Mathematics
for Science & Engineering

Second Edition

PHILIP L. ALGER

Consulting Professor of Electrical Engineering
Rensselaer Polytechnic Institute

BASED ON *Engineering Mathematics* BY CHARLES PROTEUS STEINMETZ

McGRAW-HILL BOOK COMPANY

NEW YORK   SAN FRANCISCO   TORONTO
LONDON   SYDNEY

MATHEMATICS FOR SCIENCE AND ENGINEERING

From the Preface to the Original Edition of
Engineering Mathematics by Charles P. Steinmetz

[CHARLES PROTEUS STEINMETZ (1865–1923) was a friendly person, with deep understanding, wide interests, and high ideals. He came to America as a young man and soon became one of our greatest scientists. Above all, he was a great teacher, who educated the electrical engineers of his day in the then mysterious science of alternating currents. His textbook, *Engineering Mathematics*, was a pioneer in its field.

"The Doctor," as Steinmetz was known to his friends, always wrote and spoke on an ascending scale. He would open a speech with a few statements so simple that everyone would understand, each thinking to himself "Why, I can see that!" After thus bringing his hearers into line, he would carry forward his train of thought, taking his audience with him. As the going became hard, one by one they would fall behind, until at the end only a few would still be in step. However, all his hearers felt they had been carried ahead a little way into new areas of understanding, as if they had hitchhiked along the road.

Dr. Steinmetz would resolve any complex problem into distinct elements, each readily understood and adapted to independent treatment. Then he conveyed to his students a clear visual picture of each of these elements, and finally he would present the necessary calculations in terms of simple arithmetic.

To him, numbers were intended to measure with, not just for counting. Every number was a "general number," $x + jy$, representing a point on a plane, not merely a point on a line, x. Thus, he dealt with two dimensions at once, and the numerical answers he obtained were "phasors," not merely abstract numbers. In this way, circular, hyperbolic, and exponential functions became interchangeable, convertible from one to another by substituting jx for x. In this way also, he encouraged the use of "equivalent electric circuits" with utmost freedom, providing a then new kind of mathematical model that is extremely helpful in visualizing mathematical equations.—P. L. A.]

It is generally conceded that a fair knowledge of mathematics is necessary to the engineer, and especially the electrical engineer. For the latter, however, some branches of mathematics are of fundamental importance, as the algebra of the general number, the exponential and trigonometric series, etc., which are seldom adequately treated, and often not taught at all in the usual textbooks of mathematics, or in the college course of analytic geometry and calculus given to the engineering students, and, therefore, electrical engineers often possess little knowledge of these subjects. As a result, an electrical engineer, even if he possess a fair knowledge of mathematics, may often find difficulty in dealing with problems, through lack of familiarity with these branches of mathematics, which have become of importance in electrical engineering, and may also find difficulty in looking up information on these subjects.

In the same way the college student, when beginning the study of electrical engineering theory, after completing his general course of mathematics, frequently finds himself sadly deficient in the knowledge of mathematical subjects, of which a complete familiarity is required for effective understanding of electrical engineering theory. It was this experience which led me some years ago to start the course of lectures which is reproduced in the following pages. I have thus attempted to bring together and discuss explicitly, with numerous practical applications, all those branches of mathematics which are of special importance to the electrical engineer. Added thereto are a number of subjects which experience has shown me to be important for the effective and expeditious execution of electrical engineering calculations. Mere theoretical knowledge of mathematics is not sufficient for the engineer, but it must be accompanied by ability to apply it and derive results—to carry out numerical calculations. It is not sufficient to know how a phenomenon occurs, and how it may be calculated, but very often there is a wide gap between this knowledge and the ability to carry out the calculation; indeed, frequently an attempt to apply the theoretical knowledge to derive numerical results leads, even in simple problems, to apparently hopeless complication and almost endless calculation, so that all hope of getting reliable results vanishes. Thus, considerable space has been devoted to the discussion of methods of calculation, the use of curves and their evaluation, and other kindred subjects requisite for effective engineering work.

Thus, the following work is not intended as a complete course in mathematics, but as supplementary to the general college course of mathematics, or to the general knowledge of mathematics which every engineer and really every educated man should possess.

In illustrating the mathematical discussion, practical examples, usually taken from the field of electrical engineering, have been given and discussed. These are sufficiently numerous that any example dealing with a phenomenon with which the reader is not yet familiar may be omitted and taken up at a later time.

CHARLES P. STEINMETZ

Schenectady, New York
December, 1910

Preface to the First Edition

This book is intended to provide a short integrated mathematics course for students in colleges, technical institutes, and industrial training programs; to supplement regular high school and college mathematics programs; and to serve as a reference for engineers, scientists, and others.

It is supposed to epitomize what an engineering student learns in high school and college mathematics courses, at least through the solution of linear differential equations. It is also supposed to be understandable to any intelligent high school graduate, technician, or engineering apprentice, so that by his own study a working knowledge of mathematics, comparable with that most college graduates carry away with their degrees, may be obtained. The aim is to make it easy to use mathematics and to "see what one is doing" throughout.

The book has grown out of my admiration for the teaching methods followed by Dr. Charles P. Steinmetz, and, especially, my appreciation of his book, *Engineering Mathematics*, which came out in three editions between 1911 and 1917. In fact, the present book follows the plan of the earlier one quite closely and incorporates about half of the original material. I have taken especial care to preserve the clear explanation of complex quantities, or "general numbers," as Steinmetz called them, and to show their usefulness in developing equivalent circuits to represent all sorts of physical phenomena. In this way, the book provides a bridge between the original ideas of Dr. Steinmetz and those of his modern counterpart, Gabriel Kron, whose tensor theory (a generalization of complex number theory) employs such circuits as mathematical models in the ready solution of problems of great variety and immense complexity with the aid of electronic digital computers.

All the lore of mathematics may be considered as stored in a tall building with many floors, each having spacious entrance halls, large rooms, closets, and cupboards of every sort. The ground floor is devoted to arithmetic, the second floor to plane and solid geometry, the next to algebra, then come trigonometry and analytic geometry. Above this are successive floors devoted to calculus, differential equations, probability, complex function theory, mathematical logic, and so on.

There are many books dealing with each of these various floors of knowledge, and there are numerous handbooks and compendia that provide formulas, tables, and other samples of knowledge taken from different floors of the building. Few of these books, however, provide easy transition between floors. The student is expected to follow well-marked routes through certain rooms in each of the lower floors in turn, before venturing to the higher levels. And, each floor has its own language and customs that need to be learned before the knowledge can be freely used.

Following Dr. Steinmetz's ideas, I have endeavored to provide in this new book a set of stairways and halls for the mathematical building, so that the reader can easily go up and down stairs and enter into any of the important rooms on whatever floor and in whatever sequence he pleases—all the time employing the basic symbolism and language that he learned from the first few floors. In this way, the reader should be enabled to use a wide variety of mathematical tools and also to pick up any book on a specialty and add the new ideas to his own store of knowledge with a minimum of time and effort. The novice should be enabled to start at a low level and go quite far into mathematics for engineering purposes, without calling upon more than a very few books.

The first seven chapters of the new book are nearly the same as in *Engineering Mathematics*, although the material has been rearranged and new sections have been added on interpolation, prime numbers, rules for division, the slide rule, determinants, the conic sections, Simpson's rules, the Fibonacci series, and the unit function.

Chapters 8, 12, 13, and 14 are entirely new, dealing with the calculus, differential equations, probability, and electric-circuit theory. The sections of engineering mathematics dealing with empirical curves and waveforms have been much condensed. New and more extensive appendixes have been provided to facilitate calculations. Also, problems have been included after each chapter, with the answers in a supplement.

I wish to express my appreciation for the help given by Mr. Robert J. Adsit in preparing the problems, by Mr. Lawrence R. Marwill in revising and editing, and by the Misses Ruth Shaver and Elizabeth A. Bibber in typing and editing the manuscript. I am indebted also to many friends for suggestions, especially Professor Albert A. Bennett, Professor Max Beberman, Professor David A. Page, Dr. J. J. Smith, and Dr. Gabriel Kron.

PHILIP L. ALGER

Preface to the Second Edition

In preparing this new edition of *Mathematics for Science and Engineering* I have had in mind the rapid development of community colleges and the remarkable growth in the use of digital computers. It appears that the trend in mathematics education over the past ten years has been to stress more abstruse and generalized concepts, so that the fun and utility to be found in applying mathematics in one's daily affairs have been somewhat neglected. It is my hope that the availability of this new edition will help the community colleges to give more emphasis to the practical uses of mathematics—by using it as a reference and a stimulant for the continuing self-education of their graduates.

Aside from some corrections and rephrasing, the changes from the original edition consist of material added to several chapters. A paragraph on preferred numbers and some comments on the use of mathematics in the art of industrial design have been added to Chap. 5. A new section on sampling, explaining the use of data obtained by tests on small samples in judging the quality level of high-production items, and another section on the use of Latin and Graeco-Latin squares in planning experiments, have been added to Chap. 13. Several pages have been added to Chap. 14 to explain the nature and use of the new electronic digital computers and to show how to work out numerical problems on a shared-time computer.

In reviewing the book and in making these changes, I have benefited from the suggestions of E. W. Boehne, Dr. James J. Smith, my sister, Miss Louisa R. Alger who is a mathematics teacher, and my son, John R. M. Alger. Miss Ruth Shaver has been very helpful in the editing.

PHILIP L. ALGER

Contents

Chapter 1 ARITHMETIC

1-1 Addition and Subtraction. From the operations of counting and measuring arose the art of "figuring," arithmetic, algebra, and, by degrees, the entire structure of mathematics.

During the development of the human race through the ages, which is repeated by every child in the first years of life, the first ideas of numbers and size were vague and crude: few and many, little and big, large and small. Later, the ability to count, that is, the knowledge of numbers, developed, and at last the ability to measure. Even today, measuring is to a large extent done by counting: spaces, steps, knots in a string, etc.

From counting arose the simplest arithmetical process—addition. Thus, we may count some apples:

$$1, 2, 3, 4, 5$$

then count another lot:

$$1, 2, 3$$

then put the two lots together and count them all. Or, after counting the first lot, we continue through the second lot:

$$1, 2, 3, 4, 5, \ldots, 6, 7, 8$$

which gives addition:

$$5 + 3 = 8$$

or, in general,[1] using letters which represent numerals instead of the numerals themselves:

$$a + b = b + a = c$$

---

[1] The assumption from common experience that the order of addition makes no difference in the result, whether $a + b$ or $b + a$, is called the *commutative* property of addition. Likewise, the *associative* property of addition is the assumption that $(a + b) + c = a + (b + c)$. These are two of the postulates of ordinary algebra that are accepted as true throughout this book. They do not hold, however, in some of the higher algebras developed by mathematicians and physicists.

[1]

Such a statement of equality, or "equation," when written in terms of letters a, b, c, gives in a single line more information than would be conveyed in a great many lines if numerals alone were used. That is, the equation $a + b = b + a$ is a generalization of the many equations, $1 + 2 = 2 + 1$, $3 + 2 = 2 + 3$, $5 + 7 = 7 + 5$, $6 + 8 = 8 + 6$, and so on. It says that whatever numeral may be put in place of a and whatever other numeral is put in place of b, the sum will always be the same, whether we add a to b or add b to a. Counting 1, 2, 3, 4, 5 and then counting three more, 6, 7, 8, gives the same result as counting 1, 2, 3 and then counting five more: 4, 5, 6, 7, 8.

We may take away the second lot of apples, which means that we count the entire lot, and then count backward those we take away, thus:

$$1, 2, 3, 4, 5, 6, 7, 8, \ldots, 7, 6, 5$$

which gives subtraction:

$$8 - 3 = 5$$

or, in general,

$$c - b = a$$

The opposite (or inverse) of putting things together is to take some away; therefore, subtraction is the inverse of addition.

When we add or subtract numbers like 3, 5, 8, etc., we are using arithmetic. When we employ letters, a, b, x, y, etc., to represent numerals, and express relations between them such as $c - b = a$, we are employing algebra. In the first case, we are dealing with a particular case, $8 - 3 = 5$. In the second case, $c - b = a$, we are describing an entire set of relations that are true when c, b, and a are given different numerical values. This use of a letter to stand in place of a numeral enables mathematics to compress a great deal of information into a small space and to derive general principles that apply to a great variety of problems.

1-2 Numbers and Numerals. Whole numbers are called *integers*. They express ideas of quantity that are first learned by counting. When we count 5 apples, we can see and feel, or eat, the apples, but the number 5 itself is intangible. The idea of the number 5 is the same, whether we speak of 5 fingers, or 5 chickens, or 5 apples. It is easy to see, or visualize, 5 apples, but it is not easy to think of the number 5 by itself (not merely the *numeral* 5) without reference to particular things.

The number zero, or 0, is neither positive nor negative. When we have no apples at all, we say we have zero apples. Or when we remain standing at a certain spot, we may say we have moved a distance of zero feet (or inches, etc.) from that position. The number zero is an essential element of our number system, with unique properties that require it be considered separately from all other numbers in many problems.

The Arabic numerals 1, 2, 3, 4, etc., or the Roman numerals, I, II, III, IV, etc., are symbols used to represent numbers. The numerals have definite shapes, and take different forms in the Arabic, Roman, and other scripts, but the numbers they represent have the same meanings in all languages, whatever the shapes of the symbols used.

In mathematics we must be precise. Therefore, the idea of a numeral must be kept distinct from the idea of the number that it represents. The real number (quantity) indicated by the symbol 8 is exactly the same, whether we represent it by a small numeral, 8, or by a large numeral, 8. The size and shape of the numeral do not affect the meaning of the number. The numeral 8 can be divided (split vertically) into two symbols for three, one normal 3, and one reversed, Ɛ, with nothing left over. But the number 8 is equal to two 3s plus a remainder of 2.

In our decimal system of numbers, we employ the number 10, or twice 5, as a unit, and we represent it by the numeral 10, that is, by placing the numeral 0 after the numeral 1. And we represent twice 10 by the numeral 20, or ten 10s by the numeral 100. Also, instead of writing twelve as 10 plus 2, we simply write the numeral 12. When two or more numerals are written together in this way to represent a number larger than 10, the separate numerals are called *digits*. Thus, the numeral, or digit, in the farthest right position represents the number of ones, the digit in the next to the right-hand position gives the number of tens, the digit in the second from the right position gives the number of hundreds, etc. A particular digit always represents the same number of objects, but the sort of objects it represents may be ones, tens, or hundreds, depending on whether the digit is in the units place, the tens place, or the hundreds place in the complete numeral.

If we are speaking of the numerals themselves, we may say that taking away 4 from 24 leaves 2, or taking away 2 from 24 leaves 4. Actually, since the 2 in 24 represents 20, taking away the number 4 from 24 leaves 20, or taking away 2 leaves 22. To keep these distinctions clear, we may use quotation marks, '3' to indicate when we are referring to the numeral '3' as a symbol, or mark on the paper; and we should assume that whenever the symbol is used without quotation marks, it represents the number itself.

One way to learn about numbers, apart from the numerals used to represent them, is to use numbers to measure with, instead of merely for counting. A line 5 inches long is clearly something quite distinct from, and longer than, a line 4 inches long. Also, when we measure something, the hands and eyes are being used as well as the mind, so that it is much easier to maintain undivided attention. Therefore, it is good to teach arithmetic to beginners by arranging blocks, or pieces of tape, into lines of different length, or to form objects of different size.

There is a difficulty with this method of learning also. The child having only red blocks may come to believe that the number 5 applies only to things that are red. To realize that a number is an idea of quantity that applies to all sorts of objects, of any size or color, and that the number is the same whether the numeral used to represent it is large or small, in Arabic or Roman or another script, requires mental effort that each student must make, with the teacher's help.

This matter of reasoning from a particular to a general case, of learning that if 3 apples added to 5 apples gives 8 apples, then also 3 eggs added to 5 eggs will give 8 eggs, is an inherent difficulty that the student of mathematics must surmount. The difficulty is illustrated by the story of the college student who was asked to calculate how high a ball would bounce, given its distance of fall, elasticity, and other needed data. After a long time without making any progress, he came to the teacher and asked, "What color is the ball?"

The great usefulness of mathematics stems from its power to express in terms of a few symbols a general truth that applies to many problems. It is helpful in the beginning to think of red balls, and perhaps of green apples, when solving particular problems, but as time goes on, the student should think more and more in abstract terms, remembering that the laws of mathematics apply equally well to balls of any color. When Alice in Wonderland watched the Cheshire Cat fade away, until nothing was left but its grin, she realized that the grin was the one thing that was important about the cat. Just so, in most mathematics problems, there are a few properties of the things dealt with that matter, and the student should learn to think of these properties only, dismissing all others from his mind when solving a particular problem.

1-3 Positive and Negative Numbers. There is a marked difference between addition and subtraction in practical affairs. If we have 5 apples, we can add 7 more and so have 12 apples: $5 + 7 = 12$. But we cannot take away 7 apples if we have only 5: $5 - 7 = -2$ is not possible in this case. Thus, a mathematical operation may or may not have physical reality, depending on the conditions to which it is applied. To keep the distinction clear between the numbers and the objects they represent, it is customary to write equations in this way:

$$5 + 7 = 12 \qquad \text{(apples)}$$

The equation is true in the abstract; how true it is in a particular case depends on how we define the objects to which it is applied: 5 green apples plus 7 rotten apples does not amount to 12 good apples.

The same relation holds in measuring. We may measure a distance from a starting point A (Fig. 1-1), in steps, for instance (or other units of distance), and then measure a second distance, and get the total dis-

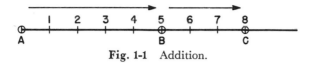

Fig. 1-1 Addition.

tance from the starting point by addition: 5 steps, from A to B, then 3 steps, from B to C, gives the distance from A to C as 8 steps:

$$5 + 3 = 8 \qquad \text{(steps)}$$

or, we may step off a distance, and then step back, that is, subtract another distance, for instance (Fig. 1-2),

$$5 - 3 = 2 \qquad \text{(steps)}$$

Thus, going 5 steps from A to B, and then 3 steps back, from B to C, brings us to C, 2 steps away from A.

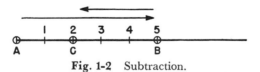

Fig. 1-2 Subtraction.

Let us try now the case of subtraction, which was impossible in the apples example, 5 steps $-$ 7 steps $=$? We go from the starting point, A, 5 steps to B and then go back 7 steps; here we find that sometimes

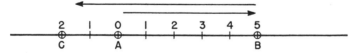

Fig. 1-3 Subtraction, negative result.

we can do it, sometimes we cannot. If back of the starting point A is a stone wall, we cannot step back 7 steps. If A is only a mark on the road, we may step back beyond it, and come to C in Fig. 1-3.

At C, we are again 2 steps away from the starting point, just as in Fig. 1-2. That is,

$$5 - 3 = 2 \qquad \text{(Fig. 1-2)}$$
$$5 - 7 = -2 \qquad \text{(Fig. 1-3)}$$

In the case where we can subtract 7 from 5, we get the same distance from A as when we subtract 3 from 5, but the distance AC in Fig. 1-3, while the same 2 steps as in Fig. 1-2, is different in character. The one is toward the left, the other toward the right. This means that we have two kinds of distance units, those to the right and those to the left, and we must find some way to distinguish them.

The distance 2 in Fig. 1-3 is toward the left of the starting point, in the direction in which we step when subtracting. It thus appears natural to distinguish it from the distance 2 in Fig. 1-2, by calling the former -2, while we call the distance AC in Fig. 1-2, $+2$, since it is in the direction we step when adding.

When numbers are used for measurements in this way, they may be called *directed numbers*. That is, a directed number is merely a number symbolized by a numeral together with a sign to indicate direction, $+2$ or -2 (or, a number that has been multiplied by a unit distance, $+1$ or -1). Generally, the $+$ sign is omitted for simplicity. Later on, in Chap. 3, we shall see that by using quadrature numbers also, either $+$ or $-$, directed numbers can be used to indicate any direction in a plane.

Therefore, besides the class of ordinary positive, nonzero, numbers,

$$+1, +2, +3, +4, +5$$

there is a corresponding class of negative, nonzero, numbers,

$$-1, -2, -3, -4, -5$$

By thus introducing negative numbers, we can always carry out the mathematical operation of subtraction:

$$c - b = a$$

If b is greater than c, a merely is negative.

1-4 Physical Interpretation of Negative Numbers. We realize, therefore, that the negative number and the negative unit, -1, when used to represent physical objects, are mathematical creations, and are not in universal agreement with experience.

In the application of numbers to the phenomena of nature, we sometimes find conditions where we can give the negative number a physical meaning, expressing the opposite of a positive number; in other cases we cannot do this. For instance, "5 apples $-$ 7 apples $=$ -2 apples" has no physical meaning. There exists no negative number of apples. At best, we can only express the relation by saying $5 - 7$ when applied to apples is an impossible transaction.

In the same way, an illumination of 5 lumens, lowered by 3 lumens, gives an illumination of 2 lumens. If we try to lower the illumination of 5 lumens by 7 lumens, it is impossible; there cannot be a negative illumination of 2 lumens. The limit is 0 lumens, or complete darkness.

From a string 5 feet long, we can cut off 3 feet, leaving 2 feet. We cannot cut off 7 feet, leaving −2 feet of string.

If the temperature is 5° above freezing and falls 3°, it will be 2° above freezing. If it falls 7°, it will be 2° below freezing. The one case is just as real, physically, as the other. Thus, in temperature measurements by the conventional scale, the negative numbers have just as much physical reality as the positive numbers. This is no longer true if the absolute zero is taken as zero on the scale, as there can be no lower temperature.

Likewise with time, we may represent future time, from the present as starting point, by positive numbers, and past time will then be represented by negative numbers. But, if we choose, we may equally well represent past time by positive numbers, and future time by negative numbers. In this, and most other physical applications that involve addition but not multiplication, the negative numbers thus appear "equivalent" to the positive numbers, and, thus, interchangeable; we may choose either direction as positive, and the other then is negative.

Therefore, in all cases where there are two opposite directions, right and left, north and south, future and past, assets and liabilities, etc., negative numbers apply. In other cases, where there is only one direction, counting apples, measuring illumination or temperatures from an absolute zero, etc., there is no physical meaning which would be represented by a negative number. There are still other cases where a meaning may sometimes be found and sometimes not. For instance, if we have 5 dollars in our pockets, we cannot pay out 7 dollars; if we have 5 dollars in the bank, we may be able to draw out 7 dollars, or we may not, depending on our credit. In the first case, 5 dollars − 7 dollars is an impossibility; in the second case, 5 dollars − 7 dollars = 2 dollars overdraft.

We see that the negative number is not a physical, but a mathematical concept, which may find a physical representation, or may not, depending on the physical conditions to which it is applied. The negative number is just as imaginary, or has just as real a physical interpretation, depending on the case, as the "imaginary" number $\sqrt{-1}$. The only difference is that we have become familiar with the negative number at an early age, when we were less critical, and have thus taken it for granted. When first learned, it was quite a step to become accustomed to say $5 - 7 = -2$, and not, simply, that $5 - 7$ is impossible. In fact, an ordinary, positive, number such as 2, or 5, is

also just an abstract concept of quantity, which has no physical reality
by itself. Later on, in Chap. 3, the ideas of quadrature numbers and of
general or directed numbers will be considered, which are just as real
as ordinary positive numbers, though less familiar.

All this illustrates the need for relating mathematical concepts to
real things, or visualizing them. If we have always in mind a physical
picture of the mathematics we are using, we can see at each stage of the
calculations whether the answers we are obtaining are in accord with
nature or common sense. This physical interpretation of mathematics
is especially important for engineers who wish to employ mathematics
to design structures or calculate forces or for other practical purposes.

This idea is expressed very simply by the statement that the engineer uses numbers to measure with (in terms of defined units), not
merely to count. Each engineer will have in his mind a different physical picture. One will think of temperatures, one of distances, and another of forces or pressures. For each, the mathematics will be the
same; hence the study of mathematics is a basic need for every kind of
engineer.

As stated before, it is very important to keep distinct the idea of the
number itself, 2, from the idea of the physical objects that are being
considered in a particular problem. If we are using numbers to count
apples, we must write 5 apples, not merely 5. If the numeral 5 appears
by itself, it is assumed to represent the abstract idea of the quantity 5,
with no more distinct physical reality than that given by the grin of the
Cheshire Cat.   For example, we know that we can add 5 to 3 and get
8, but what do we get when we add 5 apples to 3 eggs? The sum may be
said to be 8 objects, but this is quite different from 8 apples or 8 eggs.
Only like objects, or as we say in engineering, things of like dimensions, can be added directly.

1-5   Multiplication and Division.   If we have 3 separate lots o
apples, with 4 in each lot, and we add together all 3 lots, we get

$$4 + 4 + 4 = 12 \qquad \text{(apples)}$$

or, as we express it,

$$3 \times 4 = 12 \qquad \text{(apples)}$$

The operation of repeated addition thus leads to the next operation,
multiplication. Multiplication of integers is multiple addition:

$$b \times a = c$$

thus means

$$a + a + a + \cdots (b \text{ terms}) = c$$

Like addition, multiplication can always be carried out.

Three lots, each of 4 apples, give 12 apples. Inversely, if we have

12 apples, and divide them into 3 equal lots, each lot will contain 4 apples. This gives us *division*, the inverse of multiplication, which is written

$$\frac{12}{3} = 4 \quad \text{(apples)}$$

or, in general,

$$\frac{c}{b} = a \quad \text{(objects)}$$

If we have a litter of 8 puppies, and divide them into 2 equal groups, we get 4 puppies in each group.

If we divide into 4 equal groups, we get 2 puppies in each.

If we now attempt to divide the litter into 3 equal groups, we find we cannot do it. Putting 2 in each leaves 2 over; if we put 3 each in the first 2 groups, we have 1 too few to fill out the last group. That is, 8 puppies divided by 3 is impossible; or, as we usually say, 8 puppies divided by 3 gives 2 puppies and 2 puppies left over, which is written

$$\frac{8}{3} = 2 \quad \text{remainder 2}$$

Thus, it is clear that division, the inverse operation of multiplication, cannot always be carried out if the numbers are used to represent physical objects which are indivisible. Also, although we can always multiply a number by zero, obtaining zero as the result, we cannot divide by zero, since this gives an indefinitely large, or infinite, result. We express this by the equation

$$\frac{a}{0} = \infty \qquad (1\text{-}1)$$

Infinity, ∞, is approached as a limit when successively larger numbers are divided by a given small number, or when a given number is divided by successively smaller numbers. Thus:

$$\frac{12}{1} = 12 \qquad\qquad \frac{12}{1} = 12$$

$$\frac{1,200}{1} = 1,200 \qquad\qquad \frac{12}{0.01} = 1,200$$

$$\frac{120,000}{1} = 120,000 \qquad\qquad \frac{12}{0.0001} = 120,000$$

$$\frac{12,000,000}{1} = 12,000,000 \qquad\qquad \frac{12}{0.000001} = 12,000,000$$

$$\frac{\infty}{1} \cong \infty \qquad\qquad \frac{12}{0} \cong \infty$$

where the symbol $\cong$ means "nearly equal to." Infinity is not a number, it is merely a limit that an indefinitely large number may approach but never reach (see Sec. 2-10).

An example may help to show the meaning of infinity. If we wish to pack 100 pounds of sugar in boxes, we shall need 20 boxes if 5 pounds go in each box, or 100 boxes if 1 pound goes in each. Or, if we divide each pound into 16 ounces, we shall need 1,600 boxes holding 1 ounce each. We may divide the 100 pounds of sugar into as many separate units as we wish, down to 1 grain in each, and by so doing the number of boxes required becomes very large. As the amount of sugar per box approaches zero, the number of boxes required increases without limit, or, as we say, approaches infinity.

1-6 Fractions. If we have 10 apples and attempt to divide them into 3 equal lots of whole apples, we get 3 apples in each group, and one over:

$$\frac{10}{3} = 3 \text{ (apples)} \qquad \text{remainder 1 apple}$$

We may now cut the leftover apple into 3 equal parts, in which case:

$$\frac{10}{3} = 3 + \frac{1}{3} = 3\frac{1}{3} \qquad \text{(apples)}$$

In the same way, if we have 12 apples, we can divide into 5 equal lots, by cutting 2 apples each into 5 equal pieces, and get in each of the 5 lots 2 apples and 2 pieces:

$$\frac{12}{5} = 2 + \left(2 \times \frac{1}{5}\right) = 2\frac{2}{5} \qquad \text{(apples)}$$

The number $2\frac{2}{5}$ is called a *compound* fraction, while $\frac{2}{5}$ is a simple fraction. The numeral above the dividing line of a fraction symbol is called the *numerator*, the numeral below is called the *denominator*. A fraction with 1 for its numerator is called the *reciprocal* of the denominator; that is, $\frac{1}{2}$ is the reciprocal of 2.

To carry the operation of division through for all numerical values, it is convenient to introduce a new unit, smaller than the original unit.

For example, if we divide a string 10 feet long into 3 equal parts, each part contains $3\frac{1}{3}$ feet. By naming the twelfth part of one foot one inch, we say each part is 3 feet, 4 inches long, avoiding the use of fractions.

Division has led us to a new kind of number: the fraction. Like the negative number, the fraction is a mathematical concept, which may apply to physical objects sometimes, and sometimes not. In the above instance of 8 puppies, divided into 3 groups, it is not applicable. We cannot have fractions of (live) puppies.

The concept of the fraction applies to those physical quantities which can be divided into smaller units, but does not apply to those which are indivisible, or individuals, as we call them.

For simplicity in writing fraction symbols, we normally convert fractions into the nearest equivalent number of tenths, or hundredths, and then into the result as a decimal numeral, with a decimal point in front. Thus, we know that one cent is one hundredth part of a dollar, and so we write the sum of one dollar and fifty-two cents as simply $1.52. In the same way, instead of writing $2\frac{2}{5}$ apples, we recognize that $\frac{2}{5}$ is exactly the same as $\frac{4}{10}$, and we, therefore, write 2.4, or 2.40, apples.

If the fraction does not give an exact number of tenths, we may carry the division out to the nearest hundredth, or thousandth, or as we say, to two or more decimal places. Thus

$$2 + \frac{2}{7} = 2 + \frac{1}{1,000} \frac{(2,000)}{7} = 2 + \frac{1}{1,000} (285 \cdots) = 2.285 \cdots$$

The $\cdots$ means that the decimal includes an indefinite number of additional digits to the right of those given. In some cases, as when the denominator of the original fraction stands for some power of 10 divided by an integer (such as 25 or 1,250) the decimal numeral, if carried to the end, will have a limited (finite) number of digits. In other cases, the decimal numeral has no definite ending; that is, it has an infinite number of digits.

In engineering, an accuracy of one or two parts in a hundred is sufficient for many purposes. Therefore an engineer would use 2.28, or 2.3, in most cases, instead of 2.285 . . . , or 228 instead of 228.5 . . . . This practice is described by saying that usually an engineer retains only the first two or three significant digits of a decimal numeral. In banking and financial accounts, however, it is customary to keep the records accurate to the nearest cent, even though the total may be many thousands of dollars. To avoid writing decimal points and zeros in front, we often multiply a small fraction by 100 and write it as 5% instead of 0.05. The % symbol means per cent, or literally per hundred. Thus, to pay interest at 3 per cent means that the borrower pays $\frac{3}{100}$ of the amount borrowed each year.

1-7 Numeration Systems—The Abacus. The people of the ancient world dealt only with whole numbers. One of the earliest Chinese treatises on numbers, written about 1100 B.C., divides all numbers into two sets, the set of odd numbers,

$$1, 3, 5, 7, \ldots$$

and the set of even numbers,

$$2, 4, 6, 8, \ldots$$

The even numbers, being perfectly divisible into two equal whole numbers, were called *female*. The odd numbers were called *male*. A number had to be either a boy or a girl.

The earliest numeral scripts reveal their origin in counting on man's fingers and toes. The Phoenicians had a symbol for unity that could be repeated up to nine times, and a symbol for 10. The Etruscans added symbols for 5, 50, and 500, which were taken over by the Romans. The Alexandrians had a numeration system that used all the letters of the alphabet. These ancient numeral scripts were hardly more than labels to record the results of counting with the abacus, a frame of beads strung on wires.

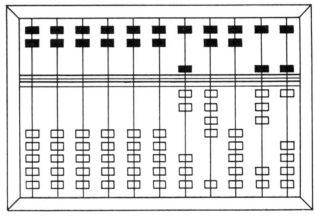

Fig. 1-4   Oriental abacus set for the number 74,086.

Figure 1-4 illustrates a form of abacus widely used in the Orient, and closely similar to those used by the early Egyptians, by the Romans, and by Europeans until about the sixteenth century. It has a number of wires, in this case 11, on which are strung two kinds of beads, or counters. Those above the dividing line each have the value 5, and those below, which may be of a different color, count 1 each. The right-hand wire indicates the unit column, the second wire is the tens, the third the hundreds, etc. In the figure, the number 74,086 is set on the abacus, as shown by a 5 and a 1 in the unit column, a 5 and a 3 in the tens column, etc.

The abacus continues to be used all over the world, especially by people of the Asiatic races. It provides a ready way of seeing the meanings of numbers and helps youngsters to have fun in doing arithmetic. Experts can make calculations with it so rapidly that they have little need for slide rules or other such devices.

Perhaps the most revolutionary step in mathematical history was the Hindu invention of the symbol 0 for the empty column of the counting frame. By simply putting each digit in its appropriate column, inserting zeros where needed, we can add on paper in the same way that addition is performed on the abacus. We do not have to introduce new symbols like the Roman X, C, and M each time we multiply by 10. Only 10 basic symbols are needed to express any number, however large.

The use of pounds, shillings, and pence as monetary units, or of degrees, minutes, and seconds to measure angles, is simply a convenience to avoid the use of fractions. The new inconvenience of multiple units that it requires is largely overcome in the modern metric system, whereby any quantity can be expressed as a multiple, or a decimal fraction, of a single unit of measurement.

In the metric system, the standard meter bar (39.37 inches) is taken as the unit of all measurements of length. We use the term *millimeter* to describe the one-thousandth part of a meter. Likewise, a centimeter is the hundredth part of a meter, and the kilometer is a unit of 1,000 meters. By means of decimals, we can thus define any quantity, however large or small, in terms of a single standard unit, and dispense with all the varied names of different-sized units employed in earlier times. How much simpler it is to measure distances in terms of meters than to employ such varied units as the inch, foot, yard, rod, furlong, mile, and league that are included in the old English measurement system!

We are so familiar with the decimal system of numerals, based on the number 10, that we usually do not realize there are other possible systems, each with advantages of its own. For example, in ancient Babylon, the base used was 12, which is exactly divisible by 2, 3, 4, and 6. The binary system, based on 2, requires only two symbols, 1 and 0. In a numeral in the binary system containing several digits, the right-hand digit stands for the number of 1s, the next digit from the right stands for the number of 2s, the second from the right stands for the number of 4s, and so on. That is, in the binary system of counting, the next larger number than 1 (which we ordinarily call 2) is represented by the numeral 10; just as in the decimal system we represent the next larger number than 9 by the numeral 10. In the binary system, 10 means 1 times 2 plus 0 times 1,[1] while in the decimal system

---

[1] Of course, a person living with the binary system would not have any such symbol as (2) and would say that (10) means 1 times 10 plus 0 times 1.

10 means 1 times 10 plus 0 times 1. Corresponding numerals in the two systems are shown in Table 1-1.

Table 1-1 Numerals in the Binary System

Name	System		Name	System	
	Decimal	Binary		Decimal	Binary
One............	1	1	Ten............	10	1,010
Two............	2	10	Twelve.........	12	1,100
Three.........	3	11	Fourteen.......	14	1,110
Four..........	4	100	Sixteen........	16	10,000
Five...........	5	101	Eighteen........	18	10,010
Six............	6	110	Twenty........	20	10,100
Seven..........	7	111	Twenty-two.....	22	10,110
Eight..........	8	1,000	Twenty-four.....	24	11,000
Nine..........	9	1,001	One hundred....	100	1,100,100

The number twelve (12) in the decimal system, or 1 times 10 plus 2, is written 1,100 in the binary system, or 1 times 8 plus 1 times 4 plus 0 times 2 plus 0. The names "one," "two," "three," etc., and the symbols 1, 2, 3, etc., are different symbols to convey abstract ideas of quantity. The Germans use the words *ein, zwei, drei,* etc., and the French say *un, deux, trois,* but they use the same Arabic symbols that we do, 1, 2, 3, because we all have agreed to use 10 as the base for our numeration systems. Some mathematicians choose to use the binary system, and they use the symbol 11 to represent our 3, but they may still read the symbol 11 as "three," since their 11 and our 3 represent exactly the same number. Although the binary system requires many more digits to represent a large number, it is very convenient for us with modern electronic digital computers, because the two symbols 1 and 0 correspond to "yes" or "no," or to an open or a closed switch, thus greatly simplifying the construction of the computer. However, engineers continue to use the decimal numeration system for all ordinary purposes.

As stated earlier, the properties of all numbers remain the same, whatever the symbols used to represent them. Thus:

In the decimal system: $9 \div 3 = 3$ and

$7 \div 3 =$ 2 plus a fraction

In the binary system: $1,001 \div 11 = 11$ and

$111 \div 11 = 10$ plus a fraction

The simplest possible way of multiplying two numbers together (except for repeated addition) requires only the ability to multiply by 2, to divide by 2, and to add, for any number A can be represented (see Sec. 1-10) as the sum of a series of powers of 2:

$$A = a(2)^0 + b(2)^1 + c(2)^2 + d(2)^3 + \cdots$$

(In the binary system of numeration, the successive digits of A, counting from the right, would be $a, b, c, d, \ldots$, where $a, b, c, d, \ldots$ are each equal to either 1 or 0.)

Therefore, to multiply B by A, we multiply B repeatedly by 2, thus:

$$A(B) = aB(2)^0 + bB(2)^1 + cB(2)^2 + dB(2)^3 + \cdots$$

The calculations are best arranged in tabular form. We place A and B at the heads of two parallel columns. In successive lower rows of the A column we put $A/2$, or if A is odd, we put $(A - 1)/2$. The number in each succeeding lower row is $\frac{1}{2}$ that in the row above. Likewise, we put $2B$, $4B$, $8B$, etc. in successive lower rows of the B column. Then, we strike out all the rows in which the number in the A column is even (because its binary digit is then zero), and add the remaining numerals in the B column. The result will be the product AB.

For example, to multiply 87 by 43

Power of 2	Binary digit of A	A	B
2^0	$a = 1$	43	87
2^1	$b = 1$	21	174
2^2	$c = 0$	[10]	[348]
2^3	$d = 1$	5	696
2^4	$e = 0$	[2]	[1,392]
2^5	$f = 1$	1	2,784

$$43 \times 87 = 3,741$$

This method is called *peasant multiplication* because of its simplicity. Similar methods exist based on the ternary and other numeration systems.

1-8 Rules of Three, Nine, and Eleven. Our everyday calculations are made in the decimal system. It is, therefore, helpful to know some of the relations among numbers that flow from the choice of 10 as the unit of counting.

The rule of nine states that, if any number is divisible by 9, the sum of its digits is also divisible by 9. This is true because any decimal numeral whose successive digits are . . . , c, b, a may be expressed as

$$cba = 100c + 10b + a = 99c + 9b + c + b + a$$

so that, dividing through by 9,

$$\frac{cba}{9} = 11c + b + \frac{c + b + a}{9} \tag{1-2}$$

If $c + b + a$ is divisible by 9, so also is cba. Thus, 8,475 is not divisible by 9, but 8,478 is. The sum of the digits of any decimal numeral, carried through to a single digit, is the amount by which the number exceeds a multiple of 9. Take 15: $1 + 5 = 6$; therefore, 15 is 6 more than 1 times 9. Or take 47: $4 + 7 = 11$, and $1 + 1 = 2$; therefore, 47 exceeds a multiple of 9 by 2.

The rule of three states that if any number is divisible by 3, the sum of its digits is also divisible by 3. The same procedure as the above gives

$$\frac{cba}{3} = 33c + 3b + \frac{c + b + a}{3} \tag{1-3}$$

If $c + b + a$ is divisible by 3, so also is cba. Thus, 11,374 is not divisible by 3, but 11,373 is.

The rule of eleven states that, if any number is divisible by 11, the sum of its digits occurring in odd-numbered positions (counting from right to left), less the sum of its even-numbered digits, is also divisible by 11. This is true, because any decimal numeral, $edcba$, may be expressed as

$$edcba = 9,999e + 1,001d + 99c + 11b + e - d + c - b + a$$

so that

$$\frac{edcba}{11} = 909e + 91d + 9c + b + \frac{e - d + c - b + a}{11} \tag{1-4}$$

If $e - d + c - b + a$ is divisible by 11, so also is $edcba$.

The rules of two and of five state, even more simply, that if any number is divisible by 2 (or by 5), its last digit is also divisible by 2 (or by 5), or is zero.

In summary, any number represented by the decimal numeral $fedcba$ is divisible by

2 if a is 0 or is divisible by 2
3 if $f + e + d + c + b + a$ is divisible by 3
4 if $2b + a$ is divisible by 4
5 if a is 0 or is divisible by 5
6 if $4f + 4e + 4d + 4c + 4b + a$ is divisible by 6

7 if $5f + 4e + 6d + 2c + 3b + a$ is divisible by 7
8 if $4c + 2b + a$ is divisible by 8
9 if $f + e + d + c + b + a$ is divisible by 9
10 if a is 0
11 if $f - e + d - c + b - a$ is divisible by 11

Rules of this kind are invaluable for checking calculations, and they often lead to short cuts. In general, it is convenient and saves time to express numbers like 989 or 491 as the difference between two simpler numbers, before multiplying them. For example, 989 times 45 is equal to 1,000 times 45, less 11 times 45, which by inspection is 44,505. Or, 491 times 32 is equal to 500 times 32, less 9 times 32, which is 16,000 less 288, or 15,712.

Another helpful rule is derived from the simple expression for the square[1] of the sum of two numbers (see Sec. 1-10):

$$(a + b)^2 = a(a + b) + b(a + b) = a^2 + 2ab + b^2 \qquad (1\text{-}5)$$

If b is replaced by $\frac{1}{2}$,

$$(a + \tfrac{1}{2})^2 = a(a + \tfrac{1}{2}) + \tfrac{1}{2}(a + \tfrac{1}{2}) = a^2 + a + \tfrac{1}{4} \qquad (1\text{-}6)$$

so that the square of the number, $a + \frac{1}{2}$, is the product $a(a + 1)$ plus $\frac{1}{4}$. Thus

$$(2\tfrac{1}{2})^2 = 2 \times 3 + \tfrac{1}{4} = 6\tfrac{1}{4} \qquad (4.5)^2 = 20.25 \qquad (85)^2 = 7,225, \text{ etc.}$$

A final example of these rules of arithmetic is the check by nines, widely used to check the accuracy of multiplication and division. Suppose a number with decimal numeral $abcd$ is to be multiplied by another number with decimal numeral ef. Expanding the numerals and separating out the multiples of 9, we obtain

$$(1,000a + 100b + 10c + d)(10e + f) =$$
$$(999a + 99b + 9c + a + b + c + d)(9e + e + f)$$

Therefore

$$(abcd)(ef) = (a + b + c + d)(e + f) + \text{a multiple of } 9 \qquad (1\text{-}7)$$

From this and the rule of nine above is derived the rule that

The product of any two numbers differs from a multiple of 9 by the same amount that the product of the sums of the digits in the two numbers differs from another multiple of 9.

[1] The square of 2 is $2 \times 2 = 4$, or the square of 3 is $3 \times 3 = 9$, etc. Instead of using the multiplication sign $\times$, it is usual to enclose the symbols for numbers to be multiplied in parentheses, ( ). Thus, 2^2, 2×2, $(2)(2)$, $2(2)$, and 4 are alternative ways of expressing the same number.

For example, this check by nines is carried out in this way:

Suppose we multiply 897 by 67, and obtain 60,099. To check this, we add the digits of 897, $8 + 9 + 7 = 24$; and add again, $2 + 4 = 6$. Put this in the top angle of an open cross (Fig. 1-5). Then, add the digits of 67; $6 + 7 = 13$; and $1 + 3 = 4$. Put this in the bottom angle of the cross. Multiply these two sums of digits, obtaining 24, and add its digits, obtaining 6. Put this at the right side of the cross. Now add the digits of the product, 60,099, obtaining $6 + 9 + 9 = 24$, and $2 + 4 = 6$. Put this in the left side of the cross. If the two numbers at the right and left sides of the cross are equal, the original multiplication has been performed correctly (unless an error has been made that is a multiple of 9). In adding the digits of each numeral, all the 9s can be ignored.

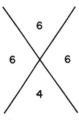

Fig. 1-5 Proof by nine.

In practice, the rule is simple to apply. We see by inspection that 897 and 67 are greater by 6 and 4, respectively, than multiples of 9. The product $6 \times 4 = 24$, and this exceeds a multiple of 9 by 6. Therefore, the product of 897 by 67 must also be greater by 6 than a multiple of 9, which evidently is true for 60,099. Or, in tabular form:

$$
\begin{array}{l}
897 \rightarrow 24 \rightarrow \quad 6 \\
\underline{\times 67 \rightarrow 13 \rightarrow \quad 4} \\
\overline{6279} \qquad\qquad \overline{24 \rightarrow 6} \\
5382 \\
\overline{60,099 \rightarrow 24 \rightarrow \quad 6}
\end{array}
$$

The check by nines is useful in locating hard-to-find errors of arithmetic. In any continued multiplication, such as $783 \times 427 \times 8,934$, it is necessary to know only that one of the factors has a digital sum which is a multiple of 9, as $783 \rightarrow 18 \rightarrow 9$, to know that the digits of the final product must also add to a multiple of 9. However, the check does not detect errors of transposed digits which make an error of a multiple of 9, as 87 for 78, nor the insertion of an extra zero, nor two compensating errors, such as putting 2,874 for 1,875.

In such ways as these, with a little practice, the ability to solve many problems by mental arithmetic can be gained, or at least a facility in checking calculations can be acquired.

1-9 Factoring and Prime Numbers. In making numerical calculations, it is often useful to separate a number into the smaller whole numbers, or factors, whose product is equal to the number itself.

Thus, the prime factors of 12 are 2, 2, and 3; or it has two factors, 3 and 4; and the factors of 111 are 3 and 37.

For example, if we wish to add two fractions, $\frac{7}{48}$ and $\frac{11}{36}$, we can proceed in either of two ways. One way is first to multiply the two numbers in each fraction, above and below, by the denominator of the other, bringing both fractions to the same denominator, then add the numerators, and finally cancel out the common factors in the combined numerator and denominator. Thus

$$\frac{7}{48} + \frac{11}{36} = \frac{7 \times 36}{48 \times 36} + \frac{11 \times 48}{36 \times 48} = \frac{252 + 528}{36 \times 48} = \frac{780}{36 \times 48}$$

$$= \frac{12 \times 65}{36 \times 48} = \frac{65}{3 \times 48} = \frac{65}{144}$$

Or we first find the largest common factor of the two denominators, then divide this out, and finally add the resulting fractions, thus:

$$\frac{7}{48} + \frac{11}{36} = \frac{1}{12}\left(\frac{7}{4} + \frac{11}{3}\right) = \frac{1}{12}\left(\frac{21 + 44}{12}\right) = \frac{65}{144}$$

The second method is much shorter and easier than the first. Another way to solve such problems is first to find the least common denominator, in this case, 144, and then to convert each fraction into an equal fraction with the common denominator before adding them. The way to find the least common denominator (LCD) is to realize that the LCD must contain each different factor of each separate denominator the maximum number of times that factor appears in any one of the denominators, but no more than that maximum number of times. Thus, we note that 36 is the product of 3, 3, and 4, while 48 is the product of 3, 4, and 4. The smallest number that contains both 36 and 48 as factors is evidently the product 3, 3, 4, and 4, or 144. By this method then

$$\frac{7}{48} + \frac{11}{36} = \frac{7 \times 3}{48 \times 3} + \frac{11 \times 4}{36 \times 4} = \frac{65}{144}$$

To find the factors of any number, the rules of 2, 5, 9, and 11 may first be applied, and any of these small numbers that are found to be factors should be divided out. Then, by successive trials of 7, 13, 17, etc., the remaining factors can be found. Familiarity with an extended multiplication table is helpful in this work. For example, one may recognize on sight that 98 is the product of 7×14, and 156 is equal to 12×13.

An integer greater than 1 whose only factors are 1 and itself is called a *prime number*. Thus 2, 3, 5, 7, 11, 13, etc., are prime numbers. All the prime numbers smaller than 500 are listed in Table 1-2. There are 95 of these,[1] and there are 73 more primes between 500 and 1,000. It is desirable to recognize the smaller prime numbers on sight, just as it is helpful to recognize the factors of a nonprime number. Every prime number greater than 3 is of the form $6n - 1$, or $6n + 1$. A prime number is always prime, regardless of whether it is expressed by a decimal numeral, a binary numeral, or a numeral in any other system.

When it is desired to have all the separate units of any task or product as much alike as possible, as in manufacturing, it is usual to divide the whole by a number with many factors, such as 12, or 1,000. When it is desired to have the units as different as possible, as to avoid lining up joints in neighboring layers of an assembly, and as in many artistic creations, it is usual to divide the whole by one or more prime numbers. The prime numbers have come to have a unique significance in many ceremonious or mystic rites.

Table 1-2   Prime Numbers Smaller than 500

2	31	73	127	179	233	283	353	401	457
3	37	79	131	181	239	293	359	409	461
5	41	83	137	191	241	307	367	419	463
7	43	89	139	193	251	311	373	421	467
11	47	97	149	197	257	313	379	431	479
13	53	101	151	199	263	317	383	433	487
17	59	103	157	211	269	331	389	439	491
19	61	107	163	223	271	337	397	443	499
23	67	109	167	227	277	347		449	
29	71	113	173	229	281	349			

1-10   Powers and Roots of Numbers.   If we have a product of several equal factors, as

$$4 \times 4 \times 4 = 64$$

it is written as

$$4^3 = 64$$

or, in general, $a^b = c$, which is read "a raised to the bth power equals c." Here b is called the *exponent* of a, and a^b is called an *exponential*, or *power*.

The operation of repeated multiplication of equal factors thus leads

[1] There are 664,579 prime numbers below 10,000,000: 135 between 1,000 and 2,000; 127 between 2,000 and 3,000; 120 between 3,000 and 4,000 and 119 between 4,000 and 5,000.

to the next algebraic operation, raising to a power, just as the repeated addition of equal numbers leads to the operation of multiplication.

The operation of raising to a power, defined as repeated multiplication, requires the exponent b to be a positive integer; b is the number of repetitions.

Dividing 4^6 repeatedly by 4, we get $4^6 \div 4 = 4^5$; $4^5 \div 4 = 4^4$; $4^4 \div 4 = 4^3$, etc., and if this successive division by 4 is carried still further, we get the following series:

$$\frac{4^3}{4} = \frac{4 \times 4 \times 4}{4} = 4 \times 4 = 4^2$$

$$\frac{4^2}{4} = \frac{4 \times 4}{4} = 4 = 4^1$$

$$\frac{4^1}{4} = \frac{4}{4} = 1 = 4^0$$

and it is natural to proceed:

$$\frac{4^0}{4} = \frac{1}{4} = 4^{-1} = \frac{1}{4^1}$$

$$\frac{4^{-1}}{4} = \frac{1}{4} \div 4 = \frac{1}{4 \times 4} = 4^{-2} = \frac{1}{4^2}$$

$$\frac{4^{-2}}{4} = \frac{1}{4^2} \div 4 = \frac{1}{4 \times 4 \times 4} = 4^{-3} = \frac{1}{4^3}$$

or, in general, $a^{-b} = \dfrac{1}{a^b}$

and

$$a^0 = 1 \tag{1-8}$$

provided that a is not given the value 0. Thus, powers with negative exponents, as a^{-b}, are the reciprocals of the same powers with positive exponents: $1/a^b$.

From the definition of raising to a power then follows:

$$a^b \times a^n = a^{b+n} \tag{1-9}$$

because a^b is the product of b equal factors a, and a^n is the product of n equal factors a; and $a^b \times a^n$ thus is a product having $b + n$ equal factors a. For instance,

$$4^3 \times 4^2 = (4 \times 4 \times 4) \times (4 \times 4) = 4^5$$

The question now arises whether by repeating the process we can reach any further mathematical operation. For instance,

$$(4^3)^2 = ?$$

may be written

$$(4^3)^2 = 4^3 \times 4^3 = (4 \times 4 \times 4) \times (4 \times 4 \times 4) = 4^6$$

and in the same manner

$$(a^b)^n = a^{bn} \tag{1-10}$$

that is, a power a^b is raised to the nth power by multiplying its exponent by n. Thus also

$$(a^b)^n = (a^n)^b \tag{1-11}$$

that is, the order of the exponents is immaterial.

Therefore, raising to a power repeatedly leads to no further algebraic operations.

The product of three equal factors 4 gives 64, that is, $4^3 = 64$.

Inversely, the problem may be to resolve 64 into a product of three equal factors. Each of the factors then will be 4. This inverse of raising to a power is called *taking the root*, and is written thus:

$$\sqrt[3]{64} = 4$$

that is, "the cube root of 64 is equal to 4," or, in general, "the bth root of c is equal to a":

$$\sqrt[b]{c} = a$$

that is, $\sqrt[b]{c}$ is defined as that number a which, raised to the power b, gives c; or, in other words:

$$\left(\sqrt[b]{c}\right)^b = c$$

When no numeral appears in the $\sqrt{\ }$ of the radical sign, it is understood to mean the square root; that is, $\sqrt[2]{c}$ is written simply $\sqrt{c}$. To avoid ambiguity, it is the rule in mathematics to assume that the positive root is always meant when the symbol $\sqrt{\ }$ is employed. Thus, $\sqrt{4}$ should always be interpreted as $+2$ (see Sec. 3-1).

Raising to a power thus far has been defined only for integral positive and negative exponents. The question arises whether powers with fractional exponents, as $c^{1/b}$ or $c^{n/b}$, have any meaning. From Eq. 1.10, writing

$$(c^{1/b})^b = c^{b \times 1/b} = c^1 = c \tag{1-12}$$

it is seen that $c^{1/b}$ is that number which, when raised to the power b, gives c; that is, $c^{1/b}$ is $\sqrt[b]{c}$, and the operation of taking the root thus can be expressed as raising to a power with a fractional exponent,

$$c^{1/b} = \sqrt[b]{c} \tag{1-13}$$

The use of the radical sign is clearly unnecessary, since the same meaning can be conveyed by fractional exponents.

From the above considerations, the following operations can be carried out with exponential numbers:

Multiplication: $$(a^b)(a^c) = a^{b+c} \tag{1-14}$$

Division: $$\frac{a^b}{a^c} = a^{b-c} \tag{1-15}$$

Raising to a power: $$(a^b)^n = a^{bn} \tag{1-16}$$

Taking the reciprocal: $$a^{-b} = \frac{1}{a^b} \tag{1-17}$$

Taking a root: $$a^{b/c} = \sqrt[c]{a^b} \tag{1-18}$$

1-11 Very Large and Very Small Numbers. As men have learned more and more about the universe of stars on the one hand, and about the mysteries of electrons, neutrons, and other atomic particles on the other, they have found it necessary to deal with both very, very large numbers and with extremely small numbers.

By listening to the echo of our voices return from the face of a cliff, we realize that it takes time for the sound to travel to the cliff and back. In fact, the speed of sound in air is about 1,080 feet per second—or 740 miles per hour. Light also takes time to travel, but it moves at a speed of 186,400 miles per second. By way of contrast, a man who runs a mile in four minutes moves at the rate of only 22 feet per second, and the tip of the hour hand of a kitchen clock moves only 1 or 2 inches per hour.

The diameter of the earth is about 8,000 miles, and that of the sun about 860,000 miles. The sun is some 93 million miles distant from the earth, on the average, so that its light takes a little more than 8 minutes to reach us. Aside from the sun, the nearest star is nearly 300,000 times as far away, or almost 5 "light-years." And, our sun is only a dwarf among the hundreds of millions of stars revealed by telescopes, some of them many millions of light-years distant from the earth.

At the other extreme, every chemical substance is made up of atoms, whose diameters are only a few tenths of a hundred-millionth of an inch. And each atom is made up of a central nucleus about one ten-thousandth as large in diameter as the atom, and of other still smaller particles.

The scientists and engineers who have to make calculations employing such extreme numbers find it convenient to express them in terms of powers of 10. That is, instead of saying the distance to the sun is 93,000,000 miles, it is expressed as 9.3×10^7, and the diameter of an atom may be expressed as 0.4×10^{-8} inch. In this way, all calculations are made with ordinary-sized numbers, and the necessary power of 10 is carried along as a common multiplier.

Numbers that differ by a factor of about 10 are said to be of one order difference in magnitude. For example, the speed of an automobile, which averages about 40 miles per hour, is one order of magnitude greater than that of a man who walks at a 4-mile-per-hour rate; and the man's speed is two orders of magnitude smaller than that of an airplane which goes some 400 miles per hour.

1-12 Irrational Numbers. Raising a whole number to a power with an integral exponent always yields a whole number. In many cases, taking the root also yields a whole number. For instance,

$$\sqrt[3]{64} = 4$$
$$\sqrt{4} = 2$$

while, in other cases, the result is not an integer. For instance,

$$\sqrt{2} = ?$$

Attempting to calculate $\sqrt{2}$, we get

$$\sqrt{2} = 1.4142135 \cdots$$

and find, no matter how far we carry the calculation (see Sec. 5-4), we never come to an end, but get an endless decimal numeral. That is, no rational number exists which is equal to $\sqrt{2}$. We can only approximate $\sqrt{2}$ in terms of rational numbers, and carry the approximation to any desired degree.

Such numbers as $\sqrt{2}$, which cannot be expressed by a rational number symbol, but merely approximated, are called *irrational numbers*. "Irrational" here means "not equal to the quotient (ratio) of any two whole numbers." Irrational numbers are just as real or "sensible" as ordinary numbers. If we draw a square, with one foot as side, the length of the diagonal is $\sqrt{2}$ feet, and the length of the diagonal of a square obviously is just as real as the length of a side. An irrational number is a real and existing number which is not equal to an integer or to a ratio of whole numbers, but can be expressed by an endless decimal whose digits do not repeat in cycles.

The term *transcendental number* is applied to certain irrational numbers, such as π, which is the ratio of the circumference of a circle to its diameter: $\pi = 3.14159 \cdots$. A transcendental number is an irrational number that is not the root of an equation with whole-number coefficients (see Chap. 4).

Endless decimal numerals frequently are met when expressing common fractions as decimals. Decimal numeral representations of common fractions, however, are *periodic* decimals; that is, the digits periodically repeat, and in this respect are different from decimal numeral representations of irrational numbers. Because of their periodic nature, they can be converted into finite common fractions. For instance, 2.1387387 . . . (where 387 repeats indefinitely):

Let

$$x = 2.1387387 \cdot \cdot \cdot$$

then

$$1{,}000x = 2{,}138.7387387 \cdot \cdot \cdot$$

subtracting,

$$999x = 2{,}136.6$$

Hence

$$x = \frac{2{,}136.6}{999} = \frac{21{,}366}{9{,}990} = \frac{1{,}187}{555} = 2\frac{77}{555}$$

1-13 Logarithms. Raising to a power, $a^b = c$, has two inverse operations: (1) c and b given, a to be found,

$$a = \sqrt[b]{c} \tag{1-19}$$

or taking the root; and (2) c and a given, b to be found,

$$b = \log_a c \tag{1-20}$$

or taking the logarithm.

The logarithm is defined as the exponent of a base number raised to a power. Thus, if $a^b = c$, then b is the logarithm of c to the base a, or $b = \log_a c$.

A logarithmic expression may be changed to an exponential, and, inversely, the laws of logarithms are the laws which the exponents obey in dealing with powers and roots.

Powers of the same base are multiplied by adding the exponents: $a^b \times a^n = a^{b+n}$. Therefore, the logarithm of a product is the sum of the logarithms of the factors. Thus

$$\log_a (c \times d) = \log_a c + \log_a d \tag{1-21}$$

A power is raised to another power by multiplying the exponents:

$$(a^b)^n = a^{bn} \tag{1-22}$$

Therefore, the logarithm of a power is the exponent times the logarithm of the base:

$$\log_a c^n = n \log_a c \tag{1-23}$$

If in taking the nth root of a number, $\sqrt[n]{c} = b$, n is given larger and larger values, b approaches 1 as a limit. Or, if we raise a number to a power, $c^m = c^{1/n} = b$, and m is given smaller and smaller values, b again approaches 1 as a limit. Therefore, $a^0 = 1$, and the logarithm of 1 is 0, or $\log_a 1 = 0$, whatever the value (except 0) of the base a.

If the base, a, is greater than 1, and if c is also greater than 1, then $\log c > 0$, or is positive.[1] If $a > 1$, and c is fractional, $0 < c < 1$, then $\log_a c < 0$, or is negative. Thus, the logarithm of c traverses all positive and negative values for positive values of c, $0 < c < \infty$.

Therefore, the logarithm of a negative number cannot be a real number, either positive, negative, or zero.

$$\log_a (-c) = \log_a c + \log_a (-1) \tag{1-24}$$

and the question of finding the logarithms of negative numbers thus resolves itself into finding the value of $\log_a (-1)$, which is considered in Sec. 3-15.

There are two standard systems of logarithms: the Napierian, or natural, system, with the base $e = 2.71828 \cdots$,[2] and the Briggs, or common, system, with the base 10. The former is generally used in algebraic, the latter in numerical calculations. If the logarithm of a number c to any base, a, is given, the logarithm of c to any other base can easily be found.

For instance, given $b = \log_a c$, to find $\log_{10} c$: since $b = \log_a c$ means $a^b = c$, taking the logarithm of this gives $b \log_{10} a = \log_{10} c$; hence

$$\log_{10} c = b \log_{10} a \tag{1-25}$$

For convenience, it is customary to write $\ln a$ instead of $\log_e a$ to represent a logarithm in the natural system, and $\log a$ instead of $\log_{10} a$ for a logarithm in the common system; thus

$$\ln a = \log_e a = (\log_e 10) \log a = 2.3026 \log a \tag{1-26}$$
$$\log a = \log_{10} a = (\log_{10} e) \ln a = 0.43430 \ln a \tag{1-27}$$

By these relations, logarithms may be changed from one base to another.

Tables of logarithms of the numbers between 1 and 10 are widely available. Their numerical values can be calculated by use of infinite series expressions, as described in Sec. 8-8. The tables are useful for performing repeated multiplications or divisions, when greater than slide-rule accuracy is desired.

---

[1] The expression $a > b$ means "a is greater than b," and "$a < b$" means "a is less than b."

[2] Regarding e, see Eq. 3-23.

Appendix A gives the logarithms of all numbers from 1 to 10 in steps of 0.01 and of all numbers from 1.000 to 1.100 in steps of 0.001. To find the logarithm of any number greater than 10 or less than 1, the number is first divided or multiplied by a power of 10 to bring it within the range of the tables, and a number equal to the exponent of the power of 10 is added to the logarithm found in the table.

By using logarithms we substitute the simple process of addition for the more involved process of multiplication. Instead of multiplying two numbers together, as

$$123 \times 456 = 56{,}088$$

we add their logarithms, and look up the corresponding number in a log table:

$$\log 123 + \log 456 = 2.08991 + 2.65896 = 4.74887 = \log 56{,}088$$

By interpolation, the logarithms of other numbers can be found directly from the table. For example, to find the logarithm of 6.8542, we find in the table that

$$\log 6.85 = 0.83569 \quad \text{and} \quad \log 6.86 = 0.83632$$

The difference between these is 0.00063. Hence, the log of 6.8542 is

$$0.83569 + 0.42(0.00063) = 0.83569 + 0.00026 = 0.83595$$

The logarithm of 68.542 is, therefore, 1.83595, and that of 68,542 is 4.83595.

The logarithm of a number can be found with a minimum of interpolation by first breaking the number into two factors, one a round number, such as 1.5, 2, 36, etc., and the other a number lying between 1.00 and 1.10.

For example,

$$\log 6.8542 = \log \left(\frac{10.2813}{1.5000}\right) = \log 10.2813 - \log 1.50$$
$$= 1.01204 - 0.17609 = 0.83595$$

To avoid the use of negative logarithms, it is customary to add 10 to the logarithm of a number between 0 and 1, and place a minus sign over the first numeral; that is, we add $10 - 10$, or 0, to the logarithm; thus

$$\log 0.010281 = \log 0.01 + \log 1.0281 = -2 + 0.01204$$

which is written $\bar{8}.01204$.

If, in making a chart, or graph, of a relation (see Sec. 4-1) such as

$y = x^2$, we consider instead the equivalent equation

$$\log y = 2 \log x$$

and then plot $\log y$ against $\log x$, the original curve is thereby changed into a straight line, as seen in Fig. 1-6. Special cross-section paper printed with logarithmic scales is widely available, and is frequently used to simplify plotting in this way. Both semilog paper (y vs. $\log x$)

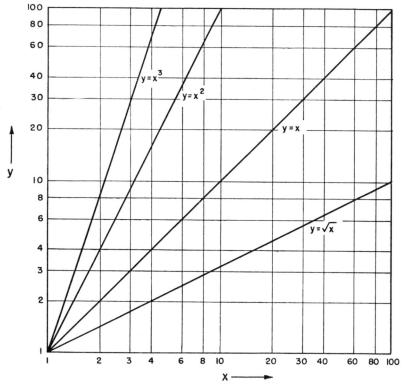

Fig. 1-6   Logarithmic chart.

and loglog paper ($\log y$ vs. $\log x$) can be obtained. The slope of a straight line on loglog paper measures the exponent, n, of x in such an equation as $y = x^n$.

1-14   The Slide Rule.   The slide rule is a device to multiply numbers by adding their logarithms. A scale is marked off in divisions proportional to the logarithms of the numbers from 1 to 10, and a like scale is arranged to slide easily beside it (Fig. 1-7). To multiply 2 by a number R, for example, the slide is moved until the 1 on its C scale is opposite 2 on the fixed D scale. Then, by looking on the D scale opposite 3 on the slide, we find 6, opposite 2 we find 4, opposite 2.04 we find 4.08, etc. By the reverse process, we can divide any two numbers. The usual 10-inch slide rule, widely employed by engineers, enables multiplication, division, and taking powers or roots to be carried out with an accuracy of about one part in 200.

The distance between 1 and 10 on the upper *A* and *B* scales, in Fig. 1-7, is only half as great as on the *C* and *D* scales. Therefore, opposite any numeral, as 3, on the lower scale, there appears the numeral for the square of the number, 9, on the upper scale, whose logarithm is twice as great as the logarithm of 3. To find the square of any number on the lower scale, look at the numeral directly above on the upper scale. Square roots can be found by the inverse process.

For three hundred years after their invention in 1614, logarithms were used for all extensive calculations. In recent years, however, the engineer's slide rule, the calculating machine, the punched-card computer, and the electronic digital computer have largely taken the place of logarithmic calculations.

1-15 The Mean of *n* Numbers. When we speak of the average or mean value of two numbers, we generally mean the arithmetic average. That is, the *arithmetic mean* of 3 and 5 is

$$\frac{3+5}{2} = 4$$

or, in general, the arithmetic mean of *n* numbers, $x_1, x_2, x_3, \ldots, x_n$, is

$$\bar{x} = \frac{x_1 + x_2 + x_3 + x_4 + \cdots + x_n}{n} \tag{1-28}$$

There are other kinds of averages, however, which are often useful. For example, the *geometric mean* of 3 and 5 is the square root of their

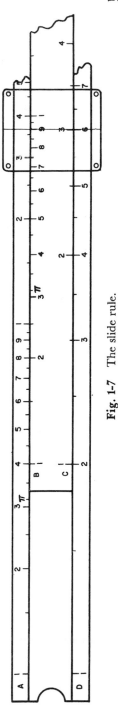

Fig. 1-7 The slide rule.

product, or

$$\sqrt{(3)(5)} = 3.873 \cdot \cdot \cdot$$

The geometric mean of x_1, x_2, x_3, . . . , x_n is

$$\sqrt[n]{x_1 x_2 x_3 \cdot \cdot \cdot x_n} \tag{1-29}$$

This is the same as the *logarithmic mean*, the number whose logarithm is the average of the logarithms of all the separate numbers. The geometric, or logarithmic, mean has the property that the mean of any power of the numbers is the same as that power of the mean of the numbers themselves. For example, the lumber in an average tree may be estimated by measuring the diameters d of a number of trees, calculating the average diameter $\bar{d}$, and then computing the total volume of the lumber by a formula in terms of $\bar{d}^2$ or $\bar{d}^3$. Or, the volume of each tree may be calculated separately and the sum of the volumes computed. If arithmetic means are used, the results will be quite different, but if geometric means are used, the same answer will be obtained both ways.

Another sort of average is the *harmonic mean*, obtained by taking the reciprocal of the arithmetic average of the reciprocals. The harmonic mean of 3 and 5 is

$$\frac{2}{(\frac{1}{3} + \frac{1}{5})} = \frac{15}{4} = 3.75$$

or the harmonic mean of x_1, x_2, x_3, . . . , x_n is given by

$$\frac{1}{\text{h.m. } (x)} = \frac{1}{n}\left(\frac{1}{x_1} + \frac{1}{x_2} + \frac{1}{x_3} + \cdot \cdot \cdot + \frac{1}{x_n}\right) \tag{1-30}$$

When we are dealing with the results of scattered experiments, still another sort of average is useful. This is the *median*, which is defined simply as the central number in the series x_1, x_2, x_3, . . . , x_n, arranged in order of magnitude. For example, in the series 1, 5, 11, 42, 45, 87, 91, the median is 42.

The reason we take the average of several quantities, usually, is that we are seeking the most probable true value, from the results of a number of different observations or from estimates from different sources. When one of these observations, say x_3, is believed to be more reliable, or more nearly correct than the others, we may give this extra weight. Thus, if we decide that x_1 is as accurate as the average of k_1 ordinary measurements, and that x_2 should be given the weight of k_2, etc., we obtain for the *weighted arithmetic* mean of x_1, x_2, x_3, . . . , x_n

$$\bar{x} = \frac{k_1 x_1 + k_2 x_2 + k_3 x_3 + \cdot \cdot \cdot + k_n x_n}{k_1 + k_2 + k_3 + \cdot \cdot \cdot + k_n} = \text{weighted mean } x \tag{1-31}$$

1-16   Interpolation.   If it is desired to calculate a large number of values of some quantity, as in making a table of the nth roots of whole numbers, a great deal of time and labor can be saved by calculating only a few of these, say every fifth one, and finding the intermediate values by interpolation. This is possible because (see Sec. 4-1) in any equation such as $y = x^2$, if y is changed by small increments, x^2 will change correspondingly, and the equation relating the two sets of increments is usually simpler than the original equation. Thus, four out of five (say) of the desired values can be calculated by a simple equation, and only one out of five by the more complex equation.

Interpolation serves as a basis for step-by-step calculations of curves that do not correspond to familiar formulas, and has many other uses.

Consider a table of squares of the natural numbers, represented by the equation

$$y = f(x) = x^2 \tag{1-32}$$

which reads "y is a function of x, equal to x^2." That is to say, the value of y, the function $f(\ \ )$ which we are considering, is equal to the square of the independent variable, or *argument*, x.

The values of y and x in Eq. 1-32 constitute what mathematicians call an *ordered pair*. That is, for any selected value of x, such as 3, there is one and only one corresponding value of y (in this case $y = 9$). When we say that "y is a function of x," we mean that a graph can be drawn, or a table can be compiled, that gives the value of y for each value of x. The letter f, and occasionally the letters g and h, are customarily used to represent a function, when followed by $(\ \ )$. On the other hand, such expressions as $a(x)$, or $3(x)$, or $y(x + 3)$ represent simple multiplication, giving ax, $3x$, and $xy + 3y$, respectively. This distinction between $f(\ \ )$ and other letters or numbers followed by $(\ \ )$ should be kept in mind.

The values given by Eq. 1-32 are shown in Table 1-3.

The argument x appears in the left-hand column of the table; the function $f(x)$, in this case x^2, is in the second column; and the differences between successive values of $f(x)$ in the third column. The descending differences of the first, second, third, etc., orders, indicated by $\Delta' f(x)$, $\Delta'' f(x)$, etc., appear along a descending diagonal from $f(x)$.

In this case, we note that the third-order differences are all zero. In general, if $f(x) = x^m$, the $(m + 1)$th-order differences are zero. The differences of higher and higher orders usually obey more and more simple laws.

The entire table can be reconstructed, or extended, if the relations

Table 1-3   Descending Differences

Argument x	Value of the function $y = f(x)$	Differences		
		First $\Delta'f(x)$	Second $\Delta''f(x)$	Third $\Delta'''f(x)$
0	0			
1	1	1		
2	4	3	2	
3	9	5	2	0
4	16	7	2	0
5	25	9	2	0
6	36	11	2	0
7	49	13	2	0

Δ is the Greek letter (capital) delta, commonly used in mathematics to represent a small difference, or increment.

between the differences are known; or a formula may be derived to represent the function. For example, since

$$\Delta'f(x) = f(x + 1) - f(x) \tag{1-33}$$

$$\Delta''f(x) = \Delta'f(x + 1) - \Delta'f(x)$$
$$= f(x + 2) - 2f(x + 1) + f(x) \tag{1-34}$$

$$\Delta'''f(x) = \Delta''f(x + 1) - \Delta''f(x)$$
$$= f(x + 3) - 3f(x + 2) + 3f(x + 1) - f(x) \tag{1-35}$$

we find, in general,

$$f(x + n) = (1 + \Delta)^n f(x) = f(x) + n\Delta'f(x) + \frac{n(n - 1)\Delta''}{2} f(x)$$
$$+ \frac{n(n - 1)(n - 2)\Delta'''}{(2)(3)} f(x) + \cdots \tag{1-36}$$

In this equation, called *Newton's interpolation formula*, n can just as well have fractional values. To find the value of (x) midway between $f(x)$ and $f(x + 1)$, we have $n = \frac{1}{2}$, and

$$f(x + \tfrac{1}{2}) = f(x) + \tfrac{1}{2}\Delta f'(x) - \tfrac{1}{8}\Delta''f(x) + \tfrac{1}{16}\Delta'''f(x) + \cdots \tag{1-37}$$

For example, the square of $4\frac{1}{2}$ is, from Table 1-3, since $x = 4$ and $n = \frac{1}{2}$,

$$f(4 + \tfrac{1}{2}) = f(4) + \tfrac{1}{2}\Delta'f(4) - \tfrac{1}{8}\Delta''f(4) + \tfrac{1}{16}\Delta'''f(4)$$

or $\quad (4\tfrac{1}{2})^2 = 16 + \tfrac{1}{2}(9) - \tfrac{1}{8}(2) + \tfrac{1}{16}(0) = 20.25$

As another example, from the table of logarithms, Appendix *A*, we have Table 1-4,

Table 1-4

	Δ′	Δ″	Δ‴
log 5.000 = 0.69897 log 5.200 = 0.71600 log 5.400 = 0.73239 log 5.600 = 0.74819	1,703 1,639 1,580	−64 −59	5

whence

$$\log 5.100 = 0.69897 + \tfrac{1}{2}(0.01703) - \tfrac{1}{8}(-0.00064)$$
$$+ \tfrac{1}{16}(0.00005) = 0.70757$$

This process of finding values of a function intermediate between those already known is called *interpolation*. By such rules as those above, values of a function can be found quite accurately, even though there are large steps between the tabulated quantities. Thus, tables of complicated functions may be compiled by interpolation from a relatively few calculated values. Or errors in tabulated values may be discovered by computing the successive differences and noting any irregularities there may be.

In every sort of computing work, a familiarity with the simple difference equation (Eq. 1-36) will be never-endingly useful.

PROBLEMS

Carry out the indicated operations:

1. $187 \times 42 = ?$

2. $\dfrac{433 \times 935}{17} = ?$

3. $86 \times 2,473 = ?$

4. $\dfrac{1}{16} \times \dfrac{41}{11} \times \dfrac{592}{7} = ?$

5. $\dfrac{92 \times 495 \times 748}{99 \times 23} = ?$

6. $\dfrac{123 \times 243 \times 7,158}{729 \times 26} = ?$

7. $\dfrac{1,331 \times 84,072}{6,642 \times 6,171} = ?$

8. $\dfrac{8,050 \times 99 \times 78}{117 \times 462} = ?$

Are the following numbers divisible by 3, by 9, by 11?

9. 81,756,429

10. 416,926,533

11. 706,584,384

12. 249,836,507,265

Express the following numbers as they would appear if the base, instead of being 10, were 3 (trinary system), 4 (quaternary system), 9 (nonary system):

13. 18	**15.** 15	**17.** 116
14. 7	**16.** 2	**18.** 83

Fill out a multiplication table for the numbers from 1 to 7 inclusive

19. in the normal base-10 numeration system.
20. in a base-5 numeration system.
21. in the binary numeration system, base 2.

Devise a rule for telling whether

22. a four-digit number is divisible by 7.
23. a five-digit number is divisible by 13.

Devise an approximate equation for

24. $(a + \frac{1}{3})^3$ **25.** $(a + \frac{1}{2})^4$

Express the following numbers as products of prime numbers:

26. 799	**28.** 1,955	**30.** 1,331
27. 2,700	**29.** 143	**31.** 1,484

Set up a table of differences and use Newton's interpolation formula to find

32. $(2.5)^3$ **33.** $(3.6)^2$

Bibliography

1. Bakst, Aaron: "Arithmetic for Adults," Appleton-Century-Crofts, Inc., New York, 1944.
2. Bell, E. T.: "Mathematics, Queen and Servant of Science," McGraw-Hill Book Company, New York, 1951.
3. Courant, R., and H. Robbins.: "What is Mathematics?" Oxford University Press, Fair Lawn, N.J., 1941.
4. Dantzig, Tobias: "Number, the Language of Science," 4th ed., The Macmillan Company, New York, 1954.
5. Dresden, Arnold: "An Invitation to Mathematics," Holt, Rinehart and Winston, Inc., New York, 1936.
6. Dubisch, Roy: "The Nature of Number, an Approach to Basic Ideas of Modern Mathematics," The Ronald Press Company, New York, 1952.
7. Eves, Howard: "An Introduction to the History of Mathematics," Rinehart & Company, Inc., New York, 1952.
8. Gardner, Martin: "Mathematical Puzzles and Diversions," Simon and Schuster, Inc., New York, 1959.

9. Jacoby, Oswald: "Mathematics for Pleasure," McGraw-Hill Book Company, New York, 1962.
10. Johnson, L. H.: "The Slide Rule," D. Van Nostrand Company, Inc., Princeton, N.J., 1949.
11. Kasner, E., and James Newman: "Mathematics and the Imagination," Simon and Schuster, New York, 1940.
12. Kline, Morris: "Mathematics in Western Culture," Oxford University Press, Fair Lawn, N.J., 1953.
13. Larsen, Harold D.: "Arithmetic for Colleges," The Macmillan Company, New York, 1950.
14. Newman, J. R.: "The World of Mathematics," pt. 1, Simon and Schuster, Inc., New York, 1956.
15. Ore, Oystein: "Number Theory and Its History," McGraw-Hill Book Company, New York, 1948.
16. Richardson, Moses: "Fundamentals of Mathematics," The Macmillan Company, New York, 1941.
17. Wilson, G. M., et al.: "Teaching the New Arithmetic," McGraw-Hill Book Company, New York, 1951.
18. Hardy, G. H., and E. M. Wright: "The Theory of Numbers" 3d ed., Clarendon Press, Oxford, 1954.

Chapter 2 TRIGONOMETRY

2-1 The Circular Functions. The simplest measurements are those of distances on a straight line, which use numbers alone, or simple arithmetic. Next are measurements on a plane, or, as we say, in two dimensions, such as are required in surveying an area of land or making the floor plan of a house. These require, besides arithmetic, a knowledge of triangles, circles, and other plane figures, or plane geometry. As usually taught, plane geometry is chiefly concerned with the construction and properties of figures that can be drawn with a ruler (unmarked straightedge) and a compass. All such figures may be represented by formulas or equations relating two variables, usually x for horizontal, or to-and-fro, distances, and y for vertical, or up-and-down, distances. To the artist, the figures themselves are more important, but to the engineer, who is concerned with exact calculations, the equations are most important, and the figures are chiefly considered as aids to understanding or visualizing the formulas.

The most important geometric figures are the circle and the right triangle, so that the study of trigonometry, which deals with their properties, is logically the next step in a mathematical course for engineers, after arithmetic.

The early astronomers divided the complete circle into 360 equal parts, or *degrees*, each of these degrees into 60 parts, called *minutes*, and each minute in turn into 60 *seconds*. In this way, they could measure any angle in degrees, minutes, and seconds, without the use of any fractions. Even today angles are usually measured in degrees, indicated by a small circle; 360° makes a whole circle, 180° a half-circle, and 90° a quadrant. It is more and more usual, however, to measure fractions of degrees in decimals, and to drop the use of minutes and seconds of arc for most engineering purposes.

Instead of degrees, angles may be measured in *radians*. One radian is the size of an angle whose circular arc length is equal to the radius. As the ratio of the circumference to the diameter of a circle is equal to

[36]

π,[1] the number of degrees in an angle of one radian is $360/2\pi$, or 57.295 . . . . And there are π radians in 180°.

For calculation purposes, it is useful to have tables, such as Appendix B, that give the ratios between any two sides of a right triangle, when the angle is known, or vice versa. These ratios are given by trigonometric functions.

For engineers, especially civil and electrical engineers, a ready familiarity with the trigonometric (circular) functions and formulas is almost as essential as familiarity with the multiplication table. To use trigonometric methods effectively, it is not sufficient merely to understand the formulas and to be able to look them up when needed. They must be learned by heart, and in both directions; that is, seeing the right side of any usual trigonometric formula should immediately suggest the left side and vice versa.

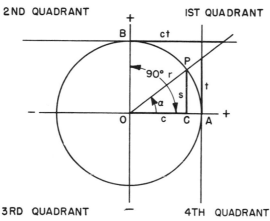

Fig. 2-1 Circular trigonometric functions.

It is usual to employ the Greek letters, alpha, beta, gamma, delta, epsilon, . . . , phi, theta, . . . , omega, written as α, β, γ, δ, ϵ, . . . , ϕ, θ, . . . , ω, to represent numerals for the size of angles, reserving the ordinary letters a, b, c, d, etc., to represent numerals for distances or other quantities.

Let, in the circle (Fig. 2-1), the directions to the right and upward be considered positive, to the left and downward as negative; and the angle α be counted from the positive horizontal, OA, counterclockwise as positive, clockwise as negative. Then OCP forms a right triangle, with angles $COP = \alpha$, $OPC = 90° - \alpha$, and $OCP = 90°$.

---

[1] The numerical value of π is, to 50 decimal places.

$$\pi = 3.14159265358979323846264338327950288419716939937510 \cdots$$

The angle α measured in radians is equal to the length of the arc AP divided by the radius OP.

The vertical *projection* s of the radius OP, divided by the radius, is called the *sine*, or simply sin α; the horizontal *projection* c of the radius OP, divided by the radius, is called the *cosine*, or cos α.

The intercept t on the vertical tangent at A, divided by the radius, is called the *tangent*, or tan α.

Thus, in Fig. 2-1,

$$\sin \alpha = \frac{s}{r} \qquad \cos \alpha = \frac{c}{r} \qquad \tan \alpha = \frac{t}{r} = \frac{\sin \alpha}{\cos \alpha}$$

(2-1)

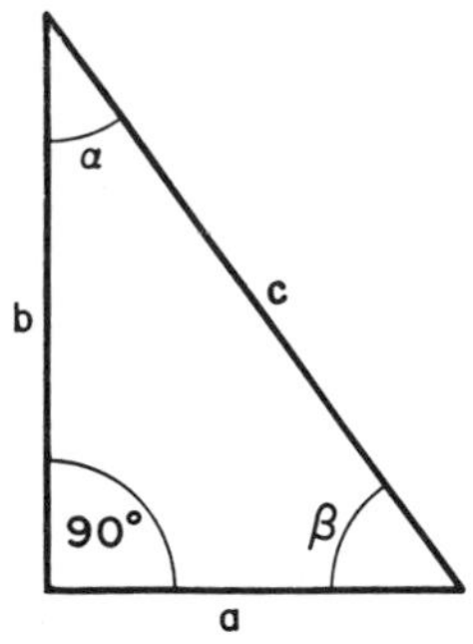

Fig. 2-2 Triangular trigonometric functions.

Names are given to the reciprocals of these functions also. They are the *cosecant*, *secant*, and *cotangent*, respectively:

$$\csc \alpha = \frac{1}{\sin \alpha} \qquad \sec \alpha = \frac{1}{\cos \alpha} \qquad \cot \alpha = \frac{1}{\tan \alpha} \quad (2\text{-}2)$$

It is quite unnecessary to use these reciprocal functions by name, since we can always write $1/\sin \alpha$ instead of csc α, without any sacrifice of clarity.

In the right triangle (Fig. 2-2) with the angles α and β opposite to the sides a and b, respectively, and with the hypotenuse c, the trigonometic functions are

$$\sin \alpha = \cos \beta = \frac{a}{c} \qquad \cos \alpha = \sin \beta = \frac{b}{c} \qquad (2\text{-}3)$$

$$\tan \alpha = \frac{\sin \alpha}{\cos \alpha} = \frac{1}{\tan \beta} = \frac{a}{b}$$

$$\tan \beta = \frac{\sin \beta}{\cos \beta} = \frac{1}{\tan \alpha} = \frac{b}{a}$$

(2-4)

By the right triangle, only functions of angles up to $90°$, or $\pi/2$ radians, can be defined, while by the circle the trigonometric functions of any angle are determined. Both representations must be so familiar to the engineer that he can see in his mind's eye the functions, their changes with a change in angle, and their approximate numerical values, from the mental picture of the diagram.

The inverse trigonometric functions, called *arc functions*, are arc sin x, arc cos x, arc tan x, etc., usually written $\sin^{-1} x$, $\cos^{-1} x$, $\tan^{-1} x$, etc.

Thus, $x = \sin \sin^{-1} x$, and the equality

$$\alpha = \sin^{-1} \frac{a}{c} = \cos^{-1} \frac{b}{c} \qquad (2\text{-}5)$$

states that α is the angle whose sine is equal to a/c, etc.

These must be distinguished from the reciprocals of the trigonometric functions, which are properly written

$$\csc \alpha = \frac{1}{\sin \alpha} = (\sin \alpha)^{-1} \qquad (2\text{-}6)$$

$$\sec \alpha = \frac{1}{\cos \alpha} = (\cos \alpha)^{-1} \qquad (2\text{-}7)$$

2-2 Signs of the Functions. In the first quadrant (Fig. 2-1) all the values of the trigonometric functions are positive.

In the second quadrant (Fig. 2-3) $\sin \alpha$ is still positive, since s is in the upward direction, but $\cos \alpha$ is negative, since c is toward the left, and $\tan \alpha$ is also negative, since t is downward.

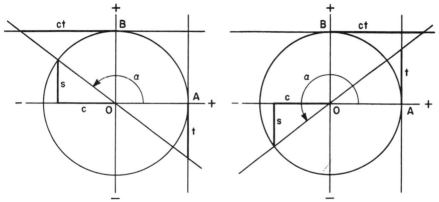

Fig. 2-3 Second quadrant. **Fig. 2-4** Third quadrant.

In the third quadrant (Fig. 2-4) $\sin \alpha$ and $\cos \alpha$ are both negative, s being downward and c to the left; but $\tan \alpha$ is again positive, as seen from t in Fig. 2-4. In the fourth quadrant (Fig. 2-5) $\sin \alpha$ is negative, since s is downward, but $\cos \alpha$ is again positive, since c is toward the right; $\tan \alpha$ is negative as seen from the downward t in Fig. 2-5.

In the fifth quadrant, all the functions again have the same value as in the first quadrant (Fig. 2-1); therefore, $360°$, or 2π, or any multiple thereof, can be added to, or subtracted from, the angle α without

Table 2-1   Signs of Trigonometric Functions

Function	Positive in quadrants	Negative in quadrants
$\sin \alpha$	1 and 2	3 and 4
$\cos \alpha$	1 and 4	2 and 3
$\tan \alpha$	1 and 3	2 and 4

changing its trigonometric functions. The trigonometric functions re-

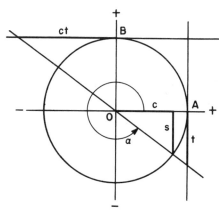

Fig. 2-5   Fourth quadrant.

peat after every 360°, or 2π radians; that is, have 360° or 2π radians as their period.

2-3   Relations between sin α, cos α, and tan α.   Figure 2-6 shows a right-angled triangle. Drawing a perpendicular line from C to the hypotenuse at D, the triangle ABC is divided into two similar, smaller, triangles, ACD and BCD. As will be shown in Sec. 2-5 (Eq. 2-20), the sum of the interior angles of any plane triangle is equal to 180°. Since

triangles ABC and ACD each have α and 90° for two of their angles, the third angle in each must be $\beta = 90° - \alpha$. Likewise, triangles

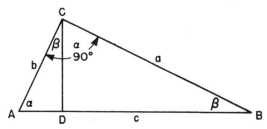

Fig. 2-6   Right triangle.

ABC and BCD have the angles 90° and β in common, and, therefore, the third angle in each is α. Hence

$$\frac{AD}{AC} = \frac{CD}{BC} = \frac{AC}{AB} = \frac{b}{c} = \cos \alpha = \sin \beta \qquad (2\text{-}8)$$

and

$$\frac{CD}{AC} = \frac{DB}{BC} = \frac{BC}{AB} = \frac{a}{c} = \sin \alpha = \cos \beta \qquad (2\text{-}9)$$

From Eq. 2-8, therefore,

$$(AC)^2 = (AB) \times (AD)$$

and from Eq. 2-9

$$(BC)^2 = (AB) \times (DB)$$

Adding gives

$$(AC)^2 + (BC)^2 = (AB) \times (AD + DB) = (AB)^2$$

or

$$a^2 + b^2 = c^2 \qquad (2\text{-}10)$$

From Eqs. 2-8 and 2-9, Eq. 2-10 may be written

$$\sin^2 \alpha + \cos^2 \alpha = 1 \qquad (2\text{-}11)$$

This gives

$$\sin \alpha = \sqrt{1 - \cos^2 \alpha} \qquad \text{and} \qquad \cos \alpha = \sqrt{1 - \sin^2 \alpha} \quad (2\text{-}12)$$

Also

$$\frac{1}{\cos^2 \alpha} = \frac{\sin^2 \alpha + \cos^2 \alpha}{\cos^2 \alpha} = \frac{\sin^2 \alpha}{\cos^2 \alpha} + 1 = \tan^2 \alpha + 1 = \sec^2 \alpha \quad (2\text{-}13)$$

Conversely, if $\tan \alpha = a/b$,

$$\sin \alpha = \frac{a}{\sqrt{a^2 + b^2}} \qquad \text{and} \qquad \cos \alpha = \frac{b}{\sqrt{a^2 + b^2}} \quad (2\text{-}14)$$

2-4 Functions of Angles in Different Quadrants. From the circle diagram of the trigonometric functions (Fig. 2-7) we see that, when changing from a positive angle (counterclockwise rotation) to a negative angle (clockwise rotation), s and t reverse their direction, but c remains the same. Therefore

$$\sin (-\alpha) = -\sin \alpha$$
$$\cos (-\alpha) = \cos \alpha \qquad (2\text{-}15)$$
$$\tan (-\alpha) = -\tan \alpha$$

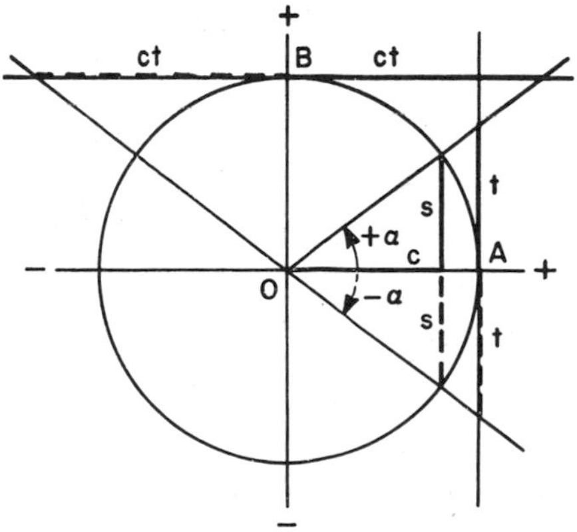

Fig. 2-7 Functions of negative angles.

Cos α is thus an *even* function, while the two others are *odd* functions. For an even function, $f(-x) = f(x)$; for an odd function, $f(-x) = -f(x)$.

From Fig. 2-8, it follows that, when changing from an angle α, to its supplementary angle $\pi - \alpha$, s remains in the same direction, but c and t reverse their directions, and all three functions retain the same

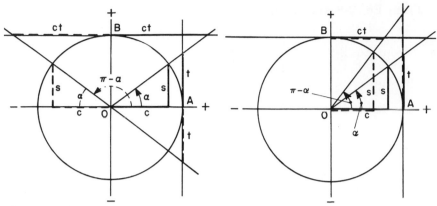

Fig. 2-8 Functions of supplementary angles.

Fig. 2-9 Functions of complementary angles.

numerical values; thus

$$\sin (\pi - \alpha) = + \sin \alpha$$
$$\cos (\pi - \alpha) = - \cos \alpha \qquad (2\text{-}16)$$
$$\tan (\pi - \alpha) = - \tan \alpha$$

Changing from an angle α to its complementary angle $\pi/2 - \alpha$, as seen in Fig. 2-9, the signs remain the same, but s and c exchange their numerical values; thus

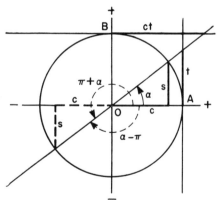

$$\sin \left(\frac{\pi}{2} - \alpha\right) = \cos \alpha$$

$$\cos \left(\frac{\pi}{2} - \alpha\right) = \sin \alpha$$

$$\tan \left(\frac{\pi}{2} - \alpha\right) = \frac{1}{\tan \alpha} = \cot \alpha$$

$$(2\text{-}17)$$

Fig. 2-10 Functions of angles plus or minus π.

Adding plus or minus 180°, or $\pm\pi$, to an angle, α, gives the same absolute values of the trigonometric functions as α, as seen in Fig. 2-10, but the directions of s and c are reversed, while t remains in the same direction:

$$\sin (\alpha \pm \pi) = - \sin \alpha$$
$$\cos (\alpha \pm \pi) = - \cos \alpha \qquad (2\text{-}18)$$
$$\tan (\alpha \pm \pi) = + \tan \alpha$$

Adding 90°, or $\pi/2$ radians, to an angle α interchanges the values of s and c and also reverses the directions of the cosine and tangent, but leaves the sine in the same direction (Fig. 2-11).

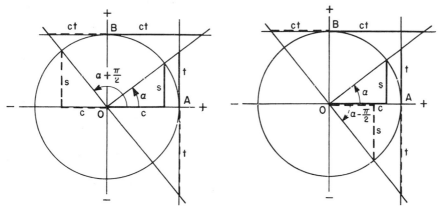

Fig. 2-11 Functions of angles plus $\pi/2$. **Fig. 2-12** Functions of angles minus $\pi/2$.

Subtracting $\pi/2$ radians from α interchanges the values of s and c and also reverses the sine and tangent, leaving the cosine in the same direction (Fig. 2-12). Thus

$$\sin\left(\alpha + \frac{\pi}{2}\right) = \cos\alpha \qquad \sin\left(\alpha - \frac{\pi}{2}\right) = -\cos\alpha$$

$$\cos\left(\alpha + \frac{\pi}{2}\right) = -\sin\alpha \qquad \cos\left(\alpha - \frac{\pi}{2}\right) = +\sin\alpha \qquad (2\text{-}19)$$

$$\tan\left(\alpha + \frac{\pi}{2}\right) = -\frac{1}{\tan\alpha} \qquad \tan\left(\alpha - \frac{\pi}{2}\right) = -\frac{1}{\tan\alpha}$$

From the circle diagrams (Figs. 2-7 to 2-12), there follow the numerical values shown in Table 2-2.

For a very small angle ϵ; $\cos\epsilon \cong 1$, $\sin\epsilon \cong \tan\epsilon \cong \epsilon$. Trigonometric functions can be expressed in the form of infinite power series, Eqs. 3-25 and 3-26, from which their numerical values can be calculated.

Figure 2-13 shows the sine, cosine, and tangent functions plotted against the angle. They are all periodic functions, repeating themselves each 360°, or each 2π radians. Values of the functions are given in Appendix B.

2-5 Laws of the Triangle. If we go around any triangle in the direction ABC (Fig. 2-14) we first go along AB to B, then turn left

Table 2-2   Numerical Values of Trigonometric Functions at 15° Intervals

Angle		Sine		Cosine		Tangent	
De-grees	Rad-ians	Exact value	Deci-mal ap-proxi-mation	Exact value	Deci-mal ap-proxi-mation	Exact value	Deci-mal ap-proxi-mation
0	0	0	0	1	1	0	0
15	$\pi/12$	$(\sqrt{6}-\sqrt{2})/4$	0.2588	$(\sqrt{6}+\sqrt{2})/4$	0.9659	$2-\sqrt{3}$	0.2679
30	$\pi/6$	$\frac{1}{2}$	0.5000	$\sqrt{3}/2$	0.8660	$1/\sqrt{3}$	0.5774
45	$\pi/4$	$1/\sqrt{2}$	0.7071	$1/\sqrt{2}$	0.7071	1	1
60	$\pi/3$	$\sqrt{3}/2$	0.8660	$\frac{1}{2}$	0.5000	$\sqrt{3}$	1.7321
75	$5\pi/12$	$(\sqrt{6}+\sqrt{2})/4$	0.9659	$(\sqrt{6}-\sqrt{2})/4$	0.2588	$2+\sqrt{3}$	3.7321
90	$\pi/2$	1	1	0	0	∞ *	∞ *
105	$7\pi/12$	$(\sqrt{6}+\sqrt{2})/4$	0.9659	$(\sqrt{2}-\sqrt{6})/4$	−0.2588	$-2-\sqrt{3}$	−3.7321
120	$2\pi/3$	$\sqrt{3}/2$	0.8660	$-\frac{1}{2}$	−0.5000	$-\sqrt{3}$	−1.7321
etc.							

* Not defined.

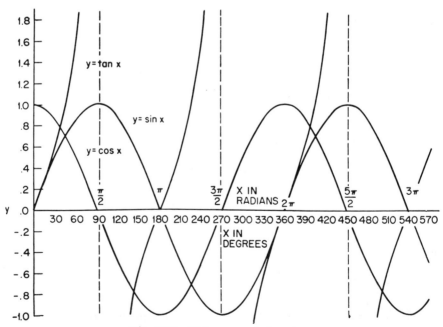

Fig. 2-13   Trigonometric functions.

through an angle of $180° - \beta$, proceed along BC to C, turn left again through an angle of $180° - \gamma$, go along CA to A, and turn left once more through an angle of $180° - \alpha$, ending the journey in the same direction that we started, having turned through $360°$ in all. Therefore, we find that

$$180° - \beta + 180° - \gamma + 180° - \alpha = 360°$$

or
$$\alpha + \beta + \gamma = 180° \qquad (2\text{-}20)$$

that is, the sum of the interior angles of any triangle is always equal to $180°$. If any two of the angles are known, the third can be found from

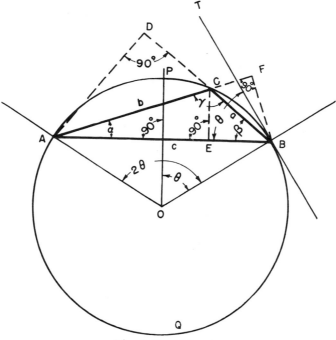

Fig. 2-14 Triangle.

Eq. 2-20. In a right triangle, one of the angles is $90°$, so that the sum of the other two angles is $90°$.

These relations can also be derived from the circle that passes through A, B, and C (Fig. 2-14). Drawing the tangent BT at B, and also the radius OP that bisects AB, we note that the angle $BOP = \theta$ is equal to the angle ABT, since OP is turned $90°$ from AB, and OB is also turned $90°$ from BT. As OP bisects AB, the angle AOB must equal 2θ. Therefore, it follows that

The angle β subtended by any chord of a circle AC at a point B on the circumference is equal to half the angle subtended by

AC at the center of the circle and, for fixed A and C, is the same wherever B may be located on the circle.

Thus, in Fig. 2-14, taking the radius of the circle as unity, we have

Angle $ABT = \theta =$ one-half arc ACB (a)

Angle $CAB = \alpha =$ one-half arc $CB =$ the angle $CBT = \theta - \beta$ (b)

Angle $ABC = \beta =$ one-half arc $AC = \beta$ (c)

Angle $BCA = \gamma =$ one-half arc $AQB = 180° - \theta$ (d)

Adding (b), (c), and (d), we find the sum of α, β, and γ to be $180°$ as before.

To find the relations between the sides and the angles, we note that the three altitudes of the triangle are, in Fig. 2-14,

$$CE = a \sin \beta = b \sin \alpha \qquad (2\text{-}21)$$
$$AD = b \sin \gamma = c \sin \beta \qquad (2\text{-}22)$$
$$BF = c \sin \alpha = a \sin \gamma \qquad (2\text{-}23)$$

These equations give the *law of sines:*

$$\frac{\sin \alpha}{a} = \frac{\sin \beta}{b} = \frac{\sin \gamma}{c} \qquad (2\text{-}24)$$

From Eqs. 2-20 and 2-24, any other sides or angles of the triangle can be found, if three sides, or two sides and one angle, or one side and two angles, are known.

Other useful relations between the sides and the cosines of the angles are derived by expressing each side as the sum of the projections on it of the other two sides:

$$\begin{aligned}
a = BC = BD - CD = c \cos \beta + b \cos \gamma \\
b = CA = FA - FC = c \cos \alpha + a \cos \gamma \\
c = AB = AE + EB = b \cos \alpha + a \cos \beta
\end{aligned} \qquad (2\text{-}25)$$

From Fig. 2-14 also, we derive the *law of cosines:*

$$\overline{AB}^2 = \overline{AD}^2 + (\overline{BC} + \overline{CD})^2$$

or $\qquad c^2 = b^2 \sin^2 \gamma + (a - b \cos \gamma)^2 = a^2 + b^2 - 2ab \cos \gamma$

so that $\qquad\qquad\qquad \cos \gamma = \dfrac{a^2 + b^2 - c^2}{2ab} \qquad (2\text{-}26)$

The area of the triangle (see Sec. 2-8) is half the product of the base by the altitude:

$$\text{Area} = \frac{ab \sin \gamma}{2} = \frac{ac \sin \beta}{2} = \frac{bc \sin \alpha}{2} = \frac{c^2 \sin \alpha \sin \beta}{2 \sin \gamma}$$

$$= \frac{b^2 \sin \alpha \sin \gamma}{2 \sin \beta} = \frac{a^2 \sin \beta \sin \gamma}{2 \sin \alpha} \qquad (2\text{-}27)$$

The above formulas are convenient for slide-rule calculation. When logarithms are used, to obtain greater accuracy the law of tangents is more convenient. This is derived by combining and rearranging Eq. 2-24:

$$\frac{a+b}{a-b} = \frac{\sin\alpha + \sin\beta}{\sin\alpha - \sin\beta} \tag{2-28}$$

This becomes, with the aid of Eqs. 2-30 to 2-43, developed in the following section,

$$\frac{a+b}{a-b} = \frac{\tan\left[(\alpha+\beta)/2\right]}{\tan\left[(\alpha-\beta)/2\right]} \tag{2-29}$$

2-6 Functions of Two Angles. Figure 2-15 enables us to find the trigonometric functions of the sum or difference of two angles, in terms of the functions of the separate angles.

Taking the radius OR as unity, we see that

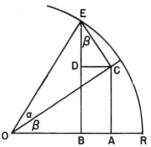

$$
\begin{aligned}
\sin(\alpha+\beta) &= BE = DE + AC \\
&= EC\cos\beta + OC\sin\beta \\
&= \sin\alpha\cos\beta + \cos\alpha\sin\beta \\
&\hspace{3em}(2\text{-}30)
\end{aligned}
$$

Also

$$
\begin{aligned}
\cos(\alpha+\beta) &= OB = OA - CD \\
&= OC\cos\beta - EC\sin\beta \\
&= \cos\alpha\cos\beta - \sin\alpha\sin\beta \\
&\hspace{3em}(2\text{-}31)
\end{aligned}
$$

Fig. 2-15 Functions of two angles.

By substituting $-\beta$ for β, and from Eq. 2-15, we find for the difference of two angles

$$
\begin{aligned}
\sin(\alpha-\beta) &= \sin\alpha\cos(-\beta) + \cos\alpha\sin(-\beta) \\
&= \sin\alpha\cos\beta - \cos\alpha\sin\beta \tag{2-32}\\
\cos(\alpha-\beta) &= \cos\alpha\cos(-\beta) - \sin\alpha\sin(-\beta) \\
&= \cos\alpha\cos\beta + \sin\alpha\sin\beta \tag{2-33}
\end{aligned}
$$

By combining these equations in pairs, we find

$$
\begin{aligned}
\cos\alpha\cos\beta &= \tfrac{1}{2}[\cos(\alpha+\beta) + \cos(\alpha-\beta)] & (2\text{-}34)\\
\sin\alpha\sin\beta &= \tfrac{1}{2}[\cos(\alpha-\beta) - \cos(\alpha+\beta)] & (2\text{-}35)\\
\sin\alpha\cos\beta &= \tfrac{1}{2}[\sin(\alpha+\beta) + \sin(\alpha-\beta)] & (2\text{-}36)\\
\cos\alpha\sin\beta &= \tfrac{1}{2}[\sin(\alpha+\beta) - \sin(\alpha-\beta)] & (2\text{-}37)
\end{aligned}
$$

By substituting α_1 for $(\alpha + \beta)$ and β_1 for $(\alpha - \beta)$ in these equations, we find the inverse equations:

$$\sin \alpha_1 + \sin \beta_1 = 2 \sin \frac{\alpha_1 + \beta_1}{2} \cos \frac{\alpha_1 - \beta_1}{2} \qquad (2\text{-}38)$$

$$\sin \alpha_1 - \sin \beta_1 = 2 \sin \frac{\alpha_1 - \beta_1}{2} \cos \frac{\alpha_1 + \beta_1}{2} \qquad (2\text{-}39)$$

$$\cos \alpha_1 + \cos \beta_1 = 2 \cos \frac{\alpha_1 + \beta_1}{2} \cos \frac{\alpha_1 - \beta_1}{2} \qquad (2\text{-}40)$$

$$\cos \alpha_1 - \cos \beta_1 = 2 \sin \frac{\alpha_1 + \beta_1}{2} \sin \frac{\alpha_1 - \beta_1}{2} \qquad (2\text{-}41)$$

Equations 2-30 to 2-41 are the most important trigonometric formulas, from which nearly all others can be derived. It is a good practice exercise to rederive Eqs. 2-16 to 2-19 by substituting β equal to 0, $\pi/2$, etc., in Eqs. 2-34 to 2-41.

The relations can be remembered more easily by noting that cosine functions lead to products of like functions, sine functions to products of unlike functions. Inversely, products of like functions resolve into cosines, products of unlike functions into sines. Also, cosine functions show a reversal of the sign, thus: the cosine of a sum is given by the difference of products; the cosine of a difference by a sum of products. This is because the cosine decreases with increasing angle; the cosine of the sum of two angles is less than the cosine of either angle.

From Eqs. 2-30 and 2-31, substituting α for β, we find the functions of a double angle:

$$\sin 2\alpha = 2 \sin \alpha \cos \alpha \qquad (2\text{-}42)$$

and

$$\cos 2\alpha = \cos^2 \alpha - \sin^2 \alpha = 2 \cos^2 \alpha - 1 = 1 - 2 \sin^2 \alpha \qquad (2\text{-}43)$$

whence follow

$$\sin^2 \alpha = \frac{1 - \cos 2\alpha}{2} \qquad \text{and} \qquad \sin \frac{\alpha}{2} = \sqrt{\frac{1 - \cos \alpha}{2}} \qquad (2\text{-}44)$$

$$\cos^2 \alpha = \frac{1 + \cos 2\alpha}{2} \qquad \text{and} \qquad \cos \frac{\alpha}{2} = \sqrt{\frac{1 + \cos \alpha}{2}} \qquad (2\text{-}45)$$

Equation 2-44 is illustrated by Fig. 2-16.

One of the most frequent trigonometric operations in electrical engineering is the transformation of the binomial, $a \cos \alpha + b \sin \alpha$, into a single trigonometric function, by the substitution $a = c \cos \beta$ and $b = c \sin \beta$, whence

$$a \cos \alpha + b \sin \alpha = c(\cos \beta \cos \alpha + \sin \beta \sin \alpha) = c \cos (\alpha - \beta) \qquad (2\text{-}46)$$

where $\quad c = \sqrt{a^2 + b^2} \quad$ and $\quad \tan \beta = b/a$

or by the alternative substitution, $a = c \sin \gamma$, $b = c \cos \gamma$, giving

$$a \cos \alpha + b \sin \alpha = c (\sin \gamma \cos \alpha + \cos \gamma \sin \alpha) = c \sin (\alpha + \gamma) \tag{2-47}$$

where $\quad c = \sqrt{a^2 + b^2} \quad$ and $\quad \tan \gamma = a/b$

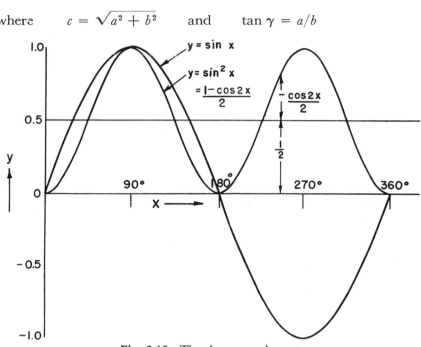

Fig. 2-16 The sine-squared curve.

2-7 Polyphase Relations. One frequently encounters in engineering the sums of a series of trigonometric functions, such as

$$S = \sin \alpha + \sin 2\alpha + \sin 3\alpha + \cdots + \sin n\alpha \tag{2-48}$$

or, more generally,

$$S = \sin \alpha + \sin \left(\alpha \pm \frac{2m\pi}{n} \right) + \sin \left(\alpha \pm \frac{4m\pi}{n} \right) + \sin \left(\alpha \pm \frac{6m\pi}{n} \right)$$
$$+ \cdots + \sin \left(\alpha \pm \frac{2km\pi}{n} \right) \tag{2-49}$$

If α represents elapsed time, or the angular position of a uniformly rotating vector, the successive terms in Eq. 2-49 will all be similar (have the same frequency) but will be displaced in angular position, or phase, from each other by the constant angle $2m\pi/n$.

Hence, the equation may represent the sum of successive voltages or currents in the symmetrically arranged windings of a polyphase alternating-current machine. The term "polyphase" describes a number (usually three) of similar windings or circuits carrying currents of the same frequency, but equally displaced in time from one another

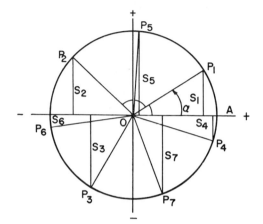

Fig. 2-17   Polyphase relations.

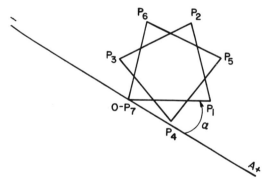

Fig. 2-18   Summation of sine series.

Any sine (or cosine) series of this type can be summed by recognizing that successive terms represent the vertical (or horizontal) projections of successive radii of a circle, spaced $2m\pi/n$ radians apart. If the radii are equally spaced over 360°, or a multiple thereof, the sum will be zero. In Fig. 2-17, for example, the radii for $m = 2$, $n = 7$ are shown as OP_1, OP_2, OP_3, etc., spaced $2\pi/7$ radian apart. These points form a closed polygon with seven sides, enclosing 360°, and the sum of the projections of the radii on either the vertical or horizontal axis is, therefore, zero (Fig. 2-18).

Hence

$$\sum_{i=1}^{n} \sin\left(\alpha \pm \frac{2mi\pi}{n}\right) = 0 \qquad (2\text{-}50)$$

and

$$\sum_{i=1}^{n} \cos\left(\alpha \pm \frac{2mi\pi}{n}\right) = 0 \qquad (2\text{-}51)$$

where $\displaystyle\sum_{i=1}^{n}$ means the sum of all the terms for which i has, successively, the values 1, 2, 3, . . . , n. If $\pm 2mi\pi/n$ is added to both α and β in Eqs. 2-34 to 2-37, 2-50 and 2-51 can be used to give

$$\sum_{i=1}^{n} \cos\left(\alpha \pm \frac{2mi\pi}{n}\right) \cos\left(\beta \pm \frac{2mi\pi}{n}\right) = \frac{n}{2} \cos(\alpha - \beta) \quad (2\text{-}52)$$

$$\sum_{i=1}^{n} \sin\left(\alpha \pm \frac{2mi\pi}{n}\right) \sin\left(\beta \pm \frac{2mi\pi}{n}\right) = \frac{n}{2} \cos(\alpha - \beta) \quad (2\text{-}53)$$

$$\sum_{i=1}^{n} \sin\left(\alpha \pm \frac{2mi\pi}{n}\right) \cos\left(\beta \pm \frac{2mi\pi}{n}\right) = \frac{n}{2} \sin(\alpha - \beta) \quad (2\text{-}54)$$

2-8 The Calculation of Areas. The area of a rectangle with sides a and b is ab. For, if each side is marked off in unit lengths, the entire area of the rectangle will be seen to consist of a rows of b unit squares (or b columns of a unit squares), making ab unit squares in all. The area of a parallelogram (Fig. 2-19) is equal to its height times its base. For, by cutting off the triangle formed at one end by the side, the altitude, and the extension of the base, as shown in the figure, and adding this triangle to the other end, the area is found to be the same as that of a rectangle with the same base and altitude.

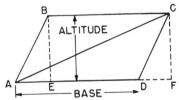

Fig. 2-19 Area of a parallelogram.

The area of the triangle formed by the diagonal and two adjacent sides of any parallelogram is evidently equal to half the area of the parallelogram, or half the altitude times the base of the triangle, as was stated in Sec. 2-5 without proof (Eq. 2-27).

The ratio of the circumference of a circle to its radius R is 2π. (The numerical value of $\pi = 3.14159 \cdots$ can be calculated from infinite series expressions derived by the calculus, as shown in Chaps. 8 and 9.) The length of an arc of angle α is $\alpha/2\pi$ times the circumference of the circle, or simply αR. Evidently, the area of a pie-shaped sector of a circle, with angle α, is equal to $\alpha/2\pi$ times the area of the entire circle. If the angle α is very small, the sector approaches a triangle, with altitude equal to the circle radius, R, and base equal to αR. Since the area of this triangle is

$$\frac{1}{2}(R)(\alpha R) = \frac{\alpha R^2}{2}$$

the area of the entire circle is $2\pi/\alpha$ times $\alpha R^2/2$, or πR^2.

By means of these simple formulas for the areas of triangles and sectors of circles, it is possible to calculate the area of any plane figure to a close approximation. For, no matter how complicated the shape of the figure, it is a simple matter to divide it up by straight lines and arcs of circles into a number of distinct triangles and sectors, whose areas may be calculated and summed by simple arithmetic. When the boundary of the area is curved or irregular, it may be necessary to break it up into a large number of short lines, or arcs, the actual number required depending on the accuracy that is wanted. Rules are given in Sec. 8-5 for making such calculations most simply.

The surveyor and the civil engineer, who make maps, lay out roads, locate dams and building sites, etc., require extensive calculations of the kind just described. While it is necessary to allow for the curvature of the earth in large-scale surveying, and other refinements are used for special purposes, the simple formulas given above for the triangle and the circle are all that are necessary for most of the surveyor's work.

2-9 Plane-table Surveying. A simple way to make a map of a limited area is by plane-table surveying. Two elevated observation stations, A and B, are chosen that overlook the area, and a base line is measured off between these, or any other convenient points that can be seen from both stations. Then, a sketch pad is placed at A, a point a on it is selected to represent A, and lines are drawn on the sketch radiating from a toward B, C, D, and various landmarks such as tall trees, houses, road intersections, etc., by sighting toward each in turn, as indicated in Fig. 2-20. A surveyor's transit, or telescope with a graduated circle for measuring horizontal angles, is used for accurate work, and the angles between the different radial lines are recorded on the sketch. Next, the process is repeated at B, the lines being now drawn from another point, b, chosen to represent B on the map. The same thing may be repeated at as many different stations as required to survey the whole area with the desired accuracy.

The location of each landmark is fixed by the intersection of the lines toward it from the several stations. If more than two stations are used, the lines may not intersect at exactly the same point, because of errors of observation, and the mid-point of the intersections will be taken as the true position. The scale of the map is determined by measuring the distance between the ends of the base line, *c* and *d*, as fixed in this way on the sketch pad, and by taking the ratio of the length of the base line, *L*, as measured on the ground, to the distance *cd* on the sketch to be the multiplier, or scale ratio, between actual and map distances.

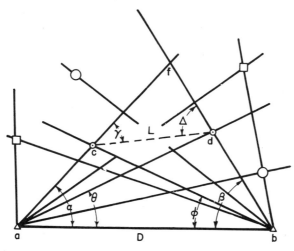

a,b   OBSERVATION STATIONS

c d   MEASURED BASE LINE

□○   LANDMARKS

Fig. 2-20   Plane-table survey.

The desired scale of the map may be chosen in advance, and the length *ab*, to represent the distance *D* between stations *A* and *B*, may be calculated before the final map is drawn. The procedure is first to calculate the ratios of *af* and *bf* to *D*, then the ratios of *fd* to *af* and of *fc* to *bf*, and finally the ratios of *fc* and *fd* to the measured length *L* of the base line. From these relations, the ratio of *D* to *L* is found.

The measured angles are

$$bac = \alpha \qquad abd = \beta$$

whence by Eq. 2-20

$$afb = 180° - \alpha - \beta$$
$$bad = \theta \qquad abc = \phi$$

whence

$$bcf = \alpha + \phi \qquad \text{and} \qquad adf = \beta + \theta$$

The unknown angles that must be calculated are $cdf = \Delta$ and $dcf = \gamma$. Since $cfd = afb = 180° - \alpha - \beta$, we have $\gamma = \alpha + \beta - \Delta$. Then, from Eq. 2-24,

$$af = \frac{D \sin \beta}{\sin (\alpha + \beta)} \quad \text{and} \quad bf = \frac{D \sin \alpha}{\sin (\alpha + \beta)}$$

or

$$af = \frac{bf \sin \beta}{\sin \alpha} \tag{2-55}$$

$$fc = \frac{bf \sin (\beta - \phi)}{\sin (\alpha + \phi)} \quad \text{and} \quad fd = \frac{af \sin (\alpha - \theta)}{\sin (\beta + \theta)} \tag{2-56}$$

$$\frac{fc}{fd} = \frac{\sin \Delta}{\sin (\alpha + \beta - \Delta)} = \frac{\sin \alpha \sin (\beta + \theta) \sin (\beta - \phi)}{\sin \beta \sin (\alpha + \phi) \sin (\alpha - \theta)} \tag{2-57}$$

From Eq. 2-57, the angle Δ can be calculated, since α, β, θ, and ϕ have all been measured directly. If Δ is known, D can be calculated from either of the equations

$$D = \frac{L \sin (\beta + \theta) \sin (\alpha + \beta - \Delta)}{\sin \beta \sin (\alpha - \theta)} \tag{2-58}$$

or

$$D = \frac{L \sin (\alpha + \phi) \sin \Delta}{\sin \alpha \sin (\beta - \phi)} \tag{2-59}$$

The two answers should agree, within the accuracy of the work.

The same methods can be used to locate ships at sea or forest fires. For this purpose, permanent stations, such as fire towers, are located on mountain tops, and their positions are accurately marked on large-scale maps. Observers in the towers sight on a fire through telescopes and telephone to headquarters the angles of their lines of sight. There, corresponding lines are drawn on the map, and fire fighters are rushed to the spot indicated by the intersection of the lines.

Similarly, heights as well as distances can be determined. Figure 2-21 shows a simple method for estimating the height of a tree or mountain. The observer holds out a stick at arm's length (L inches away from his eyes) and marks on it the vertical distance d spanned by the full height of the tree. Knowing the distance to the tree, D, as well as L and d, the height of the tree is given by the ratio formula

$$H = \frac{dD}{L} \quad \text{approximately} \tag{2-60}$$

Or, if the sun is shining, a vertical rod of known height may be set up, the distance from its base to the tip of its shadow may be measured, and the length of the shadow of the tree may be measured also. The height of the tree is then equal to the height of the rod multiplied by the ratio of the tree's shadow length to that of the rod.

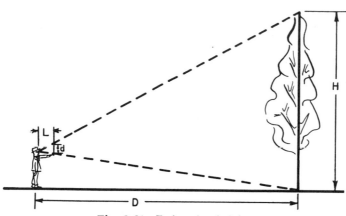

Fig. 2-21 Estimating heights.

2-10 Geometrical Concepts of Infinity. It is interesting to note in Fig. 2-13 that, if the angle is $\pi/2 - \epsilon$, and ϵ is made smaller and smaller, the tangent of the angle becomes larger and larger, approaching infinity as ϵ approaches zero. On the other hand, if the angle is $\pi/2 + \epsilon$, as ϵ is made smaller and smaller, the tangent of the angle is large and negative and approaches minus infinity as ϵ approaches zero. Thus, as the angle passes through $\pi/2$, the tangent goes to plus infinity, crosses over to minus infinity, and then returns from the negative region.

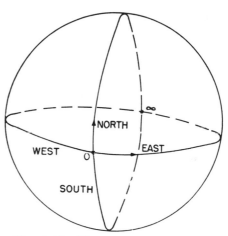

Fig. 2-22 The curvature of the earth.

This provides a fresh concept of the meaning of infinity that is well to consider here. Suppose that the sphere in Fig. 2-22 represents the earth on which we live and that we are at point O. The surface of the earth that we see at O appears to be flat (except for local ups and downs), and we are not conscious that it has any curvature. Therefore, if we sent off an airplane in a due-west direction, for example, and we knew that the pilot would not deviate far north or south from the east-west line, we would naturally expect it to come back, if at all, from the west. Actually the airplane, if it continues on a due-west course, will ultimately go completely around the earth and will return to its starting point, coming out of the east. If we really believed the earth to be flat, the return of the plane from the east would be surprising. As soon as we realize that the earth is a sphere, however, we explain the airplane's return very simply, saying that it made use of the third dimension to make the journey. The same result would occur if the airplane, after passing out of sight in the west, had turned vertically upward to a height beyond the range of our vision, returned over our heads, then descended to a low level far to the east, and at last returned home from that direction. This too will appear impossible if we believe the world has only two dimensions.

In a similar way, functions occurring in mathematics that go to plus infinity as the variable increases toward a particular value from one direction may approach minus infinity when the variable decreases toward the same value. In such cases, we can think of the function as crossing over from plus to minus infinity through an extra dimension of space, with which we are not otherwise concerned.

Just as in our life on the earth's surface we are seldom concerned with its curvature, so in the geometry of space, we are conscious of only three dimensions, forward or back, right or left, and up or down. In mathematics, however, there is no reason to limit ourselves to only three dimensions. We can imagine that there is a fourth dimension in space, of which we are not aware in our daily living, so that a ray of light sent out from the earth might ultimately return to the earth from the opposite direction. This idea of a curved space has been considered by astronomers, but the curvature is so slight (that is, the size of the universe is so great) that no direct evidence of such a return of light to its source has been obtained.

Man's imagination, however, has ranged far afield, and many different kinds of geometry in n dimensions, instead of only two or three, have been highly developed by mathematicians.

PROBLEMS

Give the values of cos α, tan α, sin $(\alpha + \pi)$, cos $(\alpha + \pi)$, tan $(\alpha + \pi)$, sin $(\alpha - \pi/2)$, cos $(\alpha - \pi/2)$, tan $(\alpha - \pi/2)$, when

1. $\sin \alpha = \frac{5}{13}$ **3.** $\sin \alpha = \frac{7}{25}$

2. $\sin \alpha = -\frac{3}{5}$ **4.** $\sin \alpha = -\frac{24}{25}$

Prove the following identities:

5. $\dfrac{\sin^3 \theta + \cos^3 \theta}{\sin \theta + \cos \theta} = 1 - \sin \theta \cos \theta$

6. $\dfrac{\csc \theta}{\cot \theta + \tan \theta} = \cos \theta$

7. $\sec^2 \theta + \cos^2 \theta = \tan^2 \theta \sin^2 \theta + 2$

8. $\cot \theta + \dfrac{\sin \theta}{1 + \cos \theta} = \csc \theta$

9. $3(\sin^4 \theta + \cos^4 \theta) - 2(\sin^6 \theta + \cos^6 \theta) = 1$

Prove that

10. $\tan (\alpha + \beta) = \dfrac{\tan \alpha + \tan \beta}{(1 - \tan \alpha \tan \beta)}$

11. $\tan (\alpha - \beta) = \dfrac{\tan \alpha - \tan \beta}{(1 + \tan \alpha \tan \beta)}$

Calculate the remaining sides and angles of a triangle ABC, given that

12. $a = 42.365$
$b = 25.863$
$C = 115° 39'$

13. $a = 365.74$
$b = 445.84$
$c = 545.62$

14. $a = 412.67$
$A = 50° 39'$
$B = 60° 8'$

15. $a = 0.062387$
$b = 0.023475$
$C = 110° 32'$

16. $a = 6.342$
$b = 7.295$
$c = 8.4177$

17. $a = 31.239$
$b = 49.001$
$A = 32° 18'$

Calculate the perimeter and the area of Figs. 2-23 and 2-24.

18. (Fig. 2-23)
$AB = 3.42$ inches
$BC = 6.16$ inches
$\angle EBA = 69°$
$\angle DBC = 16°$

19. (Fig. 2-24)
$ED = 6.42$ feet
$BD = 8.33$
$\angle EDF = 48°$
$\angle DBC = 63°$

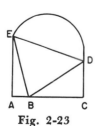

Fig. 2-23

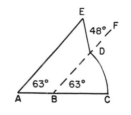

ED = 6.42
BD = 8.33

Fig. 2-24

Given a length a, with a compass and ruler, construct a line whose length is

20. $\sqrt{3}\, a$ **21.** $\sqrt{7}\, a$

Calculate the length of a side of the following regular polygons when the radius of the circumscribed circle is 1. Construct by trial and error the regular polygons with ruler and compass, and then compare the measured and calculated lengths:

    22. Pentagon (5-sided)   **24.** Heptagon (7-sided)
    23. Hexagon (6-sided)   **25.** Nonagon (9-sided)

Bibliography

1. Axelrod, Aaron: "Machine Shop Mathematics," 2d ed., McGraw-Hill Book Company, New York, 1951.
2. Coxeter, H. S. M.: "Elements of Geometry," John Wiley & Sons, Inc., New York, 1961.
3. Dubisch, Roy: "Trigonometry," The Ronald Press Company, New York, 1955.
4. Hart, W. W., and W. L. Hart: "Plane Trigonometry, Solid Geometry, and Spherical Trigonometry," D. C. Heath and Company, Boston, 1942.
5. Kells, L. M., W. F. Kern, and J. R. Bland: "Plane and Spherical Trigonometry," 3d ed., McGraw-Hill Book Company, New York, 1951.
6. Palmer, C. I., and S. F. Bibb, "Practical Mathemtics," 5th ed., McGraw-Hill Book Company, New York, 1952.
7. Wylie, C. R., Jr.: "Plane Trigonometry," McGraw-Hill Book Company, New York, 1955.

Chapter 3 DIRECTED NUMBERS

3-1 Quadrature Numbers. When we multiply a number by -1, we are reversing it. Therefore, multiplying by -1 twice, a double reversal, leaves the original number unchanged. When we say we are not *not* going to take action, we mean that we *are* going to do so. "Two negatives make a positive." Thus

$$(-1) \times (-1) = 1$$

Also $\qquad (+1) \times (+1) = 1$

and $\qquad\qquad (-1)^{2n} = +1 \qquad (-1)^{2n+1} = -1$

where n is any integer.

Therefore, we have

$$(+2)^2 = 4 \qquad \text{or} \qquad \sqrt{4} = +2$$

and also $\qquad (-2)^2 = 4 \qquad \text{or} \qquad \sqrt{4} = -2$

In extracting roots, we thus find the interesting feature that one and the same operation, with the same numbers, gives two different results. Since all the positive and negative numbers are used up as the square roots of positive numbers, the question arises, "What is the square root of a negative number?" For instance, $\sqrt{-4}$ cannot be -2, since -2 squared gives $+4$ nor can it be $+2$.

Since $\sqrt{-4} = \sqrt{4 \times -1} = 2\sqrt{-1}$, the question resolves itself into, "What is $\sqrt{-1}$?"

One of the ways we visualized numbers is by measuring distance, or counting steps, along a line (Fig. 3-1), from a starting point A. Going to the right gave us one kind of distance, to the left gave us the same numbers, but a different kind of distance. The first we chose to call positive $(+)$, the second negative $(-)$.

If we take a number, such as $+2$, which represents AB in Fig. 3-1, and multiply by -1, we get the distance $AC = -2$, opposite to AB. If we multiply again by -1, AC is changed back into $AB = +2$.

[59]

That is, multiplying by -1 has the effect of turning a distance through a half-circle, or 180°.

If we multiply $+2$ by $\sqrt{-1}$ once, we get $2\sqrt{-1}$. Multiplying again by $\sqrt{-1}$, we get -2, or AC. That is, multiplying twice by $\sqrt{-1}$ rotates a distance through 180°. Therefore, multiplication by $\sqrt{-1}$ gives a rotation of 90°. Thus, $2\sqrt{-1}$ is represented by the distance AD in Fig. 3-2.

Such numbers as $2\sqrt{-1}$ are *quadrature numbers*, which represent an upward direction; if we say that a $+$ number is in a direction to the right, and a $-$ number to the left, $-2\sqrt{-1}$ is in a downward direction.

If we lived in a one-dimensional world and were unaware of the existence of anything outside of the straight line on which we lived, the idea of a quadrature number would be purely imaginary. In fact, quadrature numbers are also called *imaginary* numbers, reflecting this

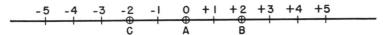

Fig. 3-1 Negative and positive numbers.

viewpoint. Just so, as we actually live in a three-dimensional world, we find it hard to imagine the existence of any fourth-or fifth-dimensional measurements. Nevertheless, mathematicians and even engineers find it useful to treat problems in more than three variables as if they were problems in an n-dimensional space (Sec. 3-5). The concept of the quadrature number, as shown in Fig. 3-2, thus opens a door to the understanding of a wide area of higher mathematics.

For convenience,[1] $\sqrt{-1}$ is usually denoted by the letter j.

Just as the operation of subtraction introduced the negative numbers, having a direction 180° away from the already familiar positive numbers, so does the operation of taking roots introduce the quadrature number, such as $2j$, a new kind of number, having a direction differing by 90°, or at right angles to the positive and negative numbers, as shown in Fig. 3-2.

Quadrature numbers are just as real, mathematically, as the negative numbers. Physically, sometimes, the negative number has a meaning—if two opposite directions exist; sometimes it has no meaning—where only one direction exists. Likewise, the quadrature number sometimes has a physical meaning, in those cases where four directions exist, and has no meaning in those physical problems where only two directions exist.

[1] The letter i is also used instead of j, but this conflicts with the use of i to represent an electric current.

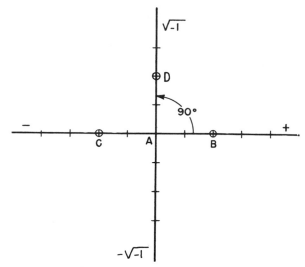

Fig. 3-2 Quadrature numbers.

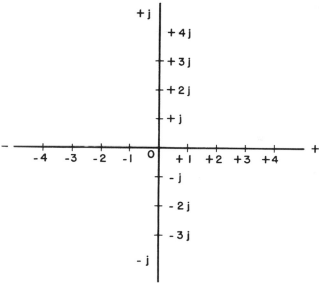

Fig. 3-3 The real and quadrature axes.

In plane geometry, and in electrical engineering when dealing with alternating current phasors (Sec. 3-4), the ordinary numbers represent the horizontal direction and the quadrature numbers the vertical. One horizontal direction is +, the other −, and so also for the vertical. Normally, positive is chosen to the right and upward, negative to the left and downward, as in Fig. 3-3; but these choices are purely a matter of convention.

In other problems, as when dealing with time, which has only the two directions of past and future, the quadrature numbers do not apply directly. In still other problems, as when dealing with absolute temperature, or illumination, or individuals, the negative numbers do not apply either, but only the positive numbers.

To sum up, just as multiplication by -1, the negative unit, means rotation through 180°, or reversal, so multiplication by $j = \sqrt{-1}$, the quadrature unit, means rotation through 90°, or change from horizontal to vertical, and conversely.

3-2 Complex Quantities. By using both quadrature and ordinary numbers, any point of a plane can be represented as a pair of distances from chosen coordinate axes, x and y. That is, any point P of the plane (Fig. 3-4) has a horizontal distance, $OB = +3$, and a ver-

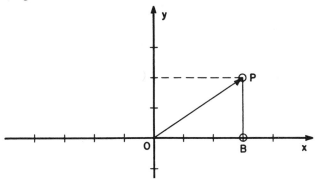

Fig. 3-4 The directed number or phasor.

tical distance, $BP = +2j$, and is, therefore, defined by a combination of the two. For convenience, the act of combining two such distances in quadrature is expressed by the plus sign. The result is thereby expressed by the equation

$$OB + BP = 3 + 2j$$

Such a combination of an ordinary number and a quadrature number is called a *complex quantity*, or sometimes a *general number*, or a *phasor*, or, more simply, a *directed number*. All these names represent the same mathematical concept. In such a combination of an ordinary and a quadrature number, either one may be positive, negative, or zero.

Physically, the directed number may be considered to represent the point P in the plane (Fig. 3-4). Or it may be considered to represent the radius vector from the origin, OP. Depending on the problem under consideration, an engineer may use either conception, or he may think of $3 + j2$ as a complex quantity, without any more physical embodiment than the grin of the Cheshire Cat. The electrical engineer calls directed numbers *phasors* because he uses them most frequently to represent the relations of periodic quantities that are displaced in time phase (see Sec. 3-13).

The quadrature number, jb, enormously extends the field of usefulness of algebra, since it provides a numerical representation of two-dimensional systems by the directed number, $a + jb$. It is especially useful in electrical engineering, since many problems in alternating currents lead to expressions with two components directed at right angles, which are directly represented by complex quantities.

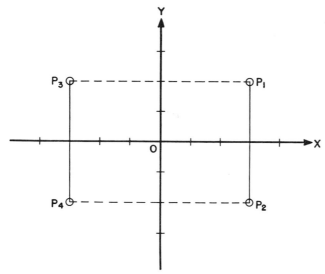

Fig. 3-5 Location of points in a plane.

Analytically, points in the plane are represented by their two coordinates: the horizontal coordinate, or *abscissa*, x, and the vertical coordinate, or *ordinate*, y. Algebraically, in the directed number, $a + jb$, the two coordinates are combined, a being the x coordinate and jb the y coordinate. Thus, in Fig. 3-5, coordinates of the points are

$$P_1: x = +3, y = +2 \qquad P_2: x = +3, y = -2$$
$$P_3: x = -3, y = +2 \qquad P_4: x = -3, y = -2$$

and the points are located in the plane by the directed numbers:

$$P_1: 3 + 2j \qquad P_2: 3 - 2j \qquad P_3: -3 + 2j \qquad P_4: -3 - 2j$$

3-3 The n Roots of Unity. Since the square root of a negative number has extended the system of numbers by giving us the quadrature number, the question arises whether still further extensions will arise from the higher roots of negative numbers. For example

$$(?)^4 = -1$$

We find the meaning of $\sqrt[4]{-1}$ in the same manner as for $\sqrt{-1}$.

A positive number a may be represented on the horizontal axis by P (Fig. 3-6). Multiplying a by $\sqrt[4]{-1}$ twice gives a $\sqrt{-1}$, or ja, whose meaning we know is a vertical line of length a. Multiplying a by $\sqrt[4]{-1}$ four times in succession gives $-a$; that is, in two steps we have rotated the distance a through 90°, and in four steps we have rotated a half-circle, or 180°. We see that a single step, or simple multiplication by $\sqrt[4]{-1}$, means a rotation through 45°.

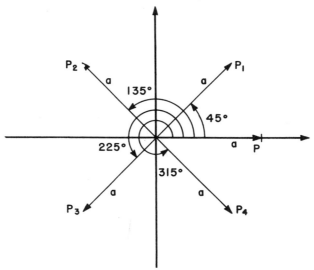

Fig. 3-6   The four fourth roots of $-\alpha^4$

Therefore, $a \sqrt[4]{-1}$ represents a point P_1 in Fig. 3-6, at a distance a from the coordinate center on a 45° radius, which has the coordinates

$$x = \frac{a}{\sqrt{2}}, y = \frac{a}{\sqrt{2}} \qquad \text{or} \qquad P_1: \frac{a(1+j)}{\sqrt{2}}$$

However, repeating a rotation of 135° to P_2 four times gives $4 \times 135 = 540°$, which is the same as 180°. Also, a rotation by 225°, or by 315°, gives 180° when repeated four times. Thus, four directed numbers exist, which equally well represent fourth roots of $-a^4$:

$$P_1: \frac{1+j}{\sqrt{2}} a \qquad\qquad P_2: \frac{-1+j}{\sqrt{2}} a$$

$$P_3: \frac{-1-j}{\sqrt{2}} a \qquad\qquad P_4: \frac{1-j}{\sqrt{2}} a$$

Therefore, all of the four roots of -1 are still directed numbers, consisting of an ordinary and a quadrature number. They do not extend our system of numbers any further.

In the same manner, $\sqrt[n]{+1}$ can be found. It is that number which multiplied by itself n times gives $+1$. It represents a rotation by $360/n°$. However, any integral multiple of this, that is, any directed number whose x coordinate is cos $(q \times 360/n)$ and whose y coordinate is sin $(q \times 360/n)$, also gives 1 when multiplied by itself n times:

$$\left(\cos \frac{360q}{n} + j \sin \frac{360q}{n}\right)^n = +1 \tag{3-1}$$

where q is any integer, positive or negative.

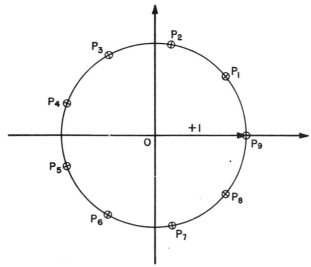

Fig. 3-7 Points determined by $\sqrt[9]{+1}$.

There are, therefore, n different directed numbers whose nth powers are equal to $+1$, which are represented by n points equally spaced on a circle with radius 1, as shown for $n = 9$ in Fig. 3-7.

3-4 Rectangular and Polar Coordinates. The best way to understand complex quantities and algebraic operations with them is to consider that they represent points in a plane. The complex quantity $a + jb = 6 + 2.5j$ represents a point P in Fig. 3-8, which has the abscissa $OA = BP = a = 6$ and the ordinate $OB = AP = b = 2.5$.

The distance of P from the coordinate center then is the hypotenuse of the right triangle OAP, or

$$OP = \sqrt{OA^2 + AP^2} = \sqrt{a^2 + b^2} = \sqrt{6^2 + (2.5)^2} = 6.5$$

The angle θ that OP makes with the x axis is given by

$$\tan \theta = \frac{AP}{OA} = \frac{b}{a} = \frac{2.5}{6} = 0.417$$

Instead of representing a complex quantity, or directed number, by its rectangular coordinates a and b in the form $a + jb$, it can be represented equally well by its polar coordinates, the distance, r, of the point from the origin, O:

$$r = \sqrt{a^2 + b^2}$$

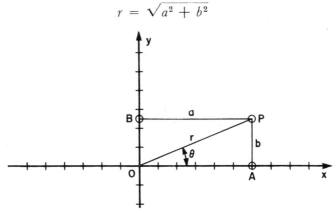

Fig. 3-8   Rectangular and polar coordinates.

and the phase angle θ between this radius and the x axis,

$$\theta = \tan^{-1} \frac{b}{a} \qquad \left(\text{the angle whose tangent is } \frac{b}{a}\right)$$

Then, referring to Fig. 3-8, we have

$$a = r \cos \theta \qquad \text{and} \qquad b = r \sin \theta$$

and the complex quantity, P: $a + jb$, can also be written in the form

$$P = r(\cos \theta + j \sin \theta)$$

or simply as $r\underline{/\theta}$, which is read as "r at the angle θ."[1]

The form $a + jb$ expresses the complex quantity by its rectangular coordinates, as used in analytic geometry; a is the x coordinate, b the y coordinate.

The form $r(\cos \theta + j \sin \theta)$ expresses the complex quantity by its polar coordinates, the radius r and the angle θ. In this expression r is called the *radius vector* or the *scalar;* θ the *phase angle.* In geometry, the

---

[1] This notation should not be interpreted as the number r times the angle θ. An alternative notation sometimes used is $r \operatorname{cis} \theta$ or $r \operatorname{cjs} \theta$, meaning $r(\cos \theta + j \sin \theta)$.

directed radius is called a *vector*. In other cases, as when the angle θ represents elapsed time, as in many electrical engineering problems, the directed radius is called a *phasor*.

The conjugate of a phasor, $r\underline{/\theta} = a + jb$, is $r\overline{\backslash\theta} = a - jb$. The two are equal in magnitude and have phase angles that are equal but opposite in sign. When a single letter is used to designate a phasor E, its conjugate is designated E^*.

Since a nonzero quadrature number cannot be equal to a real number, it follows that if two directed numbers are equal, their real components, or ordinary numbers, are equal and their quadrature numbers, or imaginary components, are also equal. Thus if

$$a + jb = c + jd$$

then $\qquad\qquad a = c \qquad$ and $\qquad b = d$

Every equation with complex quantities thus can be resolved into two equations, one containing only the ordinary numbers, the other only the quadrature numbers. For instance, if

$$x + jy = 5 - 3j$$

then $\qquad\qquad x = 5 \qquad$ and $\qquad y = -3$

3-5 Directed Numbers of More than Two Dimensions. Since, by the introduction of the quadrature number, the application of numbers was extended from the line, or one-dimensional quantities, to the plane, or two dimensions, the question arises whether the use of numbers can be still further extended. In space geometry, and in mechanics, problems often lie in three dimensions. In electrical engineering, problems occur which depend on the relations between the currents in three, four, or even more separate circuits. For all these, it may be useful to express the relations in complex algebra, using numbers generalized to three or more dimensions.

To extend the general number $a + jb$ to three dimensions, it is necessary to add the third axis in space at right angles to the x and y axes (Fig. 3-9). Also, instead of merely using j to represent rotation from the positive to the quadrature axis, we must employ three unit multipliers: j to represent rotation from the x direction to the y direction, h to rotate from y to z, and k to rotate from z to the x axis, as shown in Fig. 3-9.

Each of these three vectors is equal to $\sqrt{-1}$, since each, applied twice, reverses the direction, that is, is the same as multiplication by -1.

As seen in Fig. 3-9, starting from $+x$, going to y, then to z, and finally to $+x$, means successive multiplication by j, h, and k. Since we come back to the starting point, the total operation produces no change; that is, it represents multiplication by $+1$. Hence, it must be that

$$jhk = 1 \tag{3-2}$$

Algebraically, this is not possible, since each of the three quantities is $\sqrt{-1}$, and $\sqrt{-1} \times \sqrt{-1} \times \sqrt{-1} = -\sqrt{-1}$, and not $+1$.

If we now proceed again from x, in positive rotation, but first turn in the xz plane, by multiplication with k we reach the negative axis, $-z$, as seen in Fig. 3-10. Further multiplication by h brings us to $+y$,

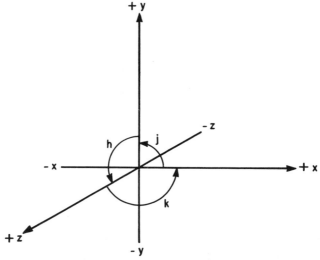

Fig. 3-9   Vectors in space, $jhk = +1$.

and multiplication by j to $-x$. In this case, the result of the three rotations by 90°, in the same directions as in Fig. 3-9, but in a different order, is a reversal, that is, represents -1. Therefore

$$khj = -1 \tag{3-3}$$

and hence

$$jhk = -khj$$

Thus, in vector analysis of more than two dimensions, we see that the fundamental law of algebra, called the *commutative* property of multiplication,

$$a \times b = b \times a$$

does not hold true. The order of the factors of a product is no longer immaterial, for changing the order of the factors of the product jhk reversed its sign. Therefore, common factors that do not occur in the same order cannot be canceled, as in ordinary algebra. For instance, if in the correct equation, $jhk = -khj$, we should cancel the j, h, and

k, as could be done in ordinary algebra, we would get $+1 = -1$, which is not true.

For this reason, the procedures devised for vector analysis in space and for the use of directed numbers in three or more dimensions are relatively difficult to apply and are little used in everyday engineering calculations. No further consideration will be given to them in this book, even though they are quite useful in advanced engineering problems.

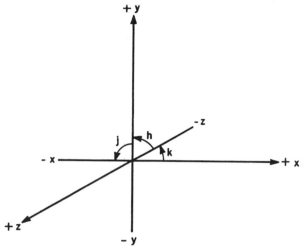

Fig. 3-10 Vectors in space, $khj = -1$.

3-6 Addition and Subtraction of Complex Quantities. If, in Fig. 3-11, P_1 represents $a_1 + jb_1 = 6 + 2.5j$, this point is reached by going from O, the horizontal distance $a_1 = 6$ and the vertical distance $b_1 = 2.5$. If P_2 represents $a_2 + jb_2 = 3 + 4j$, this point is reached by going the horizontal distance $a_2 = 3$ and the vertical distance $b_2 = 4$.

The sum of the two complex quantities, or directed numbers,

$$(a_1 + jb_1) + (a_2 + jb_2) = (6 + 2.5j) + (3 + 4j)$$

then is given by point P_0, which is reached by going from O a horizontal distance equal to the sum of a_1 and a_2:

$$a_0 = 6 + 3 = 9$$

and a vertical distance equal to the sum of b_1 and b_2:

$$b_0 = 2.5 + 4 = 6.5$$

Hence the point P_0 is given by the directed number

$$P_0: 9 + 6.5j$$

Geometrically, P_0 is derived from points P_1 and P_2 by constructing the diagonal OP_0 of the parallelogram $OP_1P_0P_2$, constructed with OP_1 and OP_2 as sides, as seen in Fig. 3-11.

It follows that the addition of complex quantities represents geometrical combination by the parallelogram law.

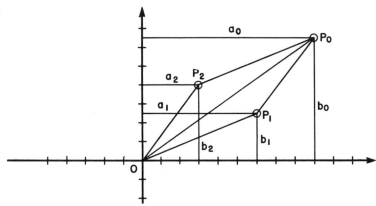

Fig. 3-11 Addition and subtraction of directed numbers.

Conversely, if P_0 represents the number

$$a_0 + jb_0 = 9 + 6.5j$$

and P_1 represents the number

$$a_1 + jb_1 = 6 + 2.5j$$

the difference of these numbers will be represented by a point P_2, which is reached by going the difference of the horizontal distances and of the vertical distances of the points P_0 and P_1. P_2 thus is represented by

$$a_2 = a_0 - a_1 = 9 - 6 = 3$$
and
$$b_2 = b_0 - b_1 = 6.5 - 2.5 = 4$$

Therefore, the difference of the two directed numbers $(a_0 + jb_0)$ and $(a_1 + jb_1)$ is given by the directed number

$$a_2 + jb_2 = (a_0 - a_1) + j(b_0 - b_1) = 3 + 4j \text{ or } P_2$$

as seen in Fig. 3-11.

This difference $a_2 + jb_2$ is represented by one side $\overline{OP_2}$ of the parallelogram $OP_1P_0P_2$, which has $\overline{OP_1}$ as the other side and $\overline{OP_0}$ as the diagonal.

Subtraction of directed numbers thus geometrically represents the resolution of a vector $\overline{OP_0}$ into two components, $\overline{OP_1}$ and $\overline{OP_2}$, by the parallelogram law.

Herein lies a great advantage of the use of the directed number in engineering calculations. If the vectors are represented by directed numbers (complex quantities), combination and resolution of vectors by the parallelogram law are carried out by simple addition or subtraction of their numerical values, that is, by the simplest operations of arithmetic.

Directed numbers are usually denoted by capitals, and their rectangular components, the ordinary number and the quadrature number, by small letters, thus:

$$A = a_1 + ja_2$$

The distance of the point which represents the directed number A from the coordinate center is called the *absolute value*, radius, or *scalar* of the directed number or complex quantity. It is the radius a in its polar representation:

$$A = a(\cos \theta + j \sin \theta)$$

and is given by $a = \sqrt{a_1{}^2 + a_2{}^2}$.

The directed number is often indicated by a boldface capital letter, in which case the scalar value may be indicated by an ordinary capital letter. However, in engineering work it is convenient to indicate the directed number by an ordinary capital letter and to indicate its scalar value either by a small letter or by a capital letter enclosed between vertical lines, thus:

$$A = a_1 + ja_2$$

and $\qquad\qquad a = \sqrt{a_1{}^2 + a_2{}^2} \qquad$ or $\qquad |A| = \sqrt{a_1{}^2 + a_2{}^2}$

and $\qquad\qquad a_1 + ja_2 = a(\cos \theta + j \sin \theta)$

or $\qquad\qquad a_1 + ja_2 = |A| (\cos \theta + j \sin \theta)$

The absolute value, or scalar, of a directed number is always an absolute number, or positive, and the sign of the rectangular component is represented in the angle θ. Thus, referring to Fig. 3-12, we have

$$A = a_1 + ja_2 = 4 + 3j$$

which gives $\qquad\qquad a = \sqrt{a_1{}^2 + a_2{}^2} = 5$

$$\tan \theta = \tfrac{3}{4} = 0.75$$

$$\theta = 37° \text{ approximately}$$

and $\qquad\qquad A = 5(\cos 37° + j \sin 37°)$

The expression $A = a_1 + ja_2 = 4 - 3j$

gives
$$a = \sqrt{a_1{}^2 + a_2{}^2} = 5$$
$$\tan \theta = -\tfrac{3}{4} = -0.75$$
$$\theta = -37° \quad \text{or} \quad \theta = 180 - 37 = 143°$$

Which of the two values of θ is the correct one is seen from the condition $a_1 = a \cos \theta$. As a_1 is positive, $+4$, it follows that $\cos \theta$ must be

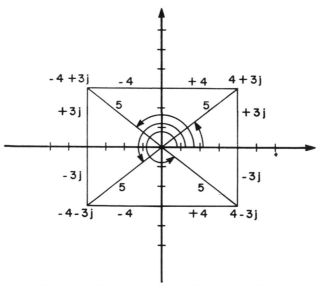

Fig. 3-12 Representation of directed numbers.

positive; $\cos (-37°)$ is positive, $\cos 143°$ is negative; hence the former value is correct:

$$A = 5[\cos (-37°) + j \sin (-37°)] = 5(\cos 37° - j \sin 37°)$$

The expression $A = a_1 + ja_2 = -4 + 3j$

gives
$$a = \sqrt{a_1{}^2 + a_2{}^2} = 5$$
$$\tan \theta = -\tfrac{3}{4} = -0.75$$
$$\theta = 37° \quad \text{or} \quad \theta = 180 - 37 = 143°$$

but since $a_1 = a \cos \theta$ is negative, -4, $\cos \theta$ must be negative; hence, $\theta = 143°$ is the correct value, and

$$A = 5(\cos 143° + j \sin 143°) = 5(- \cos 37° + j \sin 37°)$$

The expression $A = a_1 + ja_2 = -4 - 3j$

gives
$$a = \sqrt{a_1{}^2 + a_2{}^2} = 5$$
$$\theta = 37° \quad \text{or} \quad \theta = 180 + 37 = 217°$$

but since $a_1 = a \cos \theta$ is negative, -4, $\cos \theta$ must be negative; hence $\theta = 217°$ is the correct value, and

$$A = 5(\cos 217° + j \sin 217°) = 5(-\cos 37° - j \sin 37°)$$

The four directed numbers, $+4 + 3j$, $+4 - 3j$, $-4 + 3j$, and $-4 - 3j$, have the same absolute value, 5, and their representations as points in a plane have symmetrical locations in the four quadrants, as shown in Fig. 3-12.

Since $A = a_1 + ja_2$ can be used equally well to represent any point in a plane, it also may be called a *plane number*, while the positive and negative numbers, $+a$ and $-a$, may be called *linear numbers*, as they represent the points of a line.

3-7 Example—The Steam Path in a Turbine. As a simple example of the use of directed numbers, we may calculate the path of the steam flowing through two bucket wheels of an impulse turbine.

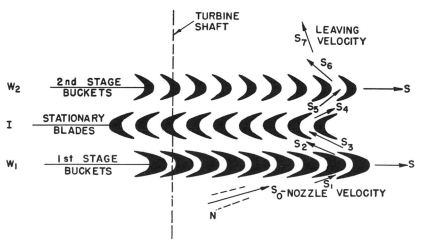

Fig. 3-13 Steam paths in two wheels of impulse turbine.

In such a turbine, high-temperature steam emerges at high velocity from a series of nozzles spaced around the outer edge of a wheel carrying curved radial blades, or buckets, as shown in Fig. 3-13. The buckets have thin edges sloped at an angle to be nearly tangent to the direction of flow of the entering steam. On entering the buckets, the steam is turned back in a smooth path, giving up its forward momentum to the wheel, and is directed into an adjoining series of stationary buckets. The edges of these stationary buckets are again shaped to be nearly tangent to the entering steam, to minimize steam eddies and friction losses. The steam path turns back again and emerges from the stationary buckets at the proper angle to enter smoothly into the buckets of the next rotating wheel.

In this way, the steam passes through a series of alternately moving and stationary buckets spaced around the entire periphery of the turbine, giving up more and more of its velocity and temperature as it proceeds, until it emerges from the last stage with very little available energy remaining. It is then condensed into water, pumped back into the boiler, reheated, and returned as steam to repeat the cycle.

The problem in designing the buckets is to make the leading bucket edges tangent to the entering steam, allowing for the steadily decreasing velocity and increasing volume of the steam as it passes through each wheel. Figure 3-13 represents a section cutting tan-

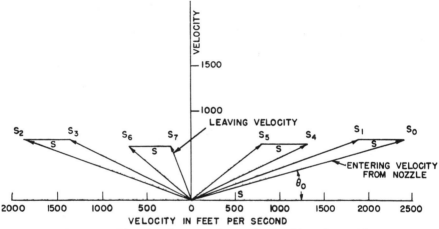

Fig. 3-14 Velocity diagram of two wheels of impulse turbine.

gentially across the buckets, as would be seen by an observer looking radially in toward the shaft. N is one of the expansion nozzles from which the steam emerges at an assumed velocity of $S_0 = 2,500$ feet per second, at an angle $\theta_0 = 16°$. W_1 and W_2 are two bucket wheels, turning together at a peripheral speed assumed to be 500 feet per second. I is an intermediate stationary ring of buckets, which turn the steam back in the direction required to enter the second bucket wheel, W_2. The buckets are assumed to be symmetrical, with equal entering and leaving angles. The friction coefficient in the buckets will be assumed to be $k_f = 0.06$; that is, the leaving velocity for each row of buckets is $1 - k_f = 0.94$ times the entering velocity.

Choosing as x axis the direction of the tangential velocity of the wheels (Fig. 3-14), the steam velocity as it enters the first wheel is represented in the figure by a vector OS_0 of length $V_0 = 2,500$ feet per second, making an angle of 16° with the x axis; hence by the directed number

$$S_0 = s_0(\cos \theta_0 + j \sin \theta_0) = 2{,}500(0.9613 + j0.2756)$$
$$= 2{,}403 + j689 \text{ fps}$$

The velocity of the wheel, W_1, is $S = 500$ feet per second, represented in Fig. 3-14 by the vector OS along the x axis. The velocity of the entering steam relative to the buckets is therefore

$$S_1 = S_0 - S = (2{,}403 - 500) + j689 = 1{,}903 + j689 \text{ fps}$$

This vector is OS_1 in the figure. The angle at which the steam enters the first buckets is therefore

$$\theta_1 = \tan^{-1} \frac{689}{1{,}903} = 19.9°$$

This angle must be given to the leading edges of the W_1 buckets. The entering steam velocity relative to the bucket is the scalar

$$s_1 = \sqrt{(1{,}903)^2 + (689)^2} = 2{,}024 \text{ fps}$$

Owing to friction, the velocity leaving W_1 will be

$$s_2 = s_1(1 - k_f) = 2{,}024(0.94) = 1{,}903 \text{ fps}$$

Since we have chosen the leaving angle to be the same as the entering angle, the steam velocity relative to W_1 is

$$OS_2 = s_2(\cos \theta_2 + j \sin \theta_2)$$
$$= 1{,}903[\cos (180 - 19.9) + j \sin (180 - 19.9)]$$
$$= 1{,}903(-0.9403 + j0.3404) = -1{,}789 + j648 \text{ fps}$$

Adding this to the wheel velocity of 500 fps gives the velocity at which the steam enters the stationary buckets, I:

$$OS_3 = -1{,}789 + j648 + 500 = -1{,}289 + j648 \text{ fps}$$

The direction of this jet is

$$\theta_3 = \tan^{-1} - \frac{648}{1{,}289} = \tan^{-1} - 0.502 = -26.7°$$

or

$$180 - 26.7 = 153.3°$$

As sin θ_3 is positive, the correct angle is $\theta_3 = 153.3°$, so that the entering angle of the intermediate buckets should be made 26.7°. The entering steam velocity for these buckets is the scalar of OS_3,

$$s_3 = \sqrt{(1{,}289)^2 + (648)^2} = 1{,}443 \text{ fps}$$

and the leaving velocity is

$$s_4 = s_3(1 - k_f) = 1{,}443(0.94) = 1{,}356 \text{ fps}$$

Since the leaving edge of the intermediate buckets is 26.7°, the leaving velocity of the steam, OS_4, is

$$S_4 = 1{,}356(\cos 26.7 + j \sin 26.7) = 1{,}212 + j609 \text{ fps}$$

This is the velocity of the steam entering the second bucket wheel, W_2. As the turning velocity of this wheel is also 500 feet per second, the entering velocity of the steam in these buckets, OS_5, is

$$S_5 = S_4 - S = 1{,}212 + j609 - 500 = 712 + j609 \text{ fps}$$

The direction of this jet is

$$\theta_5 = \tan^{-1} {}^{609}\!/_{712} = 40.5°$$

Therefore, the entrance angle of the second wheel buckets should be made 40.5°. The entering velocity in these buckets is the scalar of S_5,

$$s_5 = \sqrt{(712)^2 + (609)^2} = 936 \text{ fps}$$

The leaving velocity for the second wheel buckets is

$$s_6 = s_5(1 - k_f) = 936(0.94) = 880 \text{ fps}$$

The leaving angle of these buckets is 40.5°, so that the relative leaving velocity, OS_6, is

$$S_6 = s_6[\cos (180 - 40.5) + j \sin 40.5]$$
$$= 880(-0.760 + j0.649) = -669 + j571 \text{ fps}$$

The remaining lost or rejected velocity of the steam, OS_7, is OS_6 less the velocity of the wheel, or

$$S_7 = S_6 + S = -669 + j571 + 500 = -169 + j571 \text{ fps}$$

with an absolute value

$$s_7 = \sqrt{(169)^2 + (571)^2} = 595 \text{ fps}$$

3-8 Multiplication of Complex Quantities. Complex quantities are multiplied in the same way as ordinary numbers. The only new feature to be kept in mind is that $j^2 = -1$, and, accordingly, all higher powers of j can be eliminated, thus:

$$j^1 = j \qquad j^2 = -1 \qquad j^3 = -j \qquad j^4 = +1 \qquad j^5 = j, \text{ etc.} \quad \text{(3-4)}$$

If $A = a_1 + ja_2$ and $B = b_1 + jb_2$ are two complex quantities, or directed numbers, their product is

$$AB = (a_1 + ja_2)(b_1 + jb_2) = a_1b_1 + ja_2b_1 + ja_1b_2 + j^2a_2b_2$$
$$= (a_1b_1 - a_2b_2) + j(a_2b_1 + a_1b_2)$$

and the product can be represented by a point

$$C = c_1 + jc_2$$

where $c_1 = a_1b_1 - a_2b_2$
$c_2 = a_2b_1 + a_1b_2$

For instance, $A = 2 + j$ multiplied by $B = 1 + 1.5j$ gives

$$C = e + jf$$

where $e = 2 \times 1 - 1 \times 1.5 = 0.5$
$f = 2 \times 1.5 + 1 \times 1 = 4$

Hence $C = 0.5 + 4j$, as shown in Fig. 3-15.

The geometrical relation between the complex quantities A and B and their product C is better shown by using polar expressions. Thus

$$A = a/\alpha = a(\cos \alpha + j \sin \alpha) = a_1 + ja_2 \qquad (3\text{-}5)$$
$$B = b/\beta = b(\cos \beta + j \sin \beta) = b_1 + jb_2 \qquad (3\text{-}6)$$

where $a = \sqrt{a_1^2 + a_2^2}$
$b = \sqrt{b_1^2 + b_2^2}$

$$\alpha = \tan^{-1} \frac{a_2}{a_1}$$

$$\beta = \tan^{-1} \frac{b_2}{b_1}$$

Then

$$C = A \times B = ab(\cos \alpha + j \sin \alpha)(\cos \beta + j \sin \beta)$$
$$= ab[(\cos \alpha \cos \beta - \sin \alpha \sin \beta) + j(\cos \alpha \sin \beta + \sin \alpha \cos \beta)]$$
$$= ab[\cos(\alpha + \beta) + j \sin (\alpha + \beta)] \qquad (3\text{-}7)$$

That is, two complex quantities are multiplied by multiplying their scalar or absolute values, a and b, and adding their phase angles, α and β.

Thus, in Fig. 3-15, to multiply $A = a_1 + ja_2 = a/\alpha$ by

$$B = b_1 + jb_2 = b/\beta$$

the phasor OA is increased by the factor b and rotated through the angle β to the position OC. A complex multiplier B turns the multiplicand *A* by the phase angle of *B* and multiplies its absolute value by the absolute value of *B*.

The multiplier *B* is sometimes called an *operator*, since it carries out the operation of rotating the direction and changing the length of the multiplicand.

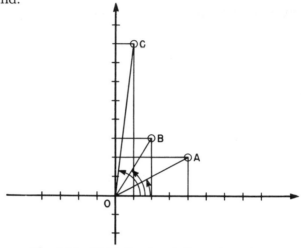

Fig. 3-15   Multiplication of directed numbers.

3-9 Physical Meaning of Multiplication.   In all algebraic operations with mathematical symbols used to represent physical quantities, it is desirable to consider whether the result of each operation, for instance the product of two factors, has a physical meaning or not. If it has a physical meaning, the question arises whether the meaning is such that the product can be represented in the same diagram as the factors.

For instance, $3 \times 4 = 12$, and 3 lots of 4 apples add up to 12 apples, but it is meaningless to multiply apples by apples. We only multiply numbers, and then interpret the result in physical terms. Thus, if we are dealing with distances, we interpret $3 \times 4 = 12$ to mean that an area 3 feet wide by 4 feet long has an area of 12 square feet. The unit of area 1 square foot is different from the unit of length 1 foot, so that the "dimensions" of the two numbers on the left side of the equation, i.e., 3 and 4, are different from the "dimension" of the right-hand number 12. In writing equations, it is essential to keep clearly in mind the distinction between a number and the physical quantity it may represent (Sec. 1-3).

If, on the line in Fig. 3-16, $OA = 3$ feet and $OB = 4$ feet, then the product, 12 square feet, while it has a physical meaning, cannot be represented any more by a point, such as $OC = 12$, on the same line.

For, if we expressed the distances OA and OB in inches, 36 and 48 inches, respectively, the product would be $36 \times 48 = 1{,}728$ square inches, while the distance $OC = 12$ feet, which might be thought to represent it, is equal to only 144 inches.

These considerations lead to the principle that for an equation to be true in physical terms, the numbers on each side must represent quantities of the same physical nature—if the terms on one side represent energy, as foot-pounds of work, those on the other side must also represent energy, perhaps kilowatt-seconds.

Exponents, and also logarithms, are merely numbers, or numerical ratios, not physical quantities. We cannot raise the number 4 to the 7 apples power, nor is the logarithm of 4 equal to any number of horses, nor of inches. From this, it follows that whenever an exponent or a logarithm in any mathematical expression is found to depend on the value of a physical quantity, this quantity must enter as a ratio to another (fixed) value of the same physical quantity. This leads to the basic principles of *dimensional analysis*, that all angles, exponents, and logarithms are dimensionless, and that all like terms in an equation between physical quantities must have the same dimensions.

O   A B   C

Fig. 3-16   Multiplication of physical quantities.

For example, we may express work done, as in lifting a weight, by the product of force times distance. In accordance with this principle, all other formulas for work done must be reducible to a product of force times distance. If any term in an equation relating different quantities of work is found to be proportional to force times (distance)^2, that term is obviously incorrect. This provides a useful method of checking formulas. An important result of this principle is that any correct equation between physical quantities will remain true whatever the units employed (whether inches or feet, for example) in measuring the quantities involved.

3-10   Per Unit Notation.   This requirement that all the terms in an equation represent similar objects, or have the same dimensions, points again to the need of precise distinctions between numbers, the symbols that represent the numbers, and the physical quantities to which the numbers apply in a particular problem. One way of keeping the distinctions clear is to add superscripts to each letter or symbol that is used, indicating which of all possible meanings is intended in the particular case. To use these superscripts in repetitive work is too burdensome. Therefore, engineers are accustomed to omitting them in their ordinary work, and relying on their own and their readers' familiarity with the conditions to avoid mistakes (as explained in a table of units that is supplied or referred to).

However, it is desirable to have a method available for making the distinctions when needed, especially for educational purposes. One such method is the *per unit notation*, as follows: Let

$^uG =$ the symbol chosen to represent the unit, or base quantity, of a particular physical entity, in terms of which the total quantity is measured. Thus ^uG may represent 1 dozen apples, or 1 bushel of apples, or 2 miles, or 10 tons, or whatever.

$G =$ an ordinary number, or measure of quantity, entirely apart from any physical concept

$G\,^uG =$ the number of dozens of apples, or tens of tons, or of other unit quantities that are being considered in a particular problem

When defined in this way, G is the "per unit" value of the quantity, and, therefore, G is a dimensionless number. Other letters, H, W, etc., may be used in place of G to represent different sorts of physical objects.

To write an equation that is physically as well as mathematically correct, the unit values, ^uG, should be included as multipliers with every quantity. Then, the effects of the units of measurement employed, whether centimeters, miles, or pounds, etc., can be separately evaluated.

For example, consider two different expressions for energy, or work done:

$$\text{Electric energy} = \text{electric power} \times \text{elapsed time}$$
$$\text{Mechanical energy} = \text{mechanical force} \times \text{distance}$$

In the English system, we usually measure force in pounds and distance in feet. To determine the relation between electric and mechanical energy, let

$^uQ =$ energy of one kilowatthour

$^uW =$ energy of one pound falling through a distance of one foot

$Q =$ number of kilowatthours measured in the particular case

$W =$ number of foot-pounds of work done in the particular case, equivalent to Q

Then

$$Q\,^uQ = W\,^uW \qquad \text{or} \qquad Q = W\left(\frac{^uW}{^uQ}\right)$$

By looking in an engineer's handbook, we find that

$$1 \text{ horsepower} = 0.746 \text{ kilowatts}$$
$$1 \text{ horsepower} = 33,000 \text{ foot-pounds per minute}$$

Therefore

$$^u Q = 1 \text{ kilowatthour}$$
$$= \left(\frac{1}{0.746}\right) \quad (1 \text{ horsepower})(60 \text{ minutes})$$
$$^u W = 1 \text{ foot-pound}$$

and

$$(1 \text{ horsepower})(1 \text{ minute}) = 33,000 \text{ foot-pounds} = 33,000 \; {}^u W$$

whence

$$^u Q = \left(\frac{60}{0.746}\right)(33,000) \; {}^u W$$

$$\frac{^u Q}{^u W} = 2,654,000$$

so that[1]

$$Q = \frac{W}{2,654,000}$$

In this way, as long as we are careful to include the appropriate unit values, $^u G$, in all equations relating physical quantities, we are free to measure quantities in terms of any unit we choose. Instead of measuring power in terms of kilowatts, for example, we may choose a base of 100,000 kilowatts, and then describe a 1,000,000-kilowatt power station as having a capacity of 10 units, or simply 10 pu. The numbers giving the results of physical measurements are all per unit values, but as long as the measurements are made in terms of familiar units, such as pounds or feet, we are likely to take the unit of measurement for granted.

3-11 Division of Complex Quantities. The division of two directed numbers is represented by

$$C = \frac{A}{B} = \frac{a_1 + ja_2}{b_1 + jb_2} \tag{3-8}$$

This fraction contains a quadrature number in the denominator as well as the numerator. The quadrature number can be eliminated

---

[1] Thus, the energy of 1 kilowatthour, which costs the typical American homeowner about 3¢, is sufficient to lift 2,654 pounds to a height of 1,000 feet.

from the denominator by multiplying both numerator and denominator by the conjugate of the denominator, $b_1 - jb_2$, giving

$$C = \frac{(a_1 + ja_2)(b_1 - jb_2)}{(b_1 + jb_2)(b_1 - jb_2)} = \frac{(a_1b_1 + a_2b_2) + j(a_2b_1 - a_1b_2)}{b_1{}^2 + b_2{}^2}$$

$$= \frac{a_1b_1 + a_2b_2}{b_1{}^2 + b_2{}^2} + j\,\frac{a_2b_1 - a_1b_2}{b_1{}^2 + b_2{}^2} \tag{3-9}$$

For instance,

$$C = \frac{A}{B} = \frac{6 + j2.5}{3 + j4} = \frac{(6 + j2.5)(3 - j4)}{(3 + j4)(3 - j4)} = \frac{28 - j16.5}{25}$$
$$= 1.12 - j0.66$$

Conversely, the quadrature number may be eliminated from the numerator by multiplying both numerator and denominator by the conjugate of the numerator:

$$C = \frac{A}{B} = \frac{6 + j2.5}{3 + 4} = \frac{(6 + j2.5)(6 - j2.5)}{(3 + j4)(6 - j2.5)} = \frac{42.25}{28 + j16.5}$$

$$= \frac{1}{0.663 + j0.390}$$

Just as in multiplication, division is more easily performed using polar forms:

$$C = \frac{A}{B} = \frac{a(\cos \alpha + j \sin \alpha)}{b(\cos \beta + j \sin \beta)} = \frac{a(\cos \alpha + j \sin \alpha)(\cos \beta - j \sin \beta)}{b(\cos \beta + j \sin \beta)(\cos \beta - j \sin \beta)}$$

$$= \frac{a[(\cos \alpha \cos \beta + \sin \alpha \sin \beta) + j(\sin \alpha \cos \beta - \cos \alpha \sin \beta)]}{b(\cos^2 \beta + \sin^2 \beta)}$$

$$= \frac{a}{b} [\cos (\alpha - \beta) + j \sin (\alpha - \beta)] \tag{3-10}$$

That is, complex quantities, or directed numbers, A and B, are divided by dividing their scalar or absolute values, a and b, and subtracting their phase angles, α and β.

3-12 Powers and Roots of Complex Quantities. Both powers, or repeated multiplications, and roots, or powers with fractional exponents, can be obtained most simply by using the polar forms of complex quantities. If

$$A = a_1 + ja_2 = a(\cos \alpha + j \sin \alpha)$$

then
$$C = A^n = a^n(\cos n\alpha + j \sin n\alpha)$$

For instance, if

$$A = 3 + 4j = 5(\cos 53° + j \sin 53°)$$

then

$$
\begin{aligned}
C = A^4 &= 5^4(\cos 4 \times 53° + j \sin 4 \times 53°) \\
&= 625(\cos 212° + j \sin 212°) = 625(-\cos 32° - j \sin 32°) \\
&= 625(-0.843 - 0.537j) = -527 - 336j
\end{aligned}
$$

If

$$A = a_1 + ja_2 = a(\cos \alpha + j \sin \alpha)$$

then

$$C = \sqrt[n]{A} = A^{1/n} = a^{1/n}\left(\cos \frac{\alpha}{n} + j \sin \frac{\alpha}{n}\right) = \sqrt[n]{a}\left(\cos \frac{\alpha}{n} + j \sin \frac{\alpha}{n}\right)$$

If, in the polar expression for A, we increase the phase angle α by 2π, or by any multiple of 2π: $2q\pi$, where q is any integer, we get the same value of A, thus:

$$A = a[\cos(\alpha + 2q\pi) + j \sin(\alpha + 2q\pi)] \qquad (3\text{-}11)$$

since the cosine and sine repeat after every 360°, or 2π.

The nth root, however, is different:

$$C^n = A = \left[\sqrt[n]{a}\left(\cos \frac{\alpha + 2q\pi}{n} + j \sin \frac{\alpha + 2q\pi}{n}\right)\right]^n$$

We hereby get n different values of C for $q = 0, 1, 2, \ldots, n-1$; $q = n$ gives again the same as $q = 0$, since it gives

$$\frac{\alpha + 2n\pi}{n} = \frac{\alpha}{n} + 2\pi \qquad (3\text{-}12)$$

that is, an increase of the phase angle by 360°, which leaves cosine and sine unchanged.

Thus the nth root of any directed number has n different values, and these values have the same scalar or absolute term $\sqrt[n]{a}$, but differ from each other by the phase angle $2\pi/n$ and its multiples.

For instance, let $A = -527 - 336j = 625(\cos 212° + j \sin 212°)$, then its four different fourth roots are

$$\sqrt[4]{625}\left(\cos \frac{212 + 360q}{4} + j \sin \frac{212 + 360q}{4}\right) \qquad \text{for } q = 1, 2, 3, 4$$

$$
\begin{aligned}
\sqrt[4]{A} &= 5(\cos 53 + j \sin 53) &&= 3 + 4j \\
&= 5(\cos 143 + i \sin 143) = 5(-\cos 37 + j \sin 37) &&= -4 + 3j \\
&= 5(\cos 233 + j \sin 233) = 5(-\cos 53 + j \sin 53) &&= -3 + 4j \\
&= 5(\cos 323 + j \sin 323) = 5(\cos \quad 37 - j \sin 37) &&= 4 - 3j \\
&= 5(\cos 413 + j \sin 413) = 5(\cos \quad 53 + j \sin 53) &&= 3 + 4j
\end{aligned}
$$

The n roots of a directed number $A = a(\cos \alpha + j \sin \alpha)$ differ from each other by the phase angles $2\pi/n$, or one-nth of $360°$, and since they have the same absolute value $\sqrt[n]{a}$, it follows that they are represented by n equidistant points on a circle with radius $\sqrt[n]{a}$, as shown in Fig. 3-17, for $n = 4$, and in Fig. 3-18 for $n = 9$. Such a system of n equal

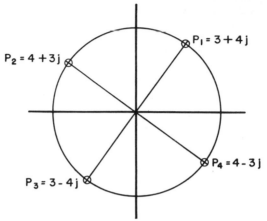

Fig. 3-17 The fourth roots of a directed number.

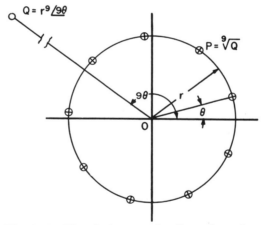

Fig. 3-18 The ninth roots of a directed number.

phasors, differing in phase from each other by one-nth of $360°$, is called a *polyphase system*, or an *n-phase system*. The n roots of unity give an *n-phase system*.

For instance (Eq. 3-1), the n roots of unity represent the phasors of an n phase alternating-current system:

$$\sqrt[n]{1} = \cos \frac{360q}{n} + j \sin \frac{360q}{n} = \left(\cos \frac{360}{n} + j \sin \frac{360}{n} \right)^q \quad (3\text{-}13)$$

where q is any integer. Expressed in radians, instead of degrees, this is

$$\sqrt[n]{1} = \left(\cos \frac{2\pi}{n} + j \sin \frac{2\pi}{n}\right)^q \tag{3-14}$$

These relations are extremely useful in electrical engineering, for the electrical pressure, or voltage, in the winding of an electric generator is produced by the magnetic flux from the rotating field magnets sweeping across the conductors. In each single coil of the winding, the voltage changes direction, or alternates, as north and south poles pass by successively. In a two-pole generator, turning at 3,600 revolutions per minute, the voltage goes through a complete reversal each time two poles pass by, or 60 times per second, and such a machine is, therefore, called a 60-cycle alternator. Usually, large generators and motors have three exactly similar stationary windings, or phases, equally spaced around the periphery and, therefore, one-third of a cycle, or 120 electrical degrees apart.

If the voltage of one phase of a balanced three-phase alternator winding is represented by E, therefore, the three phase voltages will be

$$E_1 = E$$

$$E_2 = E(\cos 120 + j \sin 120) = E\left(-\frac{1}{2} + j\frac{\sqrt{3}}{2}\right)$$

$$E_3 = E(\cos 240 + j \sin 240) = E\left(-\frac{1}{2} - j\frac{\sqrt{3}}{2}\right)$$

and the sum,

$$E_1 + E_2 + E_3 = 0$$

The meaning of these relations is that, at any instant, the relative values of the voltages of the three phases are proportional to the projections of E_1, E_2, and E_3, on a uniformly turning radius, whose position corresponds to the instant considered (Fig. 3-19). At the moment when the radius is vertical,

$$E_1 = 0 \qquad E_2 = \frac{\sqrt{3}\,E}{2} \qquad E_3 = -\frac{\sqrt{3}\,E}{2}$$

One quarter-cycle, or 90°, earlier, when it was horizontal,

$$E_1 = E \qquad E_2 = -\frac{E}{2} \qquad E_3 = -\frac{E}{2}$$

and when it is horizontal, in the 180° position,

$$E_1 = -E \qquad E_2 = \frac{E}{2} \qquad E_3 = \frac{E}{2} \qquad \text{etc.}$$

or the three voltage phasors may be assumed to revolve together, and the instantaneous voltages will be given by their projections on a fixed axis.

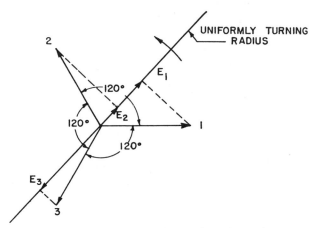

Fig. 3-19 Relations of the three phase voltages of an alternating-current generator.

3-13 Example—Electric Circuit Calculations. Figure 3-20 shows a simple direct-current electric circuit. An electric "force" E, measured in volts, is applied to the terminals, forcing an electron flow, or current I, measured in amperes, through the circuit. As long as the current is constant, the only limitation to its flow is the resistance R, measured in ohms, which is a measure of the frictional opposition the electrons meet with in passing through the conductors. The current is then given by the simple formula, called *Ohm's law*,

$$I = \frac{E}{R} \tag{3-15}$$

The power W, or rate of energy consumption in the circuit, is measured in watts and is equal to EI, or I^2R.

If the current varies from instant to instant, the energy of its magnetic field varies also, just as the energy of a baseball varies with its velocity. The inductance of the circuit, L, is a measure of the magnetic field, or electric inertia, corresponding to the mass of the baseball. To allow for this, we must include the reactance, X, as well as the resistance in an alternating-current circuit, as shown in Fig. 3-21.

The reactance is measured in ohms and is equal to $2\pi fL$, where f is the frequency of the current, or number of cycles of variation per second.

The voltage of an alternating-current circuit, such as universally used in American homes, varies sinusoidally in time (usually at

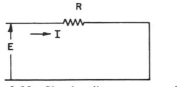

Fig. 3-20 Simple direct-current circuit.

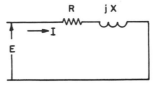

Fig. 3-21 Simple alternating-current circuit.

60-cycles-per-second frequency), so that it may be represented by the equation

$$e = \sqrt{2}\,E \sin(2\pi ft + \phi) \qquad \text{volts} \qquad (3\text{-}16)$$

where t is the elapsed time in seconds and ϕ is the phase angle of the voltage at time zero. Since the average power depends on the average value over a cycle of the square of the voltage (or current) and since

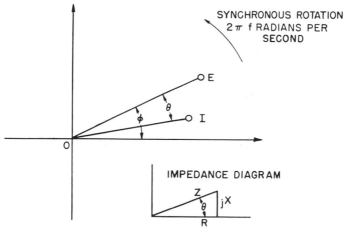

Fig. 3-22 Emf and current phasor diagram.

the average[1] of $\sin^2 x$ is $\frac{1}{2}$, it is customary to use the square root of the mean-square value of current and voltage, called the *rms value*, for measurements and engineering calculations. Hence the value of E in the above equation is 0.707 times the peak value of voltage.

The rms voltage, E, is represented by the phasor in Fig. 3.22:

$$E\underline{/\phi} = E(\cos\phi + j\sin\phi) \qquad \text{volts} \qquad (3\text{-}17)$$

[1] $\sin^2 x = \frac{1}{2}(1 - \cos 2x)$ (Fig. 2-16).

in which the horizontal reference axis, and with it the entire plane, is revolving uniformly in a counterclockwise direction at synchronous speed, or $360f$ degrees $= 2\pi f$ radians per second. Thus the observer is assumed to be riding on the rotating field structure.

The rms current that flows in response to the impressed voltage is found by dividing E by the impedance Z:

$$I = \frac{E}{Z} \qquad \text{amperes} \qquad\qquad (3\text{-}18)$$

where the impedance Z is the combined ohmic value of the resistance and the reactance. Since the resistance merely opposes the current flow, the voltage across the resistance is in time phase with the current. The reactance, however, delays the rise and fall of the current, but does not oppose its steady flow, just as the flow of water in a pipe is affected by its mass. Hence the inductance forms a j term in the impedance, and Z is given by the equation

$$Z = R + jX \qquad \text{or} \qquad Z\underline{/\theta} = \sqrt{R^2 + X^2}\ \underline{/\theta} \qquad (3\text{-}19)$$

where $\theta = \tan^{-1} X/R$, as indicated in Fig. 3-22.

The rms current flowing in the inductive circuit[1] is then

$$I = \frac{E\underline{/\phi}}{Z\underline{/\theta}} = \frac{E(\cos\phi + j\sin\phi)}{Z(\cos\theta + j\sin\theta)} = \frac{E}{Z}\underline{/\phi - \theta}$$

$$= \frac{E}{Z}[\cos(\phi - \theta) + j\sin(\phi - \theta)] \qquad (3\text{-}20)$$

The current is represented on the same diagram (Fig. 3-22) as the voltage by a phasor lagging θ behind the voltage phasor. In terms of R and X, it is

$$I = \frac{E}{R + jX} = \frac{E(R - jX)}{R^2 + X^2} = \frac{E}{\sqrt{R^2 + X^2}}(\cos\theta - j\sin\theta) \quad (3\text{-}21)$$

The current in any static circuit, however complicated, may be found by combining the branch-circuit impedances into a single equivalent impedance and dividing this into the impressed voltage. For example, Fig. 3-23 represents the circuit of a double squirrel-cage induction motor at standstill.

---

[1] There is a third circuit element, the capacitive (negative) reactance, representing the electrostatic energy stored in the dielectric field, as a consequence of voltage stress. This is opposite in phase to the inductive reactance and is much smaller in usual wire and machine circuits. It will not be considered here (see Sec. 14-5.)

R_1 is the resistance and jX_1 is the leakage reactance of the primary winding; jX_m is the magnetizing reactance; R_2 is the secondary end-ring resistance; jX_2 is the leakage reactance of the top bars in the squirrel cage; R_B is the top-bar resistance; R_A is the bottom-bar resistance; and jX_A is the additional leakage reactance of the bottom bars. If we put, for example, $E = 200$ volts; $R_1 = 2$; $X_1 = 8$;

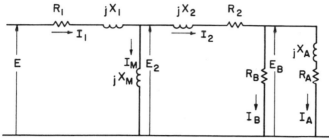

Fig. 3-23 Equivalent electric circuit of double squirrel-cage induction motor at standstill.

$X_m = 300$; $X_2 = 6$; $R_2 = 1$; $R_B = 8$; $X_A = 8$; $R_A = 2$, the numerical solution for the current proceeds in this way:

Since the voltage E_B is applied to both R_B and $R_A + jX_A$, the total secondary current I_2 is the sum of I_B and I_A, or

$$I_2 = E_B \left(\frac{1}{R_B} + \frac{1}{R_A + jX_A} \right) = E_B \left(\frac{1}{8} + \frac{1}{2 + j8} \right)$$
$$= E_B(0.125 + 0.029 - j0.117) = E_B(0.154 - j0.117)$$

The impedance of A and B in parallel is then

$$Z_{A+B} = \frac{E_B}{I_2} = \frac{1}{0.154 - j0.117} = \frac{0.154 + j0.117}{0.0374} = 4.10 + j3.12$$

Adding this to $R_2 + jX_2$ gives the total impedance of the secondary:

$$Z_2 = R_2 + jX_2 + Z_{A+B} = 5.10 + j9.12$$

The total primary current is equal to the sum of I_M and I_{A+B}, or

$$I_2 = E_2 \left(\frac{1}{jX_M} + \frac{1}{Z_2} \right) = E_2 \left(\frac{1}{j300} + \frac{1}{5.10 + j9.12} \right)$$
$$= E_2 \left(-j0.0033 + \frac{5.10 - j9.12}{109.1} \right) = E_2(0.0467 - j0.0869)$$

The total impedance is then

$$Z = R_1 + jX_1 + \frac{1}{0.0467 - j0.0869} = 2 + j8 + 4.80 + j8.93$$

$$= 6.80 + j13.73$$

and the primary current is

$$\frac{E}{Z} = \frac{220}{6.80 + j13.73} = 6.36 - j12.85 \text{ or } 14.3 \,\overline{\,\big\backslash 63.7°} \text{ amperes}$$

The I^2R loss, or power expended in the circuit, is

Power $= EI$ (power factor) $= 220(14.3) \cos 63.7° = 220(6.36)$
$= 1,400$ watts

3-14 Exponential Form of the Directed Number. By the methods of elementary calculus (see Sec. 8-2), it can be shown that the base of natural logarithms, e, when raised to the uth power, is equal to the sum of all the integral powers of u; 0, 1, 2, 3, . . . , k, . . . , each divided by its factorial. The *factorial* of a number k is defined as the product of all the positive integers up to and including k and is written

$$k! = 1 \times 2 \times 3 \times 4 \times \cdots \times k \qquad (3\text{-}22)$$

For example, $1! = 1$, $2! = 2$, $3! = 6$, $4! = 24$, etc. Also, $0! = 1$. Hence, e^u is given by the equation

$$e^u = 1 + u + \frac{u^2}{2} + \frac{u^3}{6} + \frac{u^4}{24} + \frac{u^5}{120} + \cdots \qquad (3\text{-}23)$$

The value of e itself, the base of natural logarithms, found by putting $u = 1$ in Eq. 3.23, is[1]

$$e = 1 + \frac{1}{1!} + \frac{1}{2!} + \frac{1}{3!} + \frac{1}{4!} + \cdots = 2.7182818 \cdots \qquad (3\text{-}24)$$

Also, the trigonometric functions $\sin x$ and $\cos x$ are given by the equations (see Sec. 8-8)

$$\sin x = x - \frac{x^3}{3!} + \frac{x^5}{5!} - \frac{x^7}{7!} + \cdots$$

$$= x - \frac{x^3}{6} + \frac{x^5}{120} - \frac{x^7}{5,040} + \cdots \qquad (3\text{-}25)$$

$$\cos x = 1 - \frac{x^2}{2!} + \frac{x^4}{4!} - \frac{x^6}{6!} + \frac{x^8}{8!} \cdots$$

$$= 1 - \frac{x^2}{2} + \frac{x^4}{24} - \frac{x^6}{720} + \cdots \qquad (3\text{-}26)$$

[1] The values of the transcendental numbers e and π have been computed (in 1949) to 2,000 decimal places, with an electronic digital computer.

By substituting $x = \theta$, $u = j\theta$ in the above three equations, we find that

$$\cos\theta + j\sin\theta = e^{j\theta} \qquad (3\text{-}27)$$

so that the polar expression of the complex quantity

$$A = a(\cos\theta + j\sin\theta)$$

can also be written in the form

$$A = ae^{j\theta}$$

where θ is expressed in radians.

The unique property of the number e, expressed by Eq. 3-27, that led to its choice as the base of natural logarithms, is that the scalar value of $e^{j\theta}$ is exactly unity, when its exponent $j\theta$ is any quadrature number.

We may regard $e^0 = 1 + j0$ as a unit vector. Multiplying this by e and raising the product to a real power x, if x is very small, extends the length of the unit vector by the distance x in the direction of the radius (Eq. 3-23). Raising it to the power jy extends it by the distance y at right angles to the radius (Fig. 3-24). The increment in length of the unit vector is thus equal to the exponent of e, when x is small, as shown by the first two terms of Eq. 3-23.

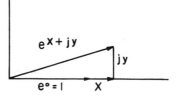

Fig. 3-24 Graph of e^{x+jy}

Since any number a can be expressed as e raised to the power $\ln a$, a directed number can be expressed in the form

$$A = \exp\ln a^{+j\theta} \qquad (3\text{-}28)$$

as well as in the forms

$$A = a_1 + ja_2 \qquad (3\text{-}29)$$

and

$$A = a(\cos\theta + j\sin\theta) \qquad (3\text{-}30)$$

Each form is most convenient in particular cases, the exponential form in differential equations and transient phenomena, the rectangular form in algebraic and circuit problems, and the polar form in problems requiring extensive multiplications or powers.

3-15 Logarithms of Complex Quantities. In taking the logarithm of a complex quantity, the exponential form is most convenient:

$$\log(a_1 + ja_2) = \log a(\cos\theta + j\sin\theta) = \log ae^{j\theta}$$
$$= \log a + \log e^{j\theta} = \log a + j\theta\log e = \log a + j0.4343\theta$$

or, in natural logarithms

$$\ln (a_1 + ja_2) = \ln ae^{j\theta} = \ln a + j\theta \qquad (3\text{-}31)$$

From this, it follows that

$$\ln j = \ln e^{j\pi/2} = \frac{j\pi}{2}$$

and $\ln (-1) = 2 \ln j = j\pi$

or, more generally,

$$\ln (-1) = j\pi(2n + 1) \qquad (3\text{-}32)$$

where n is any positive integer.

These relations are summed up in De Moivre's theorem

$$e^{jn\theta} = (\cos \theta + j \sin \theta)^n = \cos n\theta + j \sin n\theta \qquad (3\text{-}33)$$

from which is derived Euler's famous formula

$$e^{j\pi} + 1 = 0 \qquad (3\text{-}34)$$

PROBLEMS

By the use of the root circle (Fig. 3-18), show by measurement that

1. $\sqrt[5]{+1} \neq -1$ 3. $\sqrt[3]{1 - j3} \neq 1.27 - j0.735$
2. $\sqrt[6]{6 + j8} = 0.57 - j1.35$ 4. $\sqrt[4]{15 + j10} = 2.04 + j0.30$

Solve for x and y in the following equations. Express the answers in polar form also, to the nearest ½ degree.

5. $x + jy = \dfrac{(2 + j5)(1 + j7)}{(6 + j3)(4 + j7)}$

6. $x + jy = \dfrac{[(11 - j) - (11 + j3)](5 + j3)}{1 + j}$

7. $x + jy = \dfrac{(9 + j10)^2(2 - j)}{\sqrt{2} + j\sqrt{3}}$

8. $x + jy = \dfrac{(3 + j3)(1 + j0)(18 - j9)}{1 + j0.5}$

9. $x + jy = \dfrac{5 + j6}{(2 + j)^2[(8 + j7) + (-4 + j3)]}$

If a voltage, $E \sin 2\pi ft$ volts, is applied to a series circuit containing a resistance R ohms and a reactance X ohms, calculate the impedance $Z = R + jX$, the current in amperes $I = E/Z$, and the voltages E_R

and E_X across the resistance and reactance separately. Give the rms values of the voltages and currents (rms value $=$ max value$/\sqrt{2}$):

10. $E = 162.7$, $R = 20$, $X = 26.63$
11. $E = 170$, $R = 50$, $X = -13$
12. $E = 120$, $R = 19$, $X = 8.73$
13. $E = 100$, $R = 49$, $X = -22.7$

Solve the following expressions for x and y, by first converting each factor into polar form, $x + jy = ze^{j\theta}$, and converting the results back to the form $x + jy$. Compare the time taken to solve these problems with that taken to solve them by direct multiplication, as in Probs. 5 to 9.

14. $x + jy = (2 + j3)^2(4 + j3)$

15. $x + jy = \dfrac{(7 + j5)(1 + j)(4 + j4)}{j}$

16. $x + jy = (3 + i)^{-\frac{1}{2}}(7 + j2)^{\frac{3}{2}}$

17. $x + jy = \dfrac{1}{(6 + j9)^3}$

18. $x + jy = \dfrac{(8 + j3)^{\frac{1}{3}}}{(3 + j5)^2}$

Bibliography

1. Bridgman, P. W.: "Dimensional Analysis," Yale University Press, New Haven, Conn., 1922.
2. Caratheodory, C.: "Theory of Functions of a Complex Variable," vol. 1, Chelsea Publishing Company, New York, 1954.
3. Churchill, R. V.: "Introduction to Complex Variables and Applications," McGraw-Hill Book Company, New York, 1954.
4. Coffin, J. G.: "Vector Analysis," 2d ed., John Wiley & Sons, Inc., New York, 1911.
5. Holmes, C. T.: "Calculus and Analytic Geometry," McGraw-Hill Book Company, New York, 1950.
6. Johnson, W. C.: "Mathematical and Physical Principles of Engineering Analysis," McGraw-Hill Book Company, New York, 1944.
7. Newell, H. E., Jr.: "Vector Analysis," McGraw-Hill Book Company, New York, 1955.
8. Schnell, L. H., and M. Crawford: "Plane Geometry," 3d ed., McGraw-Hill Book Company, New York, 1953.

Chapter 4 ALGEBRAIC EQUATIONS

4-1 The Nature of Equations. An equation is a statement, expressed in mathematical symbols, that two quantities are equal to each other. For example,

$$8 = 2 + 6 \tag{4-1}$$

is an arithmetic equation.

An algebraic equation enables the relations between unknown or varying quantities to be expressed in a form that can be manipulated in various ways, and can be understood, or "seen," readily. For example, the equation

$$x = y^2 \tag{4-2}$$

states that for every value of y, there is one and only one value of x, equal to y^2, and that for every nonzero value of x there are two values of y, equal to $\sqrt{x}$ and $-\sqrt{x}$, respectively. In order to see the relationship more clearly, we may plot successive pairs of values of x and y on graph paper, obtaining the curve shown in Fig. 4-1, a parabola with the $y = 0$ axis as its center line. Equation 4-2 is an algebraic equation, because it is true over a range of values of x and y, and these variables are represented by letter symbols. When numbers are substituted in an algebraic equation, it becomes an arithmetic equation. Putting $x = 3$, Eq. 4-2 gives

$$3 = y^2 \quad \text{or } y = \pm \sqrt{3} = 1.732 \quad \text{or } -1.732 \tag{4-3}$$

Equation 4-3 represents a single point on Fig. 4-1, while Eq. 4-2 represents the entire curve. Thus, an equation enables a good deal of information to be conveyed in a simple, compact form. Otherwise, extensive tables of corresponding values of x and y, or an actual drawing, would be required to give the same information. Also, one equation can be combined with others, enabling new relationships to be worked out, a process not possible with tables or charts.

Letters such as x and y, used in place of numerals in this way, are

[94]

properly called *pronumerals*.[1] Instead of writing $x = y^2$, we could have written $\square = \triangle^2$, where the $\square$ indicates a vacant space into which a particular numeral may be inserted. If a value of 4 is put in the $\square$, the numeral 2 must go in the $\triangle$, to comply with the requirement that $4 = \triangle^2$. We write x, y, and other letters instead of using blank spaces such as $\square$, $\triangle$, because the letters are easier to write and to talk about. In either case, the symbols stand in place of any one of a great many possible sets of numerals, for each of which the algebraic equation is equally true.

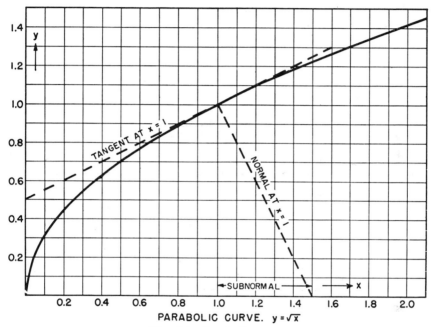

PARABOLIC CURVE. $y = \sqrt{x}$

Fig. 4-1 Parabolic curve.

With a little experience, one recognizes at a glance the form of curve that any simple equation represents, or, as we say, the graph of the equation. For example, if x represents the horizontal and y the vertical distance from two axes at right angles, we see that

$$ax + by = c \qquad \text{or} \qquad y = -\frac{ax}{b} + \frac{c}{b} \qquad (4\text{-}4)$$

represents a straight line cutting the horizontal axis ($y = 0$) at $x = c/a$ and the vertical axis ($x = 0$) at $y = c/b$ (Fig. 4-2). With such a linear, first-order, equation, for every value of x there is one and only one value of y, and vice versa.

[1] This term has been proposed by Dr. Max Beberman.

A quadratic equation, having second-order terms in x^2 and y^2, will, in general, have two values of x for each value of y, and vice versa. The most general form of a quadratic curve, therefore, will cut each of the two axes in two points, either real or imaginary. For example,

$$ax^2 + bx + dy^2 + ey + fxy + c = 0 \tag{4-5}$$

has two possible values of x when y is 0, and two possible values of y when x is 0. Such a curve is called a *conic section*, because all its possible forms correspond to the various curves formed by the intersection of a plane with a right circular cone (Fig. 4-3) (see Sec. 4-9).

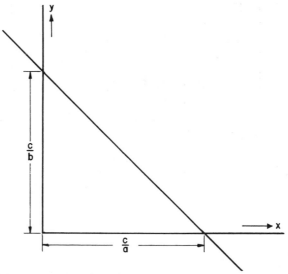

Fig. 4-2   Straight line.

The plane can form four kinds of curve, by cutting the cone in the four different ways that are possible. If the plane is

(*a*) At an acute angle with the axis of the cone, the intersection is an ellipse (Fig. 4-3*A*).

(*b*) Perpendicular to the axis of the cone, the intersection is a circle (Fig. 4-3*B*).

(*c*) Parallel to the axis of the cone, the intersection is a hyperbola (Fig. 4-3*C*).

(*d*) Parallel to an element of the cone, the intersection is a parabola (Fig. 4-3*D*).

There are also degenerate cases, as an ellipse of zero width, which becomes a straight line.

These various forms of curve are expressed algebraically by giving appropriate values to the coefficients in Eq. 4-5, thus:

(*a*) If $f = 0$, the curve is an ellipse with its axes parallel to the x and y axes (Fig. 4-4).

(*b*) If $a = d$ and $f = 0$, the curve is a circle.

(*c*) If $a = b = d = e = 0$, the curve is an equilateral hyperbola, represented by the equation

$$fxy + c = 0$$

or simply,
$$xy = k \qquad \text{(Fig.4-5)} \qquad (4\text{-}6)$$

(*d*) If a or $d = 0$, but not both, and $f = 0$, the curve is a parabola (Fig. 4-1).

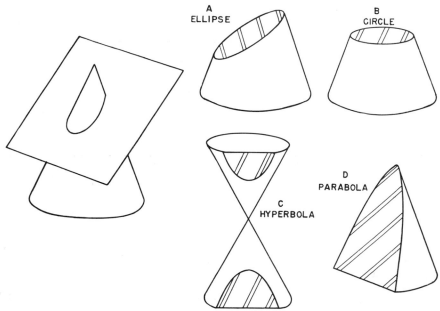

Fig. 4-3 Curves formed by intersection of a plane with a right circular cone.

If the highest exponent of x or y occurring in an equation is 2, 3, 4, or n, it is called a quadratic, cubic, quartic, or nth-order equation, respectively.

For an nth-order equation in x, there will be n values of x for which $y = 0$, in general, or n points at which the curve representing the equation cuts the horizontal axis. These values of x that make $y = 0$ are called the *roots* of the equation. Some of the roots may be directed numbers, that is, will have j components. These are said to be imaginary, as contrasted with the real roots. If an nth-order equation has m real roots and $n - m$ imaginary ones, the curve will cross the y axis only m times (in the real plane).

Algebraic Equations

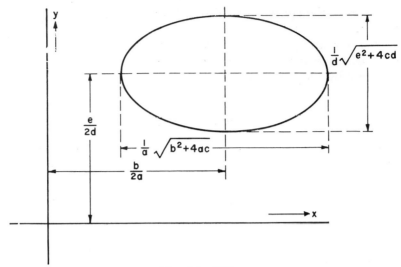

Fig. 4-4   Ellipse.

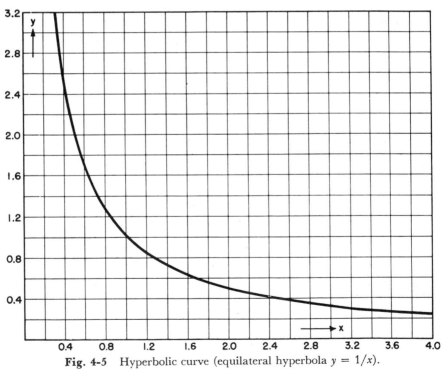

Fig. 4-5   Hyperbolic curve (equilateral hyperbola $y = 1/x$).

By employing three or more letters, shapes in three or more dimensions can be defined by such equations. By using two or more equations relating the same variables, the curves of intersection of the shapes can be defined. The representation of algebraic equations by curves and the study of their properties are the subject of analytic geometry.

4-2 Quadratic Equat ns. To find the roots of a quadratic equation (Eq. 4-5), or values of x that make $y = 0$, we substitute $y = 0$, when it becomes

$$ax^2 + bx + c = 0 \qquad (4\text{-}7)$$

To solve this, we rearrange it,

$$x^2 + \frac{bx}{a} = -\frac{c}{a} \qquad (4\text{-}8)$$

and complete the square, by adding to each side an amount sufficient to make the left-hand side a perfect square. Since we know that $(a + b)^2 = a^2 + 2ab + b^2$, the new term to be added is equal to the second term divided by $2x$ and squared, or $(b/2a)^2$. This gives

$$x^2 + \frac{bx}{a} + \left(\frac{b}{2a}\right)^2 = \left(\frac{b}{2a}\right)^2 - \frac{c}{a} \qquad (4\text{-}9)$$

Taking the square root of both sides:

$$x + \frac{b}{2a} = \pm \frac{1}{2a} \sqrt{b^2 - 4ac}$$

or

$$x = \frac{-b \pm \sqrt{b^2 - 4ac}}{2a} \qquad (4\text{-}10)$$

If $b^2 > 4ac$, both values of x given by Eq. 4-10 are real numbers, and the graph of Eq. 4-5 will actually cut the x axis at the two points. If $b^2 = 4ac$, there will be two identical roots, each equal to $-b/2a$. If $b^2 < 4ac$, the two roots will be conjugate complex numbers,

$$-\frac{b}{2a} + j\frac{\sqrt{4ac - b^2}}{2a} \qquad \text{and} \qquad -\frac{b}{2a} - j\frac{\sqrt{4ac - b^2}}{2a}$$

In this case, the curve does not cross the x axis at all (in the real plane).

4-3 Higher-order Equations. Cubic and higher-order equations cannot be solved (or their roots found) by such simple explicit formulas as Eq. 4-10. In ·engineering, therefore, it is usual to solve them by some method of approximation. For example, putting $y = k$ in an nth-order equation between x and y gives an nth-order equation in x alone:

$$x^n + ax^{n-1} + bx^{n-2} + \cdots + cx^2 + dx + e = 0 \qquad (4\text{-}11)$$

Solving this equation will give the n values of x at which the graph of the original equation between x and y cuts the line $y = k$.

Equation 4-11 may be written, alternatively, as the product of n factors, each of the form $x - a$, or as

$$(x - x_1)(x - x_2)(x - x_3) \cdots (x - x_n) = 0 \qquad (4\text{-}12)$$

where $x_1, x_2, x_3, \ldots, x_n$ are the n roots of the equation, or the values of x which satisfy Eq. 4-11.

The process of finding the roots is essentially that of resolving the left-hand member of the equation into factors. If any root, x_1, is known, dividing by $(x - x_1)$ will yield a new equation of order $n - 1$, whose roots are the remaining roots of the original equation.

If two roots, x_1 and x_2, can be found, dividing Eq. 4-11 by $(x - x_1)(x - x_2)$ will reduce it to an equation of order $n - 2$. Each root that is found makes it simpler to find the remaining roots.

If we expand Eq. 4-12 and compare it with its identity, Eq. 4-11, we note that the coefficients of like powers of x must be equal. Hence

$$a = -(x_1 + x_2 + \cdots + x_n)$$
$$b = (x_1x_2 + x_1x_3 + \cdots + x_2x_3 + x_2x_4 + \cdots)$$
$$c = -(x_1x_2x_3 \cdots x_{n-1} + x_2x_3x_4 \cdots x_n + \cdots) \qquad (n \text{ equations})$$
$$d = x_1x_2x_3 \cdots x_n \qquad (4\text{-}13)$$

That is, the coefficients of Eq. 4-11 are, respectively, equal to plus or minus the sum of the products of all the roots, taken 1, 2, 3, . . . at a time.

If any of the coefficients $a, b, \ldots, e$ are numbers with j components, the equation can be separated into two independent equations, one with real and one with j coefficients, which can be solved separately. If the coefficients are all real numbers, it follows from Eq. 4-13 that the sum of all the roots is a real number. Therefore, any roots that have j components must occur as conjugate pairs, just as in Eq. 4-10. Thus, a cubic equation with real coefficients can have three real roots, or one real and two roots with j components, but cannot have three roots with j components.

Equations 4-13 give a great deal of information about the values and the signs of the roots, which help in locating them, especially after one root has been found.

A straightforward method of finding one root, x_1, is to calculate the sum of the left-hand terms of Eq. 4-11 for successive (arbitrarily chosen) values of x and to plot these sums against x on graph paper, proceeding in this way until the sum, or graph, passes through zero. Evidently the value of x at this point satisfies the equation and therefore is a root, x_1. The graph, or an equivalent method of estimation, need be used only to find a rough approximation to x_1. The exact value of the root may then be found by substituting $x_1 + \epsilon$ for x in Eq. 4-11, giving a new equation in ϵ instead of in x:

$$\epsilon^n + p\epsilon^{n-1} + q\epsilon^{n-2} + \cdot \cdot \cdot + r\epsilon + s = 0 \qquad (4\text{-}14)$$

If the chosen value of x_1 is nearly equal to a root of Eq. 4-11, $\epsilon = x - x_1$ will be small and therefore the ϵ^2 and higher-order terms of Eq. 4-14 may be neglected. Considering only the last two terms, therefore, we find $\epsilon = -s/r$. Putting a new value, $x_1 - s/r + \epsilon'$, for x in Eq. 4-11, a third equation, in ϵ', is found, similar to Eq. 4-14 with coefficients p', q', etc. Solving this for ϵ', we find, finally, $x = x_1 - s/r - s'/r'$. Depending on the accuracy with which x_1 was originally chosen, this method of solving Eq. 4-11 may be very brief and direct, or it may require several repetitions. The whole process may be repeated n times, choosing appropriate initial values for x_2, x_3, etc., to find the n roots of the original equation.

Or, preferably, after one root, x_1, is found, the entire Eq. 4-11 may be divided by $x - x_1$, giving a new equation of order $n - 1$. If $n = 3$, this leaves a quadratic which can be solved directly by Eq. 4-10.

A quick way of estimating the largest root of Eq. 4-11 is to start with

$$x_1 = -a + \epsilon$$

for, if x is large, the two largest terms in the equation will normally be those in x^n and x^{n-1}. Neglecting the other terms gives the reduced equation

$$x_1{}^n + ax_1{}^{n-1} = 0 \qquad \text{or} \qquad x_1 = -a \qquad (4\text{-}15)$$

if x_1 is large. On the other hand, the smallest roots can be estimated by neglecting all but the last three terms, and solving these as a quadratic, by Eq. 4-10. Or, whichever terms in the equation appear to be smallest may be dropped out, until the remaining terms constitute an equation simple enough to be readily solved. Then, the numerical value of x, so found, may be substituted in the neglected terms, and the resulting equation solved for a new value of x_1, the process being repeated until sufficient accuracy is obtained. Which is the better way to start will depend on the relative values of the coefficients a, b, c, etc. An additional method of finding the roots, by Taylor's theorem, is given in Sec. 9-3.

An alternative procedure, especially useful in solving cubic equations, is to substitute a new variable for x, in Eq. 4-11, such that the new equation in y will have no term in y^{n-1}. This is done by putting $x = y - a/n$. For, making this substitution and considering the terms in y, y^{n-1}, and y^{n-2} only, we find that Eq. 4-11 becomes (see Eq. 1-36)

$$\left(y - \frac{a}{n}\right)^n + a\left(y - \frac{a}{n}\right)^{n-1} + b\left(y - \frac{a}{n}\right)^{n-2} + \cdots = 0$$

or

$$y^n - \frac{na}{n}y^{n-1} + \frac{n(n-1)a^2}{2n^2}y^{n-2} + \cdots + ay^{n-1} - \frac{(n-1)a^2}{n}y^{n-2}$$
$$+ \cdots + by^{n-2} + \cdots = 0$$

which is

$$y^n + \left(b - \frac{a^2}{2} + \frac{a^2}{2n}\right)y^{n-2} + \cdots = 0 \qquad (4\text{-}16)$$

Following the same approximate method as before, we may estimate two of the roots of Eq. 4-16 by placing the sum of its first two terms equal to zero, whence

$$y_1 = \pm\sqrt{\frac{a^2(n-1) - 2bn}{2n}} \qquad \text{approximately} \qquad (4\text{-}17)$$

Putting $y = y_1 + \epsilon$ in Eq. 4-16, we find a new equation in ϵ for each value of y_1, similar to Eq. 4-14. Solving these for ϵ (neglecting terms in ϵ^2 and higher orders) and adding this to y_1, we find, finally,

$$x = y - \frac{a}{n} = \sqrt{\frac{a^2(n-1) - 2bn}{2n}} - \frac{a}{n} + \epsilon_1$$

and

$$- \sqrt{\frac{a^2(n-1) - 2bn}{2n}} - \frac{a}{n} + \epsilon_2 \qquad (4\text{-}18)$$

for the two roots of Eq. 4-11.

If n is 3, Eq. 4-16 has only three terms in all, becoming

$$y^3 + py + q = 0 \qquad (4\text{-}19)$$

This can be solved directly on a slide rule, in the form

$$y^2 + p = -\frac{q}{y} \qquad (4\text{-}20)$$

An assumed value of y on the sliding scale is set opposite q on the lower fixed scale of the rule. The value of y^2 on the (upper) square scale on the slide is then read off and mentally added to p. The slide is moved until this sum is equal to the ratio q/y that appears on the fixed scale opposite 1 on the slide (Fig. 4-6). In the figure, the rule is set to solve $y^2 + 3 = 6.10/y$, and y is found to be 1.30, since

$$\frac{6.10}{1.30} = 4.69 = (1.30)^2 + 3$$

4-4 Example Solution of a Cubic Equation. To solve the equation:

$$x^3 - 6x^2 + 4x + 10 = 0 \qquad (4\text{-}21)$$

we may estimate x_1, from Eq. 4-18, to be (since $a = -6$, $b = 4$, $n = 3$):

$$x = \frac{6}{3} \pm \sqrt{\frac{36(2) - 8(3)}{6}} = 2 \pm \sqrt{8}$$

$$= 4.83 \qquad \text{or} \qquad -0.828$$

Taking the plus sign, we have as a first approximation $x_1 = 4.83$. Putting $x = 4.83 + \epsilon_1$ in Eq. 4-21, it reduces to

$$\epsilon_1{}^3 + 8.5\epsilon_1{}^2 + 16\epsilon_1 + 2.03 = 0$$

or $\qquad \epsilon_1 = -0.13$ approximately

Hence, one root of Eq. 4-21 is

$$4.83 - 0.13 = 4.70 \text{ approximately}$$

The exact value is 4.695, to three decimals.

Taking the minus sign, we have for the second root

$$x_2 = -0.828 + \epsilon_2$$

which gives

$$\epsilon_2{}^3 - 8.5\epsilon_2{}^2 + 16.0\epsilon_2 + 2.00 = 0$$

or $\qquad \epsilon_2 = -0.126$ approximately

Hence, the second root of Eq. 4-21 is

$$-0.828 - 0.126 = -0.954$$

The exact value is -0.946.

From Eq. 4-13, the last term of Eq. 4-11 is equal to the product of all the roots times

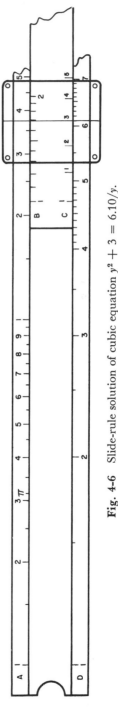

Fig. 4-6 Slide-rule solution of cubic equation $y^2 + 3 = 6.10/y$.

$(-1)^n$, or

$$e = (-1)^n (x_1)(x_2)(x_3) \cdots (x_n) \qquad (4\text{-}22)$$

The third root of Eq. 4-21 is therefore given by the quotient

$$x_3 = \frac{10}{(-1)^3(-0.946)(4.695)} = 2.252$$

We note, also, from Eq. 4-13, that the coefficient of the x^{n-1} term in Eq. 4-11 must equal minus the sum of all the roots, or

$$a = -(x_1 + x_2 + x_3 + \cdots + x_n) \qquad (4\text{-}23)$$

As a check, therefore, we find that the sum of the roots is

$$4.70 - 0.954 + 2.252 = 5.998$$

which equals minus the coefficient of x^2 in Eq. 4-21, or 6, as expected.

The success achieved with any one of these approximate methods depends on adapting it to the particular case. For example, the accuracy within which Eq. 4-18 gives a root of an nth-order equation will be better the larger the coefficients a, b, and c in Eq. 4-11 are with respect to d and e.

4-5 Simultaneous Equations. When a problem deals with two, three, or more variables, that is, x, y, z, etc., instead of only one variable, x, the relations between them usually will be expressed in a corresponding number of equations. For example, we may find that the three equations

$$\begin{aligned}
7x + 5y - z &= 14 \qquad &(4\text{-}24\text{a}) \\
4x - 4y + 3z &= 5 \qquad &(4\text{-}24\text{b}) \\
x + 2y + z &= 8 \qquad &(4\text{-}24\text{c})
\end{aligned}$$

fit the conditions of a problem. To solve these three simultaneous equations in x, y, and z, the normal procedure is to find the value of z in terms of x and y from one of the equations; substitute this in the other two; then find the value of y in terms of x from one of these new equations; and finally substitute this in the remaining equation and solve for x.

For example, Eq. 4-24a gives

$$z = 7x + 5y - 14 \qquad (4\text{-}24\text{a})$$

Putting this in Eqs. 4-24b and 4-24c, we find

$$\begin{aligned}
4x - 4y + 21x + 15y - 42 &= 5 \qquad &(4\text{-}25\text{a}) \\
\text{or} \qquad 25x + 11y &= 47 \qquad &(4\text{-}25\text{b}) \\
\text{and} \qquad 8x + 7y &= 22 \qquad &(4\text{-}25\text{c})
\end{aligned}$$

From Eq. 4-25b

$$y = \frac{47 - 25x}{11}$$

Putting this in Eq. 4-25c, we have

$$8x + \frac{7(47 - 25x)}{11} = 22$$

or

$$88x - 175x = 242 - 329$$

giving, finally,

$$x = 1$$

Putting this in Eq. 4-25b, we find

$$y = \frac{47 - 25}{11} = 2$$

and these values in Eq. 4-24a give

$$z = 7 + 10 - 14 = 3$$

Thus, $x = 1$, $y = 2$, $z = 3$ are the solutions of Eq. 4-24.

4-6 Determinants and Matrices. Depending on the number and complexity of the separate equations, it may be very easy or very difficult to solve them. The process of solving such linear simultaneous equations as Eq. 4-24, in n variables, is simplified by arranging the coefficients in tables, or rectangular arrays, called matrices, and calculating their *determinants*.

For example, the two equations

$$a_{11}x + a_{12}y = k_1$$
$$a_{21}x + a_{22}y = k_2 \tag{4-26}$$

are represented by the matrix

$$\begin{matrix} & x & y & k \\ 1 & \begin{bmatrix} a_{11} & a_{12} & k_1 \\ 2 & a_{21} & a_{22} & k_2 \end{bmatrix} \end{matrix} \quad \text{or, merely} \quad \begin{bmatrix} a_{11} & a_{12} & k_1 \\ a_{21} & a_{22} & k_2 \end{bmatrix}$$

If there are n equations in n variables, their matrix has n rows and $n + 1$ columns. The square array formed by a table of n of the columns and n rows, such as

$$\begin{bmatrix} a_{11} & a_{12} \\ a_{21} & a_{22} \end{bmatrix}$$

gives rise to a number, called a *determinant* of the nth order and expressed analogously by use of vertical bars, thus:

$$\begin{vmatrix} a_{11} & a_{12} \\ a_{21} & a_{22} \end{vmatrix}$$

In this case, where $n = 2$, the determinant is merely another way of writing down the difference of the diagonal products. This is

$$\begin{vmatrix} a_{11} & a_{12} \\ a_{21} & a_{22} \end{vmatrix} = a_{11}a_{22} - a_{12}a_{21}$$

The solution of Eqs. 4-26 is found by multiplying the first by a_{22} and the second by a_{12}, and subtracting, whence

$$x = \frac{a_{22}k_1 - a_{12}k_2}{a_{22}a_{11} - a_{12}a_{21}} \tag{4-27}$$

and, similarly, multiplying the first by a_{21} and the second by a_{11}, and subtracting

$$y = \frac{a_{11}k_2 - a_{21}k_1}{a_{22}a_{11} - a_{12}a_{21}} \tag{4-28}$$

In the method of determinants, this procedure is expressed more formally by writing down the matrix formed of the equation coefficients

$$\begin{array}{c} \\ 1 \\ 2 \end{array} \begin{array}{ccc} x & y & k \\ \left[\begin{array}{ccc} a_{11} & a_{12} & k_1 \\ a_{21} & a_{22} & k_2 \end{array}\right] \end{array}$$

forming from this the three determinants

$$D = \begin{vmatrix} a_{11} & a_{12} \\ a_{21} & a_{22} \end{vmatrix} \qquad D_x = \begin{vmatrix} k_1 & a_{12} \\ k_2 & a_{22} \end{vmatrix} \qquad D_y = \begin{vmatrix} a_{11} & k_1 \\ a_{21} & k_2 \end{vmatrix} \tag{4-29}$$

and finding

$$x = \frac{D_x}{D} \qquad y = \frac{D_y}{D} \tag{4-30}$$

where D is merely a symbolic way of representing the difference of the products of the elements in the two diagonals:

$$D = \begin{vmatrix} a_{11} & a_{12} \\ a_{21} & a_{22} \end{vmatrix} = a_{11}a_{22} - a_{12}a_{21} \tag{4-31}$$

By an orderly development of this symbolism, the whole procedure of solving n simultaneous equations is reduced to a routine, which may be stated as follows:

1. Write the matrix of the n^2 equation coefficients and the n con-

stant terms in n rows and $n + 1$ columns:

$$
\begin{array}{c|ccccc}
 & x & y & z & \cdots & & k \\
\hline
1 & a_{11} & a_{12} & a_{13} & \cdots & a_{1n} & k_1 \\
2 & a_{21} & a_{22} & a_{23} & \cdots & a_{2n} & k_2 \\
\cdots & \cdots & \cdots & \cdots & \cdots & \cdots & \cdots \\
n & a_{n1} & a_{n2} & a_{n3} & \cdots & a_{nn} & k_n
\end{array}
$$

2. Form a determinant, D, of the nth order from the n^2 coefficients alone:

$$
D = \begin{vmatrix}
a_{11} & a_{12} & a_{13} & \cdots & a_{1n} \\
a_{21} & a_{22} & a_{23} & \cdots & a_{2n} \\
\cdots & \cdots & \cdots & \cdots & \cdots \\
a_{n1} & a_{n2} & a_{n3} & \cdots & a_{nn}
\end{vmatrix} = |a_{nn}| \tag{4-32}
$$

3. Calculate the numerical value of D as the sum of all the $n!$ different products that can be found by taking one element from each row and one from each column, the sign of the product depending upon the relative positions of the elements:

$$
D = |a_{nn}| = \Sigma \pm a_{1x}a_{1y}a_{1z} \cdots a_{1n} \tag{4-33}
$$

where the sequence $x, y, z, \ldots, n$ assumes in turn each of the $n!$ possible sequences of $1, 2, 3, \ldots, n$. The sign of each product is $+$ or $-$ according as an even or odd number of interchanges is necessary to derive the particular sequence from the normal sequence, $1, 2, 3, \ldots, n$.

4. Calculate in the same manner in turn the numerical value of each of the different determinants $D_x, D_y, D_z, \ldots, D_n$ formed by substituting in D the values of $k_1, k_2, k_3, \ldots, k_n$ for the coefficients in the column belonging to one of the unknown variables, $x, y, \ldots$.

5. Find the values of $x, y, z, \ldots$, by dividing the determinant of each variable by D:

$$
x = \frac{D_x}{D}, \quad y = \frac{D_y}{D}, \quad z = \frac{D_z}{D}, \cdots \tag{4-34}
$$

For example, Eqs. 4-24 expressed in matrix form are

$$
\begin{array}{c|cccc}
 & x & y & z & k \\
1 & 7 & 5 & -1 & 14 \\
2 & 4 & -4 & 3 & 5 \\
3 & 1 & 2 & 1 & 8
\end{array}
$$

The value of D is

$$D = \begin{vmatrix} a_{11} & a_{12} & a_{13} \\ a_{21} & a_{22} & a_{23} \\ a_{31} & a_{32} & a_{33} \end{vmatrix} = \begin{vmatrix} 7 & 5 & -1 \\ 4 & -4 & 3 \\ 1 & 2 & 1 \end{vmatrix}$$

$$= (a_{11}a_{22}a_{33} + a_{12}a_{23}a_{31} + a_{13}a_{21}a_{32})$$
$$- (a_{13}a_{22}a_{31} + a_{12}a_{21}a_{33} + a_{11}a_{23}a_{32})$$

$$= [(7)(-4)(1) + (5)(3)(1) + (-1)(4)(2)]$$
$$- [(-1)(-4)(1) + (5)(4)(1) + (7)(3)(2)]$$

$$= -28 + 15 - 8 - 4 - 20 - 42 = -87$$

The product $a_{13}a_{22}a_{31}$ is given a minus sign because the sequence of its second subscripts, 3, 2, 1, requires three interchanges (321:231: 213:123) to bring them into the normal sequence, 123. The products $a_{12}a_{21}a_{33}$ and $a_{11}a_{23}a_{32}$ each require one interchange to bring their sequences of 2, 1, 3 and 1, 3, 2 to normal, and, therefore, they also are given a minus sign. In general, products found by elements that lie on diagonals sloping down to the right are positive and those on diagonals sloping down to the left are negative.

Similarly, the values of D_x, D_y, D_z are

$$D_x = \begin{vmatrix} 14 & 5 & -1 \\ 5 & -4 & 3 \\ 8 & 2 & 1 \end{vmatrix} = \begin{aligned} &[(14)(-4)(1) + (5)(3)(8) + (-1)(5)(2)] \\ &- [(-1)(-4)(8) + (5)(5)(1) + (14)(3)(2)] \end{aligned}$$
$$= -56 + 120 - 10 - 32 - 25 - 84 = -87$$

$$D_y = \begin{vmatrix} 7 & 14 & -1 \\ 4 & 5 & 3 \\ 1 & 8 & 1 \end{vmatrix} = \begin{aligned} &[(7)(5)(1) + (14)(3)(1) + (-1)(4)(8)] \\ &- [(-1)(5)(1) + (14)(4)(1) + (7)(3)(8)] \end{aligned}$$
$$= 35 + 42 - 32 + 5 - 56 - 168 = -174$$

$$D_z = \begin{vmatrix} 7 & 5 & 14 \\ 4 & -4 & 5 \\ 1 & 2 & 8 \end{vmatrix} = \begin{aligned} &[(7)(-4)(8) + (5)(5)(1) + (14)(4)(2)] \\ &- [(14)(-4)(1) + (5)(4)(8) + (7)(5)(2)] \end{aligned}$$
$$= -224 + 25 + 112 + 56 - 160 - 70 = -261$$

Therefore

$$x = \frac{D_x}{D} = \frac{-87}{-87} = 1 \qquad y = \frac{D_y}{D} = \frac{-174}{-87} = 2$$

$$z = \frac{D_z}{D} = \frac{-261}{-87} = 3$$

agreeing with the values found in Sec. 4-5.

If it is found that $D = 0$, it means that the equations are not independent; that is, two of the equations are equivalent. For example, if two identical equations are used in forming D, two of the rows will be the same and it will then be found that $D = 0$. In such a case, another independent equation must be found before x, y, . . . can be determined.

Determinants have many interesting properties, and an extensive theory of their use has been developed, but the engineer's use for them is principally in the solution of first-order simultaneous equations, as in the example given.

4-7 Diophantine Equations. Sometimes, in engineering, problems arise in which there are more unknown quantities than there are equations: for instance, two equations and three unknowns. Mathematically, this gives not one, but an indefinite number of possible solutions. Physically, however, the number of permissible solutions may be limited by conditions entirely apart from the algebra. For instance, it is often the case that the answer must be a whole number, as when the problem is to decide between buying two large machines or several smaller ones of the same total capacity.

In other cases, also, when the solution is indefinite or provides some freedom of choice, it is often desirable to choose a positive integer, or a "preferred number" for the answer. A familiar example of this is the calculation of the number of turns to be used in each coil of an electric motor. Obviously, each coil has a whole number of turns, either 3 or 7 or some other integer. Other integers also must be selected for the number of parallel circuits in a winding, the number of slots in an armature, etc., and often these several integers must satisfy joint equations.

Suppose that in a proposed electric supply system for an industrial area, the physical and economic conditions indicate that the following equations should be satisfied, for best results:

$$8x + 3y + \ \ z = 49 \tag{4-35}$$
$$2x + \ \ y + 3z = 21 \tag{4-36}$$

where x = number of substations

y = number of transformers per substation

z = number of load supply lines per substation

There are two equations with three unknowns, but these unknowns must all be integers.

Eliminating z from Eqs. 4-35 and 4-36 gives

$$11x + 4y = 63$$

or
$$y = \frac{63 - 11x}{4} = 15 - 2x + \frac{3 - 3x}{4} \tag{4-37}$$

Since y must be an integer, $(3 - 3x)/4$ must be an integer. Call this u; it is

$$u = \frac{3 - 3x}{4} \qquad (4\text{-}38)$$

whence $x = 1 - u - u/3$. Since x must be an integer, $u/3$ must also be an integer; that is,

$$u = 3v \qquad (4\text{-}39)$$

Substituting Eq. 4-39 in Eqs. 4-36, 4-37, and 4-38 gives

$$\begin{aligned} x &= 1 - 4v \\ y &= 13 + 11v \\ z &= 2 - v \end{aligned} \qquad (4\text{-}40)$$

The number of possible answers to the problem has thus been reduced to those few that come out when successive integer values of v are substituted in Eq. 4-40. The simplest choices are those for $v = -2$, -1, 0, 1, or 2:

v	$+2$	$+1$	0	-1	-2
x	-7	-3	1	5	9
y	35	24	13	2	-9
z	0	1	2	3	4

There are only two solutions, those for $v = 0$ and $v = -1$, that give positive integers for x, y, and z. All other values of v lead to negative or fractional values of x, y, or z, and, therefore, are not real answers. The first of the two real solutions, giving only one substation with 13 transformers, is not attractive. Therefore, the one and only practical solution is to have $x = 5$ substations, with $y = 2$ transformers per substation, and $z = 3$ load supply lines each.

Such equations, relating integral numbers, are called *Diophantine equations*, after Diophantus of Alexandria, who first studied them.

4-8 Right Triangles with Integral Sides. As another example, consider the problem of finding all possible combinations of whole numbers x, y, and z, such that

$$x^2 + y^2 = z^2 \qquad (4\text{-}41)$$

that is, of finding all possible right triangles whose sides are integers. To solve this,[1] let

$$z = y + a \qquad (4\text{-}42)$$

and $$y = bn^2 + cn + d \qquad (4\text{-}43)$$

where n is an integer that assumes successive values 0, 1, 2, 3, . . . , n,

---

[1] The most general solution is $x = 2ab$, $y = a^2 - b^2$, $z = a^2 + b^2$.

and a, b, c, and d are also integers, whose values are to be found. Then, by factoring Eq. 4-41 and substituting, we have

$$x^2 = z^2 - y^2 = (y + a)^2 - y^2 = 2ay + a^2 = 2abn^2 + 2acn + 2ad + a^2 \tag{4-44}$$

Since this must be true for any value of n, and since x must be a whole number, it follows that the right-hand side of Eq. 4-44 must be a perfect square, or

$$x = n \sqrt{2ab} + \sqrt{a^2 + 2ad} \tag{4-45}$$

and

$$2ac = 2 \sqrt{2ab} \sqrt{a^2 + 2ad} \quad \text{or} \quad c = \sqrt{2b(a + 2d)} \tag{4-46}$$

For x to be an integer, $2ab$ must be a perfect square. The solution will take different forms, therefore, depending on the value of a:

For $\qquad\qquad a = k^2, b = 2m^2$ $\qquad\qquad$ (4-47)
For $\qquad\qquad a = 2k^2, b = m^2$ $\qquad\qquad$ (4-48)
For $\qquad\qquad a = 3k^2, b = 6m^2$, etc. $\qquad\quad$ (4-49)

where k and m are any integers, 0, 1, 2, 3, ... The simplest solution is found by taking $a = k = 1$ and $m = 1$, whence

$$a = 1 \qquad b = 2 \qquad c = \sqrt{4(1 + 2d)} \tag{4-50}$$

For c to be an integer, d must be 0, or 4, or 12, etc. Taking $d = 0$, we have $c = 2$ and

$$x = 2n + 1 \qquad y = 2n^2 + 2n \qquad z = 2n^2 + 2n + 1 \tag{4-51}$$

This defines the series of right triangles with sides 3, 4, 5; 5, 12, 13; 7, 24, 25; etc., found by making $n = 1, 2, 3, \ldots$

Taking $d = 4$, we have $c = 6$, and

$$x = 2n + 3 \qquad y = 2n^2 + 6n + 4 \qquad z = 2n^2 + 6n + 5 \tag{4-52}$$

which is the same result as found by putting $(n + 1)$ for n in Eq. 4-51. Thus, Eq. 4-52 gives no new triangles not already given by Eq. 4-51.

For $a = 2$, taking $k = 1$ and $m = 1$, we have

$$a = 2 \qquad b = 1 \qquad c = 2 \sqrt{1 + d} \tag{4-53}$$

so that $d = 0$ and $c = 2$. This gives

$$x = 2n + 2 \qquad y = n^2 + 2n \qquad z = n^2 + 2n + 2 \tag{4-54}$$

This defines the series of right triangles with sides 4, 3, 5; 6, 8, 10; 8, 15, 17; etc.

For $a = 9$, $k = 3$, and $m = 1$,

$$a = 9 \qquad b = 2 \qquad c = 6 \qquad d = 0 \qquad (4\text{-}55)$$

and $\qquad x = 6n + 9 \qquad y = 2n^2 + 6n \qquad z = 2n^2 + 6n + 9 \qquad (4\text{-}56)$

which describes the series of right triangles 15, 8, 17; 21, 20, 29; 27, 36, 45; etc.

Continuing in this way, we can readily construct tables that will give all possible right triangles with integral sides.

4-9 The Conic Sections. In Sec. 4-1, we found that any quadratic equation represents one of the conic sections (Fig. 4-3) and that by inspection of the equation coefficients we can determine

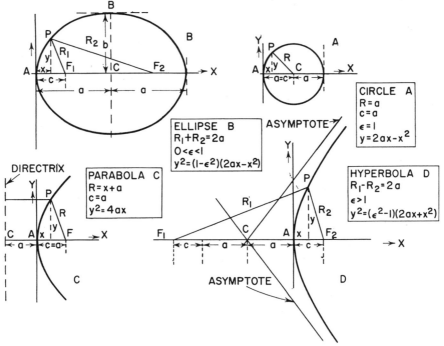

Fig. 4-7   The conic sections.

whether it is a circle, an ellipse, a parabola, or a hyperbola. Conversely, from a knowledge of the properties of such curves, their equations can be derived.

For example, the circle is defined as the locus of (path followed by) a point P, whose distance R from a fixed center C is equal to a constant a. Taking the origin of coordinates at the end of a diameter, or vertex, A, in Fig. 4-7A, and the center C at $x = a$, $y = 0$, we find

$$R = \sqrt{(a - x)^2 + y^2} = a$$

Squaring and combining terms give for the equation of the circle

$$y^2 = 2ax - x^2 \tag{4-57}$$

when the origin is at one end of a diameter.

The ellipse is defined as the locus of a point P the sum of whose distances $R_1 + R_2$ from two fixed points F_1 and F_2, called *foci*, is equal to a constant $2a$. In Fig. 4-7B, taking the origin A at the end of a major axis, the distance from the vertex to the center is a and from the vertex to a focus is c. The major axis of the ellipse is then $2a$, and the minor axis is $2b$, where

$$b = \sqrt{a^2 - (a - c)^2} = \sqrt{2ac - c^2} \tag{4-58}$$

From the figure

$$R_1 + R_2 = \sqrt{(c - x)^2 + y^2} + \sqrt{(2a - c - x)^2 + y^2} = 2a$$

Transferring, squaring, and combining terms give

$$2a - \sqrt{(c - x)^2 + y^2} = \sqrt{(2a - c - x)^2 + y^2}$$

or

$$a\sqrt{(c - x)^2 + y^2} = ac + (a - c)x$$

Squaring again, and simplifying, we find for the equation of the ellipse

$$a^2 y^2 = c(2a - c)(2ax - x^2) \tag{4-59}$$

Substituting Eq. 4-58 in Eq. 4-59 gives a more familiar form of the ellipse equation in Fig. 4-7B:

$$\frac{y^2}{b^2} + \frac{x^2}{a^2} = \frac{2x}{a} \tag{4-60}$$

The eccentricity of the ellipse, ϵ, is defined as

$$\epsilon = \sqrt{1 - \left(\frac{\text{minor axis}}{\text{major axis}}\right)^2} = \sqrt{1 - \frac{b^2}{a^2}} = \frac{a - c}{a} \tag{4-61}$$

so that still another form of the ellipse equation is

$$y^2 + (1 - \epsilon^2)x^2 = 2px \tag{4-62}$$

where $p = b^2/a = a(1 - \epsilon^2)$

The parabola is defined as the locus of a point P whose distance a from a straight line, called the *directrix*, is always equal to its distance from the focus F, as shown in Fig. 4-7C. From the figure

$$R = \sqrt{(a - x)^2 + y^2} = x + a$$

which gives for the equation of the parabola in Fig. 4-7C

$$y^2 = 4ax \tag{4-63}$$

The directrix passes through the center C, at a distance a from the vertex, so that the distance from the vertex to the focus c must also be equal to a, just as in the case of the circle. In the circle, the focus and the center coincide at $x = a, y = 0$, while in the parabola the focus is at $x = a$ and the center at $x = -a$.

The hyperbola is defined as the locus of a point P, the difference of whose distances from the two foci F_1 and F_2, $R_1 - R_2$, is equal to a constant $2a$. In Fig. 4-7D, the center C is at $x = -a$ and the two foci are at $x = c$ and $x = -(2a + c)$.

The major axis of the hyperbola, or twice the distance from the center to the vertex, is $2a$. The asymptotes are lines passing through the center C that are tangent to the curve when $x = \infty$, and the minor axis of the hyperbola, $2b$, is twice the value of y for the asymptote when $x = 0$ in Fig. 4-7D. From the figure

$$R_1 - R_2 = \sqrt{(x + 2a + c)^2 + y^2} - \sqrt{(c - x)^2 + y^2} = 2a$$

Transferring, squaring, and combining terms give

$$a\sqrt{(c - x)^2 + y^2} = ac + (a + c)x$$

Squaring again and simplifying give

$$a^2y^2 = c(2a + c)(2ax + x^2) \tag{4-64}$$

The slope of the asymptote (which passes through the center C) is the ratio of y to x, when x is very large (when the x term can be neglected):

$$\frac{y}{x} = \frac{1}{a}\sqrt{c(2a + c)}$$

so that the equation of the asymptote is

$$y^2 = \frac{c(2a + c)(x - a)^2}{a^2} \tag{4-65}$$

and the half-minor axis b is the value of y found by making $x = 0$ in Eq. 4-65:

$$b = \sqrt{c(2a + c)} \tag{4-66}$$

Substituting Eq. 4-66 in Eq. 4-64 gives the more familiar form of the equation for the hyperbola in Fig. 4-7D:

$$\frac{y^2}{b^2} - \frac{x^2}{a^2} = \frac{2x}{a} \qquad (4\text{-}67)$$

The eccentricity of the hyperbola, ϵ, is

$$\epsilon = \sqrt{1 + \left(\frac{\text{minor axis}}{\text{major axis}}\right)^2} = \sqrt{1 + \frac{b^2}{a^2}} = \frac{a+c}{a} \qquad (4\text{-}68)$$

so that another form of the hyperbola equation is

$$y^2 - (\epsilon^2 - 1)x^2 = 2px \qquad (4\text{-}69)$$

where $p = b^2/a = a(\epsilon^2 - 1)$

Comparing Eqs. 4-57, 4-62, 4-63, and 4-69, we see that all of the conic sections are represented by the equation

$$y^2 = 2px - (1 - \epsilon^2)x^2 \qquad (4\text{-}70)$$

if the origin is taken at the vertex of the curve. For the circle, $\epsilon = 0$; for the ellipse, $0 < \epsilon < 1$; for the parabola, $\epsilon = 1$; and for the hyperbola, $\epsilon > 1$. For the circle, the ellipse, and the hyperbola, $p = b^2/a$.

In this way, the equations for curves having any specified properties can be developed, and the relations between can then be studied. Such studies lie in the field of analytic geometry.

4-10 Other Plane Curves. A great many plane curves, whose properties have been studied by mathematicians, have been given distinctive names. One of these is the cissoid of Diocles (Fig. 4-8) whose equation is

$$y^2 = \frac{x^3}{2a - x}$$

or, in polar form,

$$r = 2a \sin \theta \tan \theta \qquad (4\text{-}71)$$

The cissoid is generated by extending a chord of a circle, OB, to its intersection C with the tangent at the opposite end of the diameter OA, and marking off on the chord a distance OP equal to the distance BC. The asymptote of the curve, or line that it approaches as y approaches ∞, is AC, or $x = 2a$; and the total area between the curve and its asymptote is 3 times the area of the circle.

Another celebrated curve is the cycloid (Fig. 4-9), formed by a point on the circumference of a circle as the circle rolls along a straight line. Its equation is

$$x = a(\phi - \sin \phi) \qquad y = a(1 - \cos \phi) \qquad (4\text{-}72)$$

The length of a single arch of the cycloid is four times the diameter of the generating circle, and the area under the arch is three times the area of the circle. The cycloid has the interesting property that, if the curve is inverted and a frictionless ball is allowed to roll from a point A to a lower point B on it under the influence of gravity, the time required to move from A to B is less than for any other possible curve that can be drawn through the two points. For this reason, the cycloid is also called a *brachistochrone*. Only one of the many possible cycloids that can be drawn through A and B has this property, however.

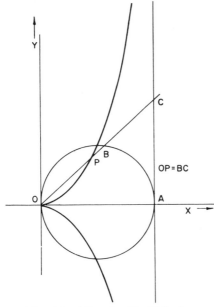

Fig. 4-8 The cissoid of Diocles.

Still another interesting curve is the catenary (Fig. 4-10), which is the form assumed by a perfectly flexible, inextensible rope of uniform weight per foot when suspended between two points under the influence of gravity. Its equation is

$$2ay = (e^{ax} + e^{-ax})$$

or
$$ay = \cosh ax \qquad \text{(see Eq. 9-23)} \qquad (4\text{-}73)$$

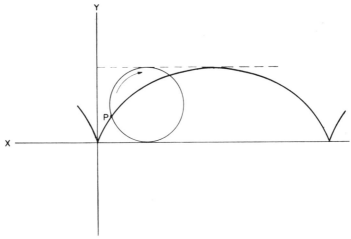

Fig. 4-9 The cycloid.

The wires of a transmission line and the cables of a suspension bridge are familiar examples of the catenary. The large number of other named curves that exist with interesting properties is suggested by the fact that we have included here only curves whose names begin with c!

4-11 Summary. It is well at this point to look back over the four chapters that have just been covered and to consider broadly the purpose or utility of the methods that have been presented.

In engineering, we generally want to design a structure or equipment or to predict some future occurrence in fairly exact numerical terms. To do this, we must assemble the necessary data on the available materials, the performance of earlier equipment, etc., and we must know, or discover, the physical laws and relationships governing the different materials and elements that are pertinent to the problem.

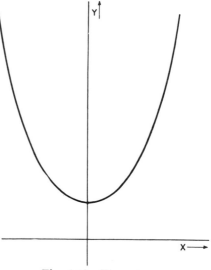

Fig. 4-10 The catenary.

Then, we formulate the needed specific relationships or equations, in which the numerical data can be inserted; and, finally, the equations must be solved, thus determining the actual dimensions and behavior of the proposed structure.

In solving the equations, it is quite immaterial what letter we choose to assign to any particular quantity. That is, we may choose to call an unknown length either y or x as we may prefer, an unknown weight w, an unknown velocity v, etc., all of which are conventional choices, or we may choose any other letters, or Greek letters, or symbols that we wish. Whatever symbols are chosen, the equations and their properties will be the same.

This illustrates a chief distinction between engineering and mathematics. In engineering, we are dealing with specific quantities and their relations under prescribed conditions, so that when we use the letter M, for example, we may naturally think of this as meaning "mass," and we may associate the letter with a physical reality in terms of pounds or weight. Actually, we should think of each factor in the equation as a pure number G, multiplied by its proper unit, ^uG, as indicated in Sec. 3-10. When all the units of measurement, or base quantities, are divided out, leaving an equation between pure numbers, or dimensionless ratios, the problem is reduced to plain mathematics.

In mathematics, the letters used represent numbers, which have no fixed physical meaning, but may be per unit measures of any quantity whatever, as long as the equation considered is a true description of the phenomena. Thus, the student should learn very early to recognize a familiar mathematical equation such as

$$ax^2 + bx + c = 0 \qquad (4\text{-}7)$$

and know that its solution is

$$x = \frac{-b \pm \sqrt{b^2 - 4ac}}{2a} \qquad (4\text{-}10)$$

no matter what symbols or letters are used in place of a, b, c, and x. For example, Eq. 4-10 gives the solution of $p\alpha^2 + q\alpha + w = 0$ just as well as it solves Eq. 4-7. We merely put p for a, α for x, q for b, and w for c in Eq. 4-10.

In this way, the x or y or z of a given algebraic equation may represent per unit quantities of apples, or horses, or dollars, or anything else. And a single mathematical equation may represent equally well the behavior of magnetic or electrostatic fields, of temperature or stress distribution, of fluid flow, etc. A relatively few mathematical equations will thus cover a great variety of engineering phenomena. The engineer does not need to know *much* mathematics, but he must be able to see through the symbols used for a particular problem and recognize the basic mathematical equations that apply, no matter how unfamiliar the symbols in which they are written.

The Greeks, who had no adequate system of numbers, developed geometry to perfection. Their mathematical ideas were expressed in drawings and geometrical models, whereby the properties of triangles, circles, polygons, and the conic sections were derived. For example, Pythagoras derived Eq. 2-10 by means of a diagram which proved that the sum of the areas of two squares erected on the sides of a right triangle is equal to the area of the square erected on the hypotenuse. This rule is still known as the theorem of Pythagoras.

However, any geometrical figure can be represented by corresponding equations, and thereby its properties can usually be derived and dealt with in a more compact, convenient, and accurate way than by a drawing. Thus, engineers nowadays generally rely on algebraic equations for their calculations and use figures only to confirm and illustrate their results or to show how to make and assemble parts for construction.

Nevertheless, when you are tackling an unfamiliar problem especially, fresh ideas and a better understanding can be obtained by drawing curves to represent a set of equations. For example, the two equations

$$x + 3y = 0 \qquad \text{and} \qquad 2x - y = 14$$

represent two straight lines in the x,y plane. Their solution, $x = 6$, $y = -2$, is their intersection, or the point at which they cross. In a similar way, by drawing curves to represent two or more separate equations, their solution often may be found graphically without using any mathematics.

An equation in three or in n variables represents a curve in three- or in n-dimensional space. And, if two or more such equations are solved simultaneously, the resulting points, or the equations in fewer variables that result, represent their intersections. The intersection of a plane with a three-dimensional surface is a two-dimensional curve. When no more than three variables, x, y, and z, are concerned, the equations can be represented by actual models, which are helpful in visualizing the relations of the variables. By keeping in mind the geometrical equivalents of his equations, the engineer may often be led to a quicker or more general solution of practical problems. This question of the use of models to represent equations is considered further in Chap. 14.

The concepts considered in this chapter are generally included under the heading of *Analytic Geometry*. The mathematician E. T. Bell has said: "The method of analytic geometry is so powerful that very ordinary boys of seventeen can use it to prove results which would have baffled the greatest of the Greek geometers—Euclid, Archimedes, and Appollonius."

PROBLEMS

Read the following values from the curve of Fig. 4-1 and compare them with values calculated directly:

1. $\sqrt{1.6}$	**3.** $(0.95)^2$	**5.** $\sqrt{1.95}$
2. $\sqrt{0.2}$	**4.** $(1.36)^2$	**6.** $(0.32)^2$

Find the roots of the following equations by expressing them as the products of factors $(x - x_1)(x - x_2)$, etc.:

7. $x^3 - 2x^2 - 5x + 6 = 0$ **9.** $2x^2 - 13x - 7 = 0$
8. $x^3 + x^2 + 3x + 3 = 0$ **10.** $x^2 + 7 = 0$
11. $x^4 - 3x^3 - 15x^2 - 19x + 30 = 0$

Determine whether the following sets of equations are consistent (have one common point), first graphically, and then by solving the equations directly:

12. $3x + 2y = 0$ $4x - y + 11 = 0$ $11x + 7y + 1 = 0$
13. $x^2 + y^2 = 16$ $4x + y = 8$ $x + 4y = 15$

Find the solution, or point of intersection, of the following sets of three:

14. $2x + y - z = -2$ $y + z = 5$ $2x - 2y + 6z = 23$
15. $3x + 8y + 4z = -11$ $x + 5y + z = -6$
     $x + y + z = -2$
16. $2x - 2y + 3z = 10$ $6y + 6z = 5$ $x + 2y - 9z = 3$
17. $x + y + 2z = 0$ $2x + y = 6$ $3x + 5y + 4z = 8$
18. $3x - 5y + z = 41$ $x - y + z = 15$ $5x + 3y - z = -7$

Bibliography

1. Aiken, D. J., and K. B. Henderson: "Algebra," books I and II, McGraw-Hill Book Company, New York, 1954.
2. Birkhoff, G., and S. MacLane: "A Survey of Modern Algebra," The Macmillan Company, New York, 1941.
3. Bradley, H. C., and E. H. Uhler: "Descriptive Geometry for Engineers," International Textbook Company, Scranton, Pa., 1943.
4. Keller, M. W.: "College Algebra," Houghton Mifflin Company, Boston, 1946.
5. Lehmann, C. H.: "Analytic Geometry," John Wiley & Sons, Inc., New York, 1942.
6. Middlemiss, R. R.: "College Algebra," McGraw-Hill Book Company, New York, 1952.
7. Murnaghan, F. D.: "Analytic Geometry," Prentice-Hall, Inc., Englewood Cliffs, N.J., 1946.
8. Osgood, W. F., and W. C. Graustein: "Plane and Solid Analytic Geometry," The Macmillan Company, New York, 1930.
9. Perlis, S.: "Theory of Matrices," Addison-Wesley Publishing Company, Inc., Reading, Mass., 1952.
10. Rowe, C. E.: "Engineering Descriptive Geometry," D. Van Nostrand Company, Inc., Princeton, N.J., 1939.
11. Stoll, R. R.: "Linear Algebra and Matrix Theory," McGraw-Hill Book Company, New York, 1952.

Chapter 5 INFINITE SERIES

5-1 Power Series. An expression such as

$$y = \frac{1}{1 - x} \tag{5-1}$$

represents a fraction, that is, the result of division. Like any fraction, it can be expressed in nonfractional form, by dividing the numerator by the denominator, thus:

$$
\begin{array}{r}
1 + x + x^2 + x^3 + \cdots \\
1 - x \overline{)\, 1} \\
\underline{1 - x} \\
+x \\
\underline{x - x^2} \\
+x^2 \\
\underline{x^2 - x^3} \\
+x^3
\end{array}
$$

Hence, the fraction (Eq. 5-1) can also be expressed as

$$y = \frac{1}{1 - x} = 1 + x + x^2 + x^3 + \cdots + x^n + \cdots \tag{5-2}$$

This is an infinite series of successive powers of x, or a *power series.* In the same way, by dividing through, the expression

$$y = \frac{1}{1 + x} \tag{5-3}$$

can be reduced to the infinite series:

$$y = \frac{1}{1 + x} = 1 - x + x^2 - x^3 + \cdots + (-1)^n x^n + \cdots \tag{5-4}$$

The infinite series, Eq. 5-2 or 5-4, is an alternate form of Eq. 5-1 or 5-3, just as the repeating decimal fraction is another representation of the common fraction (for instance, $0.636363 \ldots = \frac{7}{11}$).

[121]

As it contains an infinite number of terms, perfect exactness can never be reached in calculating numerical values from such a series. Only a finite number of terms can be calculated, and the result can be only approximate. By taking a sufficient number of terms of the series, numerical values can be calculated as accurately as need be.

For engineering purposes, the infinite series gives just as useful values as calculation by a finite expression, provided a sufficient number of terms is used. In most engineering calculations an exactness of 0.1 per cent is sufficient; rarely is an exactness of 0.01 per cent or closer required. On the one hand, the unavoidable variations in the materials used in structures or in manufacturing and the inaccuracies of measuring instruments impose a limit of this order on the exactness of the result. On the other hand, customers will rarely pay anything extra for unneeded precision.

No one cares in the least whether a given motor develops 100 or 101 foot-pounds of torque at exactly rated voltage, rated frequency, normal temperature, etc. The motor must develop enough torque to bring the pump, or whatever else it drives, up to speed promptly, however the voltage, frequency, or temperature may vary in that particular location. This usually requires that the motor have a reserve of at least 25 per cent more torque capacity than normally required, so that a matter of 1 per cent or less is insignificant.

One of the first principles an engineer should learn is that he must economize time and effort in his work. Methods of approximation, which enable the result to be obtained accurately enough, without the use of any abstruse mathematics or extended calculations, are invaluable to this end.

5-2   Convergent and Divergent Series.   For $x = 0.5$, Eq. 5-1 gives $y = 1/(1 - 0.5) = 2$, while the series (Eq. 5-2) gives

$$y = 1 + 0.5 + 0.25 + 0.125 + 0.0625 + 0.03125 + \cdots \quad (5\text{-}5)$$

The successive approximations given by including more and more terms are shown in Table 5-1.

Table 5-1   Values of a Converging Series Using Five Terms

		Sum	Error
Using one term....	$y = 1$	1	−1
Using two terms...	$y = 1 + 0.5$	1.5	−0.5
Using three terms...	$y = 1 + 0.5 + 0.25$	1.75	−0.25
Using four terms...	$y = 1 + 0.5 + 0.25 + 0.125$	1.875	−0.125
Using five terms....	$y = 1 + 0.5 + 0.25 + 0.125 + 0.0625$	1.9375	−0.0625

The successive approximations come closer and closer to the correct value, $y = 2$, but in this case always remain below it. The series approaches its limit, or asymptote, from below, as shown in Fig. 5-1.

For the value $x = 0.5$, the approach to the limit is rather slow, and to get an accuracy of 0.1 per cent, that is, to bring the error down to less than 0.002, requires a large number of terms.

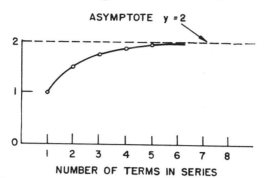

Fig. 5-1 Convergent series with one-sided approach.

For $x = 0.1$, Eq. 5-2 gives

$$y = 1 + 0.1 + 0.01 + 0.001 + 0.0001 + \cdots \qquad (5\text{-}6)$$

and the successive approximations are

$$1, 1.1, 1.11, 1.111, 1.1111, \ldots$$

As, by Eq. 5-1, the limiting value is

$$y = \frac{1}{1 - 0.1} = \frac{10}{9} = 1.1111 \cdots$$

the fourth approximation already brings the error well below 0.1 per cent. Only four terms of the series, therefore, are needed for engineering purposes in this case.

Equation 5-3 gives, for $x = 0.5$, the value

$$y = \frac{1}{1 + 0.5} = \frac{2}{3} = 0.6666 \cdots$$

By Eq. 5-4, we have

$$y = 1 - 0.5 + 0.25 - 0.125 + 0.0625 - 0.03125 + \cdots \qquad (5\text{-}7)$$

The successive approximations are given in Table 5-2.

The successive values for this series come closer and closer to the correct value, $y = 0.6666 \cdots$, but are alternately above and below the limiting value. The series approaches its limit from both sides, as

Table 5-2 Successive Values for an Alternating Convergent Series

		Sum	Error
First..........	$y = 1$	1	$+0.3333$
Second........	$y = 1 - 0.5$	0.5	-0.1666
Third.........	$y = 1 - 0.5 + 0.25$	0.75	$+0.0833$
Fourth.........	$y = 1 - 0.5 + 0.25 - 0.125$	0.625	-0.04166
Fifth..........	$y = 1 - 0.5 + 0.25 - 0.125 + 0.0625$	0.6875	$+0.020833$

seen in Fig. 5-2, while the series of Eq. 5-2 approached its limit from below and other series may approach their limits from above.

With such an alternating approach to the limit, as shown by Eq. 5-4, the final value is between any two successive approximations; that is, the error of any one approximation is smaller than the next

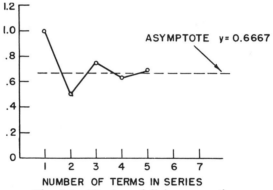

Fig. 5-2 The law of divine proportion.

term of the series. Such a series is preferable for engineering calculations, since it gives information on the maximum possible error. A series with a one-sided approach does not do this without special investigation, since the error is greater than the absolute value of the next term of the series.

Substituting $x = 2$ in Eq. 5-1 gives

$$y = \frac{1}{1 - 2} = -1$$

while the infinite series (Eq. 5-2) gives

$$y = 1 + 2 + 4 + 8 + 16 + 32 + \cdots$$

and the successive approximations of y, found by including more and more terms, are

$$1, 3, 7, 15, 31, 63, \ldots$$

that is, the successive approximations do not approach a final value, but, on the contrary, get further and further away from each other and give entirely wrong results. They give increasing positive values, which seem to approach infinity when all terms are included, while the correct value for the expression, by Eq. 5-1, is -1.

Therefore, for $x = 2$, the series (Eq. 5-2) gives unreasonable results and thus cannot be used for calculating numerical values.

The same is the case with the representation (Eq. 5-4) of the expression (Eq. 5-3) for $x = 2$. Equation 5-3 gives

$$y = \frac{1}{1 + 2} = \frac{1}{3} = 0.333 \ldots$$

while the infinite series (Eq. 5-4) gives

$$y = 1 - 2 + 4 - 8 + 16 - 32 + \cdots$$

whose successive approximations are

$$1, \; -1, \; 3, \; -5, \; 11, \; -21, \; \ldots$$

Hence, while the successive values are alternately above and below the correct value, they do not approach it more and more closely, but diverge further and further from it.

Such a series, in which the values derived by including more and more terms do not approach a final value more and more closely, is called *divergent*. A series is called *convergent* if the differences between the successive values and the final value, or limit, approach zero.

In a convergent series, successive terms are smaller and smaller, while in a divergent series they are larger and larger, or at any rate they get smaller at a very slow rate. Equation 5-2 is divergent if $x > 1$, because x^{n+1} will be greater than x^n and successive terms will be continually larger. If $x < 1$, however, Eqs. 5-2 and 5-4 will be convergent, because x^{n+1} will then be less than x^n and successive terms will be continually smaller.

Thus, a finite expression such as Eq. 5-1 or 5-3 holds good for all values[1] of x, and numerical values may be calculated with it whatever the value of x may be. An infinite series, as Eq. 5-2 or 5-4, frequently does not give a finite result for any value of x, but only for values within a certain range. For instance, in the above, for $-1 < x < +1$, the series are convergent, while for values of x outside this range, the series are divergent and thus useless for engineering purposes.

---

[1] Except those that make the expression infinite.

When representing an expression by an infinite series, it is necessary to determine that the series is convergent, that is, approaches with increasing number of terms a finite limiting value; otherwise, the series cannot be used. When the series is convergent within a certain range of x and divergent outside of this range, it can be used only in the range of *convergency;* outside of this range some other form of representation must be found which is convergent.

This can frequently be done, and an expression thus represented by one series in one range and another series in another range. For instance, Eq. 5-1, $y = 1/(1 + x)$—by substituting $x = 1/u$—can be written in the form

$$y = \frac{1}{1 + 1/u} = \frac{u}{1 + u} \qquad (5\text{-}8)$$

Dividing yields the infinite series

$$y = u - u^2 + u^3 - u^4 + \cdots + (-1)^{n+1} u^n + \cdots$$

and resubstituting $1/x$ for u gives

$$y = \frac{1}{x} - \frac{1}{x^2} + \frac{1}{x^3} - \frac{1}{x^4} + \cdots + (-1)^{n+1} \left(\frac{1}{x}\right)^n + \cdots \qquad (5\text{-}9)$$

This is convergent for values of $x > 1$. For $x = 2$, it gives

$$y = 0.5 - 0.25 + 0.125 - 0.0625 + \cdots$$

with the successive approximations

$$0.5, \ 0.25, \ 0.375, \ 0.3125, \ \ldots$$

which approach the limiting value $y = 0.3333 \ldots$.

5-3   Some Useful Numerical Series.   An infinite series is useful for computation only if it converges. There are mathematical methods for determining whether a series is convergent or not. In engineering, however, these methods are rarely needed. For practical purposes, it is not sufficient that a series converge. It must converge so rapidly, that is, the successive terms of the series must decrease at such a great rate, that accurate numerical results are derived by calculating only a few terms, two or three, or at most four terms. This, for instance, is true with the series 5-2 and 5-4 if $x = 0.1$ or less. For $x = 0.5$, these two series are still convergent, but are useless for most engineering purposes, since too large a number of terms has to be calculated to get sufficient accuracy. There is no time in engineering work for such lengthy calculations. Any series whose terms decrease at such a rapid rate that all but the first three or four can be neglected is certain to be convergent.

In a series, therefore, where there is a question whether it converges or diverges, as for instance the series

$$y = 1 + \tfrac{1}{2} + \tfrac{1}{3} + \tfrac{1}{4} + \tfrac{1}{5} + \tfrac{1}{6} + \cdots \qquad \text{(divergent)} \qquad (5\text{-}10)$$
$$\text{or } y = 1 - \tfrac{1}{2} + \tfrac{1}{3} - \tfrac{1}{4} + \tfrac{1}{5} - \tfrac{1}{6} + \cdots \qquad \text{(convergent)} \qquad (5\text{-}11)$$

the matter of convergence is of no importance to an engineer, since the series is useless in any case; that is, it does not give accurate results with a reasonable amount of calculation.

The great advantage of an infinite power series over other forms of expression is that it requires only the simplest mathematical operations, of taking powers and of addition or subtraction. Whenever such a series can be substituted for another expression, such as a logarithmic, trigonometric, or hyperbolic form, the resulting equations will generally be simpler, easier to visualize, and easier to calculate. Success in solving engineering problems, therefore, hinges to a considerable degree on skill in using series to obtain approximate answers quickly.

A series that often arises in engineering work is one whose successive terms differ by a constant amount, called an *arithmetic* series:

$$S_n = A(1 + 2 + 3 + 4 + \cdots + n) \qquad (5\text{-}12)$$

To sum this finite series, we assume that it can be expressed by a simple polynomial

$$S_n = an^2 + bn + c \qquad (5\text{-}13)$$

so that

$$S_{n+1} = a(n + 1)^2 + b(n + 1) + c = an^2 + (2a + b)n + a + b + c$$

We know that the difference between S_{n+1} and S_n is $A(n + 1)$, so that

$$S_{n+1} - S_n = A(2an + a + b) = A(n + 1)$$

whence $a = b = \tfrac{1}{2}$.

The value of c must be zero, because S_n is zero when $n = 0$. Therefore

$$S_n = A\left(\frac{n^2}{2} + \frac{n}{2}\right) = \frac{n(n + 1)A}{2} \qquad (5\text{-}14)$$

In a similar way, we find that the sum of the squares of the first n

numbers is

$$1^2 + 2^2 + 3^2 + 4^2 + \cdots + n^2 = \frac{n(n + 1)(2n + 1)}{6} \qquad (5\text{-}15)$$

the sum of the cubes is

$$1^3 + 2^3 + 3^3 + 4^3 + \cdots + n^3 = \frac{n^2(n + 1)^2}{4} \qquad (5\text{-}16)$$

and that of the fourth powers is

$$1^4 + 2^4 + 3^4 + \cdots + n^4 = \frac{n(n + 1)(2n + 1)(3n^2 + 3n - 1)}{30}$$
$$(5\text{-}17)$$

The geometric series, in which each term is a constant ratio r times the preceding term is another common type:

$$S_n = A(1 + r + r^2 + r^3 + \cdots + r^n) \qquad (5\text{-}18)$$

To sum this, we multiply the series by r and subtract S_n from the result. All but the first and last terms, cancel out, giving

$$(r - 1)S_n = A(r^{n+1} - 1)$$

so that the sum is

$$S_n = \frac{A(r^{n+1} - 1)}{r - 1} \qquad (5\text{-}19)$$

If r is less than 1 and n is ∞, Eq. 5-19 reduces to Eq. 5-1.

This result can be used to find the series of perfect numbers, which are defined as numbers that are equal to the sum of all their factors. For example, the number 6 can be factored in only two ways:

$$6 = 1 \times 6 \qquad \text{or} \qquad 2 \times 3$$

The only factors of 6, therefore, are 1, 2, and 3, and the sum of these is equal to 6:

$$6 = 1 + 2 + 3$$

Therefore, 6 is a perfect number.

In general, the perfect numbers have the form

$$N = 2^n(2^{n+1} - 1) = 2^n P = \frac{(P + 1)P}{2}$$

subject to the condition that $2^{n+1} - 1 = P$ must be a prime number. For, the sum of the first n successive powers of 2 is, by Eq. 5-19,

$$1 + 2 + 4 + 8 + \cdots + 2^n = 2^{n+1} - 1 = P$$

or, for $n = 0, 1, 2 \ldots$ in succession,

$$P = 1, 3, 7, 15, 31, 63, 127 \ldots$$

And, for those values of P that are prime numbers, the factors of $2^n P$ will be those of 2^n and P times each of the factors of 2^n, including 1 but excluding 2^n itself. The sum of the factors of 2^n is $2^{n+1} - 1 = P$, so that the sum of the factors of $2^n P$, when P is prime, is

$$P + P(P - 2^n) = P + P\left(P - \frac{P+1}{2}\right) = \frac{P(P+1)}{2}$$

as before. Thus, the first six perfect numbers, corresponding to $n = 0, 1, 2, 4, 6,$ and 12, and to $P = 1, 3, 7, 31, 127,$ and 8,191, are

$$N = 1;\ 6;\ 28;\ 496;\ 8,128;\ 33,550,336$$

Some of the numerical series that are met with in engineering work are given in Appendix C.

5-4 Continued Fractions. As we saw in Sec. 1-12, a common fraction may be expressed, alternatively, as a repeating decimal. Conversely, an irrational number, such as π, or a number raised to a fractional power, may be approximated by a common fraction. For example, $\sqrt{2}$, $\sqrt{3}$, etc., are represented by simple *continued fractions* (or chain fractions):

$$\sqrt{2} = 1 + \sqrt{2} - 1 = 1 + \frac{(\sqrt{2} - 1)(\sqrt{2} + 1)}{\sqrt{2} + 1}$$

$$= 1 + \cfrac{1}{2 + \sqrt{2} - 1} = 1 + \cfrac{1}{2 + \cfrac{1}{2 + \cfrac{1}{2 + \cfrac{1}{2 + \cdots}}}} \tag{5-20}$$

Considering only the first n 2s in this continued fraction and reconverting it into a common fraction give successive approximations to its true value of 1.4142134 · · · (See Table 5-3):

$$1, \tfrac{3}{2}, \tfrac{7}{5}, \tfrac{17}{12}, \tfrac{41}{29}, \tfrac{99}{70}, \tfrac{239}{169}, \tfrac{577}{408}, \cdots$$

Table 5-3   Approximations of $\sqrt{2}$ by Continued Fractions

Fraction	Decimal equivalent	Error
1	1	−0.4142
$\tfrac{3}{2}$	1.5	0.0858
$\tfrac{7}{5}$	1.4	−0.0142
$\tfrac{17}{12}$	1.41666 . . .	0.00245
$\tfrac{41}{29}$	1.413793 . . .	−0.000420
$\tfrac{99}{70}$	1.4142857 . . .	0.0000724
$\tfrac{239}{169}$	1.4142012 . . .	−0.0000123
$\tfrac{577}{408}$	1.4142157 . . .	0.0000024

Similarly, the continued fractions representing the square roots of 3, 5, etc., are

$$\sqrt{3} = 1 + \cfrac{2}{2 + \cfrac{2}{2 + \cfrac{2}{2 + \cdots}}} \qquad \text{or} \quad \sqrt{3} = 1 + \cfrac{1}{1 + \cfrac{1}{2 + \cfrac{1}{1 + \cfrac{1}{2 + \cdots}}}}$$

$$\sqrt{5} = 2 + \cfrac{1}{4 + \cfrac{1}{4 + \cfrac{1}{4 + \cdots}}} \qquad \sqrt{6} = 2 + \cfrac{1}{2 + \cfrac{1}{4 + \cfrac{1}{2 + \cfrac{1}{4 + \cdots}}}} \qquad (5\text{-}21)$$

$$\sqrt{7} = 2 + \cfrac{3}{4 + \cfrac{3}{4 + \cfrac{3}{4 + \cdots}}}$$

$$\sqrt{11} = 3 + \cfrac{2}{6 + \cfrac{2}{6 + \cfrac{2}{6 + \cdots}}} \qquad \text{or} \quad \sqrt{11} = 3 + \cfrac{1}{3 + \cfrac{1}{6 + \cfrac{1}{3 + \cfrac{1}{6 + \cdots}}}}$$

Likewise

$$\pi = 3.141593 \cdots = 3 + \cfrac{1}{7.0625 \cdots}$$

$$= 3 + \cfrac{1}{7 + \cfrac{1}{15 + \cfrac{1}{1 + \cfrac{1}{288 + \cdots}}}}$$

The common fractions that represent these values to three decimal places are shown in Table 5-4.

Table 5-4 Common Fractions Representing Square Roots and Irrational Numbers

	Equivalent fraction	Corresponding value	True value
$\sqrt{2}$	$99\frac{9}{70}$	1.4143 . . .	1.4142 . . .
$\sqrt{3}$	$97\frac{7}{56}$	1.7321 . . .	1.7321 . . .
$\sqrt{5}$	$161\frac{1}{72}$	2.2361 . . .	2.2361 . . .
$\sqrt{6}$	$218\frac{8}{89}$	2.4494 . . .	2.4495 . . .
$\sqrt{7}$	$233\frac{3}{88}$	2.6477 . . .	2.6458 . . .
$\sqrt{11}$	$199\frac{9}{60}$	3.3167 . . .	3.3166 . . .
π	$355\frac{5}{113}$	3.141593 . . .	3.141593 . . .
e	$193\frac{3}{71}$	2.71831 . . .	2.71828 . . .

It is often more convenient to find the square root of a number by this method of continued fractions than to look it up in tables or extract it by another process (Sec. 5-6). This illustrates a cardinal principle of engineering mathematics—that the simplest processes of arithmetic, properly employed, are adequate to solve many problems generally thought to require elaborate techniques.

5-5 The Binomial Series. Multiplying $(a - b)$ by itself repeatedly leads to the expressions

$$(a - b)^2 = a^2 - 2ab + b^2$$
$$(a - b)^3 = a^3 - 3a^2b + 3ab^2 - b^3$$
$$(a - b)^4 = a^4 - 4a^3b + 6a^2b^2 - 4ab^3 + b^4$$

which leads to the general formula, or *binomial theorem:*

$$(a + b)^n = a^n + na^{n-1}b + \frac{n(n - 1)}{2!} a^{n-2}b^2$$

$$+ \frac{n(n - 1)(n - 2)}{3!} a^{n-3}b^3 + \cdots \quad (5\text{-}22)$$

The successive coefficients are the same as those found in the inter-polation formula (Eq. 1-36). The factorial $k!$ is defined by Eq. 3-22.

Equation 5-22 may be used to expand many complicated functions into series forms, more convenient for calculation. It is particularly useful when $b \ll a$,* so that b/a is a very small quantity, and terms in b^2/a^2 and higher orders can be neglected. For example, the impedance of an alternating-current circuit is $Z = \sqrt{R^2 + X^2}$ ohms, where R and X are the circuit resistance and reactance, respectively. In nearly all power circuits, R is much smaller than X. Hence, instead of calcu-lating the current by the formula

$$I = \frac{E}{Z} = \frac{E}{\sqrt{R^2 + X^2}} \qquad \left(\text{amperes} = \frac{\text{volts}}{\text{impedance}} \right)$$

we may expand this by Eq. 5-22:

$$
\begin{aligned}
I &= \frac{E}{X(1 + R^2/X^2)^{\frac{1}{2}}} = \frac{E}{X}\left(1 + \frac{R^2}{X^2} \right)^{-\frac{1}{2}} \\
&= \frac{E}{X}\left(1 - \frac{R^2}{2X^2} + \frac{1}{2}\frac{1}{2}\frac{3}{2}\frac{R^4}{X^4} - \frac{1}{6}\frac{1}{2}\frac{3}{2}\frac{5}{2}\frac{R^6}{X^6} + \cdots \right) \\
&= \frac{E}{X}\left(1 - \frac{R^2}{2X^2} + \frac{3R^4}{8X^4} - \frac{5R^6}{16X^6} + \cdots \right)
\end{aligned}
\qquad (5\text{-}23)
$$

Usually R/X will be less than 0.10, so that for practical purposes we need use only

$$I = \frac{E}{X}\left(1 - \frac{R^2}{2X^2} \right) \qquad (5\text{-}24)$$

The correction term, $R^2/2X^2$, need be calculated to only one or two decimal places in most cases, so that it can frequently be estimated by mental arithmetic and written down directly.

As another example of the usefulness of Eq. 5-22, suppose we are given the following expression to calculate

$$F = \frac{\sqrt{a}\,\sqrt[4]{(a + s)^3}}{(a + 2s)\,\sqrt{a - 2s}} \qquad (5\text{-}25)$$

* The symbol $\ll$ means very much less than.

and we know that s is less than $0.1a$. Expanding by Eq. 5-22, we have

$$F = \frac{a^{3/4}(1 + s/a)^{3/4}}{a^{3/2}(1 + 2s/a)(1 - 2s/a)^{1/2}}$$

$$= a^{-1/4}\left(1 + \frac{3s}{4a} - \frac{3s^2}{32a^2} + \cdots\right)\left(1 - \frac{2s}{a} + \frac{4s^2}{a^2} - \cdots\right)$$

$$\times \left(1 + \frac{s}{a} + \frac{3s^2}{2a^2} + \cdots\right)$$

or

$$F = a^{-1/4}\left(1 - \frac{s}{4a} + \frac{85s^2}{32a^2} - \cdots\right) \tag{5-26}$$

Equation 5-26 is ever so much simpler for repetitive calculations than Eq. 5-25. It is just as accurate, from an engineering point of view, when $s < 0.10a$, approximately, and it permits easy visualization of the effects of changes in a or s.

5-6 Finding Square and Cube Roots. Algebra books usually give rules for long-hand extraction of the square and the cube roots of ordinary numbers. Rather than remember such rules, it is convenient to employ the binomial theorem for this purpose. For example, to find the square root of x, we first select the nearest perfect square, a^2, that comes to mind, and write down the equation

$$y = \sqrt{x} = [a^2 + (x - a^2)]^{1/2} \tag{5-27}$$

Expanding this by the binomial theorem (Eq. 5-22), we have

$$y = a + \frac{(x - a^2)}{2a} + \cdots \tag{5-28}$$

If $(x - a^2)$ is small, this gives the desired answer directly. For example, to find $\sqrt{9.475}$, we take $a = 3$, and find

$$y = \sqrt{9.475} = (9 + 0.475)^{1/2} = 3 + \frac{0.475}{6} = 3.079 \tag{5-29}$$

The square of 3.079 is 9.4802. Repeating the process, we have

$$y = 3.079 + \frac{9.475 - 9.4802}{2(3.079)} = 3.079 - 0.00084 = 3.07816 \tag{5-30}$$

The square of 3.07816 is 9.4751, so that 3.07816 is the answer required.

Generally, an engineer has a slide rule within easy reach, and he finds the square root with the rule directly, by moving the slider to the point x on the top scale and reading y opposite it on the bottom scale (Fig. 1-7). If greater accuracy is required, solving Eq. 5-28 with the slide rule gives the answer simply and speedily. Even without a slide rule, Eq. 5-28 usually can be solved by mental arithmetic, since only one or two decimal places are required in the correction term.

In a similar way, to find the cube root, we have

$$y = \sqrt[3]{x} = [a^3 + (x - a^3)]^{1/3} = a + \frac{(x - a^3)}{3a^2} + \cdots \quad (5\text{-}31)$$

For example, to find the cube root of 24,

$$y = \sqrt[3]{24} = [27 + (24 - 27)]^{1/3} = 3 - \frac{3}{3(9)} = 3 - 0.111 = 2.889$$

The cube of 2.90 is 24.389, so as a second approximation

$$y = 2.90 - \frac{0.389}{3(8.41)} = 2.90 - 0.0154 = 2.8846$$

The exact answer to four decimal places is 2.8845.

5-7 Interest Calculations. These infinite series relations are useful in commerce as well as in engineering and science. For example, when money is borrowed, the lender expects to receive interest in addition to the return of his principal. A man may borrow 1,000 dollars for 10 years, with yearly interest payments at a 5 per cent rate. He will then pay the lender 50 dollars each year for 9 years, and at the end of the tenth year will pay 1,050 dollars. His total payments are

$$S = 1,000 + 10(50) = 1,500$$

He has paid 500 dollars for the privilege of using the 1,000 dollars for 10 years.

Such fixed annual payments are called *simple* interest. Often, the lender requests interest payments in advance. Thus, a man borrowing 1,000 dollars from a bank for 3 months ($\frac{1}{4}$ year) at 6 per cent will receive only

$$R = 1,000 - (0.06)(1,000)(\tfrac{1}{4}) = 1,000 - 15 = 985 \text{ dollars}$$

At the end of the 3 months, he will pay the bank 1,000 dollars. In a similar way, a man who has lent money may take the borrower's note (written promise to pay) to a bank and receive for it a sum equal to the principal amount due, less the estimated amount of interest for the remaining period of the loan. This practice is called *discounting*, since the seller of the note receives for it less than the principal sum.

When money is deposited in a savings bank, the interest due is added to the principal after each year, or other period agreed upon, and correspondingly larger interest payments will be made after each successive period as the total increases. For example, a sum of 1,000 dollars deposited in a savings account at an interest rate of 100 x per cent will increase after n interest periods to a total amount

$$S = 1,000(1 + x)^n \qquad (5\text{-}32)$$

This plan of increasing payments is called *compound* interest. Tables of compound interest are available in any bank. The amount can be estimated to engineering accuracy by expanding Eq. 5-32 by the binomial theorem (Eq. 5-22):

$$S = 1,000 \left[1 + nx + \frac{n(n-1)x^2}{2} + \cdots \right] \qquad (5\text{-}33)$$

In business transactions, a great many calculations of this kind are required, such as:

What is the amount remaining to be paid after n years when a loan A dollars made at 100 x per cent interest is repaid at a uniform rate of a dollars each year?

After the first year the amount due, less the first payment, is

$$S_1 = A(1 + x) - a$$

After the second year, it is

$$S_2 = [A(1 + x) - a](1 + x) - a$$

And, after the nth year, it is

$$S_n = A(1 + x)^n - a[(1 + x)^{n-1} + (1 + x)^{n-2} + \cdots + 1] \qquad (5\text{-}34)$$

which reduces by Eq. 5-19 to

$$S_n = \left(A - \frac{a}{x} \right)(1 + x)^n + \frac{a}{x} \qquad (5\text{-}35)$$

Such formulas as these enable the engineer to estimate the interest charges and the payments due with sufficient accuracy for most purposes. The banker, however, must calculate the amounts to the last penny, and for this purpose he uses a calculating machine, or tables.

5-8   The Fibonacci Series.   Through the ages, men have sought to define beauty in mathematical terms. Emerson said, "We ascribe beauty to that which is simple; which has no superfluous parts, which exactly meets its end; which stands related to all things; which is the mean of many extremes." In the papyrus of Ahmes, which tells of the building of the great pyramid of Gizeh, about 4700 B.C., the statement appears: "The sacred quotient, seqt, was used in the proportions of our pyramids." This sacred quotient of the Egyptians was known to the Greeks as the "golden section," and in medieval times its formula came to be known as the law of divine proportion:

> The most beautiful division of any given length into two parts is such that the lesser is to the greater as the greater is to the whole length.

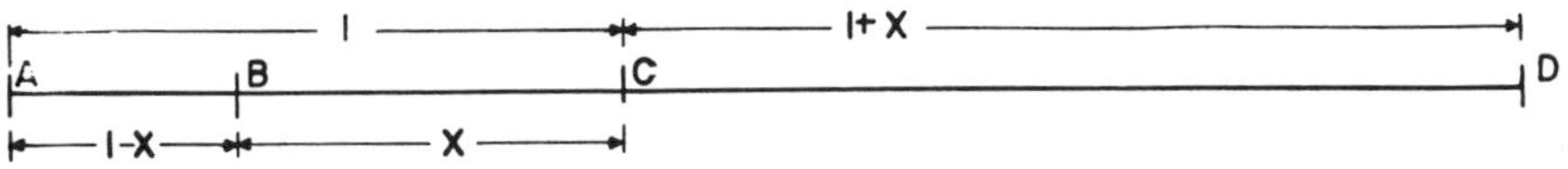

$$\frac{1-x}{x} = \frac{x}{1} = \frac{1}{1+x} = \frac{1+x}{2+x} = \frac{\sqrt{5}-1}{2} = 0.618$$

Fig. 5-3

That is, in Fig. 5-3, if the length AC is 1 and the greater of its two parts, BC, is x, the equation that defines the most beautiful proportion is

$$\frac{1-x}{x} = \frac{x}{1} \qquad \text{or} \qquad x^2 + x - 1 = 0 \tag{5-36}$$

Completing the square, as in Eq. 4-9, and taking the square root, we find

$$x = \frac{-1-\sqrt{5}}{2} \text{ or } \frac{1-\sqrt{5}}{2} = -1.618 \cdots \text{ or } +0.618 \cdots \tag{5-37}$$

To divide the line AC in Fig. 5-3 externally, we lay off $CD = 1.618$ to the right of C and find that

$$\frac{AC}{CD} = \frac{CD}{AD} = \frac{1}{1+x} = \frac{1+x}{2+x} = 0.618$$

To divide AC internally, we lay off $CB = 0.618$ to the left of C and find that

$$\frac{AB}{BC} = \frac{BC}{AC} = \frac{1-x}{x} = \frac{x}{1} = 0.618$$

The ratio of the base of a regular polygon with ten sides inscribed in a circle to the radius of the circle is also equal to 0.618, and the same number appears over and over again in the construction of five-sided polygons and stars (see Prob. 28).

The "golden rectangle" of Fig. 5-4, with a ratio of base to altitude equal to 1.618, has been used by architects and artists since ancient times in proportioning rooms, buildings, pictures, windows, etc. A

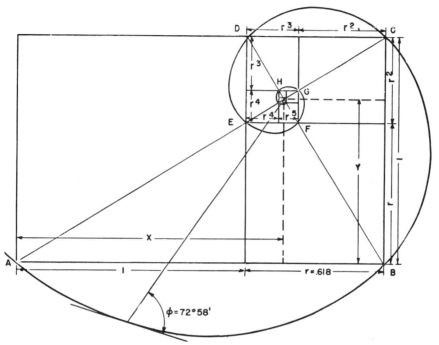

Fig. 5-4   The golden rectangle and the logarithmic spiral.

series of increasing panels, such as might be used from the top to the bottom of any structure, has been thought to be most aesthetic if the successive sizes are proportional to

$$1, (1 + x), (1 + x)^2, (1 + x)^3, (1 + x)^4, \ldots$$
$$1, 1.618, 2.618, 4.236, 6.854, \ldots$$

This "golden series" has the interesting property that each number is the sum of the two preceding numbers, while the ratio of any one to the preceding number is always 1.618. In Fig. 5-4, the series is applied to develop a logarithmic spiral, whose radius increases by a constant factor when its angle increases by a fixed amount. A rectangle of the "divine proportions" is drawn, with a base 1.618 and an altitude 1, and a square is marked off on the left side, leaving a smaller rectangle at the right, with sides 0.618 and 1. This second rectangle is similar to the first, but is turned 90°. Marking off a second square on its base leaves a third rectangle with sides 0.618 and $(0.618)^2$, turned 180° from the first. Continuing in this way, an infinite series of similar diminishing rectangles is formed, spiraling around the center fixed by the intersection of corresponding diagonals.

The logarithmic spiral, *ABCDEFGH*, formed by connecting consecutive corners of these whirling squares, has the property that its radius is changed by the factor 1.618 for each 90° increase in its angle. The polar equation of such a spiral is

$$R = R_0 e^{c\theta} \tag{5-38}$$

where c is a constant that determines the proportions of the curve. The logarithmic spiral is also called the *equiangular* spiral, because the radius cuts the curve at a fixed angle, ϕ, that is determined by the relation $\tan \phi = 1/c$. For the particular spiral formed by the golden-rectangle series (Fig. 5-4), the radius increases by the factor 1.618 for each 90°, so that

$$e^{c\pi/2} = 1.618$$

whence

$$c = 0.3063$$
$$\tan \phi = 3.264$$
$$\phi = 72°58' \text{ or } 1.274 \text{ radians}$$

The horizontal coordinate of the center of the spiral is

$$X = 1 + r^4 + r^8 + r^{12} + \cdots$$

where $r = 0.618 = 1/1.618$. From Eq. 5-2, this is

$$X = \frac{1}{1 - r^4} = \frac{3\sqrt{5} + 5}{10} = 1.171 = 0.724(1.618)$$

The vertical coordinate of the center, or eye, of the spiral is

$$Y = rX = \frac{5 + \sqrt{5}}{10} = 0.724$$

The center is located at the intersection of the corresponding diagonals of the successive rectangles, which cut each other at right angles. From an artistic viewpoint, the eye of the spiral is considered the best place to locate a picture on a blank wall, or to put the central feature of a display, etc.

If one doubts the truth of the statement that the golden rectangle truly does have the most beautiful shape, it is easy to test this by giving the members of a class, or a large group, a strip of paper about three times as long as it is wide and asking each one to fold it to give a rectangle of the most pleasing shape to him (or her). Figure 5.5 shows the results of such an experiment with 200 people. The horizontal scale shows the chosen ratio of the two sides, divided into blocks 0.05 wide. The vertical scale shows the number of persons choosing values in each block. When a choice fell on a dividing line, one half was

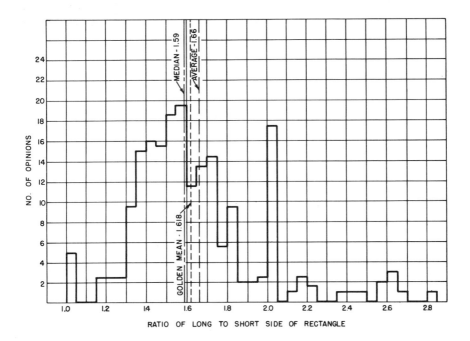

Fig. 5-5 Distribution curve for 200 individual judgements of the most pleasing proportions of a rectangle.

added to the ordinate on each side. Thus, the chart shows that 5 persons chose a ratio between 1.00 and 1.05; 34 chose between 1.45 and 1.55; and only 1 chose a ratio greater than 2.7. The median value of the ratio was 1.59, and the average was 1.66, values which are remarkably close to the golden ratio of 1.618. It would be interesting to learn whether all sorts of people of different ages, colors, and origins would choose 1.62.

The logarithmic spiral occurs in nature in many forms, such as the snail's shell and the horns of a ram. Figure 5-6 shows the shell of the pearly nautilus, which forms a perfect logarithmic spiral. For this particular shell, the ratio between successive radii 90° apart is 1.32, giving $c = 0.164$ and $\phi = 81°$. The logarithmic spiral is also the "curve of pursuit" that will be followed by each of three dogs, placed at the corners of an equilateral triangle, that start at the same moment to chase each other at equal speeds.

The seeds of a sunflower are arranged with exquisite uniformity in curved lines radiating in spokes from the center. Some of the curves turn to the left, and these are crossed by others turned to the right. The curves are logarithmic spirals, and the ratio of those going clockwise to those going counterclockwise is normally 1.618.

Fig. 5-6 Shell of the chambered nautilus.

Leonardo of Pisa, called Fibonacci, about the year 1200, gave to the world a series of increasing numbers that were supposed to express the laws of nature governing the growth of plants. The Fibonacci series, starting with 1, is

$$1, 1, 2, 3, 5, 8, 13, 21, 34, 55, 89, 144, 233, \ldots$$

each term after the second being the sum of the two preceding terms. Whatever two numbers are used at the start of the series, the ratio of any terms to the next preceding approaches 1.618 as a limit. For example, the successive ratios in the series given are

$$1, 2, \tfrac{3}{2}, \tfrac{5}{3}, \tfrac{8}{5}, \tfrac{13}{8}, \tfrac{21}{13}, \tfrac{34}{21}, \tfrac{55}{34}, \tfrac{89}{55}, \tfrac{144}{89}, \tfrac{233}{144}, \ldots$$

the last three of which are equal to 1.61818, 1.61798, and 1.61806.

Starting with 2 and 5 instead of 1 and 1, the successive ratios become

$$\tfrac{5}{2}, \ \tfrac{7}{5}, \ \tfrac{12}{7}, \ \tfrac{19}{12}, \ \tfrac{31}{19}, \ \tfrac{50}{31}, \ \tfrac{81}{50}, \ \tfrac{131}{81}, \ \tfrac{212}{131}, \ \ldots$$

the last three of which are 1.62000, 1.61728, 1.61832. This property of the Fibonacci series can help to make teaching arithmetic easy and pleasant. For example, the teacher may ask each pupil in a class to choose any two numbers, as 2 and 5; to form a series by repeated addition, as 2, 5, 7, 12, 19, . . . ; and then to divide each term by the preceding one. After the tenth term or so, all the pupils should obtain the same answer, 1.618034 . . . , a fact that will excite their wonder

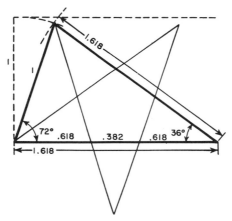

Fig. 5-7   Golden triangle and five-pointed star.

and make the correction of papers very simple. Making whirling square drawings like Fig. 5-4, but starting with inner rectangles of different shapes such as by 2 by 1 or 2 by 5 is another instructive exercise.

The golden triangle is formed by removing one end of the golden rectangle, and bringing the two open corners together, as in Fig. 5-7. The acute angle of the golden triangle is one-tenth of a circle, or 36°, so that the ratio of the golden series is 0.618 . . . = 2 sin 18° exactly (see Prob. 5-28). Each arm of a five-pointed star is approximately a golden triangle, so that the starfish as well as the snails on an ocean beach are shaped by the law of divine proportion.

The Fibonacci series is an approximation to the golden series. The numbers in this series continually recur in the arrangements of the leaves and petals of plants and flowers. It has been suggested that this is Nature's way of arranging the leaves to make the best possible use of the available sunlight, by minimizing the shading of one leaf by those above it.

In electrical engineering also, the Fibonacci numbers occur. For example, if a series of unit resistances are connected alternately in

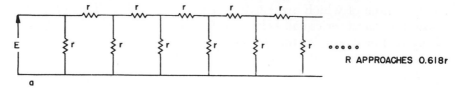

R APPROACHES 0.618r

a

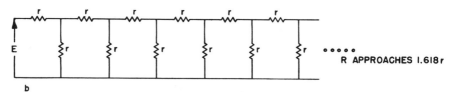

R APPROACHES 1.618r

b

Fig. 5-8 Ladder network of resistances.

series and in parallel, as shown in Fig. 5-8*b*, the resistance of the entire circuit is expressed by the continued fraction:

$$R = r + \cfrac{1}{\cfrac{1}{r} + \cfrac{1}{r + \cfrac{1}{\cfrac{1}{r} + \cfrac{1}{r + \cfrac{1}{\cfrac{1}{r} + \cdots}}}}}$$

For successively larger numbers of resistances, the value of R/r is

$$\frac{R}{r} = 1, 2, \frac{3}{2}, \frac{5}{3}, \frac{8}{5}, \frac{13}{8}, \frac{21}{13}, \frac{34}{21}, \ldots, 1.618$$

in accordance with the Fibonacci series. If the first resistance in the circuit is in parallel instead of in series, as in Fig. 5-8*a*, the initial term in the equation for R is omitted, and the successive values of R/r become

$$\frac{R}{r} = 1, \frac{1}{2}, \frac{2}{3}, \frac{3}{5}, \frac{5}{8}, \frac{8}{13}, \frac{13}{21}, \frac{21}{34}, \ldots, 0.618$$

5-9 Mathematics and Beauty. The mathematician G. H. Hardy said: The mathematician's patterns, like the painter's or the poet's, must be beautiful; the ideas, like the colors or the words, must fit together in a harmonious way. Beauty is the first test: there is no permanent place in the world for ugly mathematics.

Along with the multiplying of ways for enhancing feminine beauty, there has grown up in recent years a whole new art of *styling*, or of making ordinary things good-looking. Nowadays a bridge builder, an architect, and a construction engineer must be sure that the structures they create will satisfy artistic standards, or else they may be deluged with public criticism. And, with the advent of self-service stores, where the customer selects a box of cereal, a TV set, or a power lawn mower without the aid of any salesman's words, the article must appeal to the eye, or it will not be chosen.

To meet these needs, a new profession of *industrial designers* has sprung up, a profession whose members are keenly aware of colors and forms that create beauty. They are also well informed about materials, costs, and manufacturing methods—so that they can *style* anything from a baby's bottle or a vacuum cleaner to an automobile or a motor boat in ways that add beauty at no extra cost.

These designers are finding new uses for geometry, a subject which has fallen into disuse by engineers, who tend to use equations and computers rather than pictures in reaching their conclusions. For brevity, the usual courses in geometry have been omitted from this book, because they are not needed by practical engineers, aside from trigonometry in Chap. 2 and some analytic geometry in Chap. 4. Those who are interested in art and in geometry for its own sake can learn much by reading Thompson, Coxeter, and Pacioli, (see Refs. 3, 7 and 10). Paoli (1445–1509) wrote about the law of divine proportion with great enthusiasm and illustrated his book with drawings made by his friend Leonardo da Vinci.

5-10 Preferred Numbers. A line of manufactured products, such as shirts, nails, or motors, must cover a wide range of sizes to fit the needs of different customers. The manufacturer cannot afford to offer an unlimited range of sizes, as his costs vary inversely with the number of units made of a single size. On the other hand, customers do not want to pay for any larger size than they need. The need is to make just that number of sizes that will give the lowest overall cost, balancing the extra cost of making and stocking more sizes against those of using a larger size than necessary in some cases.

To obtain the least overall cost, it is desirable to choose sizes that form a geometric series, since in this way the percentage by which an

Table 5-5 Preferred-Numbers—Decimal Series

5 Series 60% Steps	10 Series 25% Steps	20 Series 12% Steps	40 Series 6% Steps
		10	10
	10		10.6
		11.2	11.2
			11.8
10		12.5	12.5
	12.5		13.2
		14	14
			15
		16	16
	16		17
		18	18
			19
16		20	20
	20		21.2
		22.4	22.4
			23.6
		25	25
	25		26.5
		28	28
			30
25		31.5	31.5
	31.5		33.5
		35.5	35.5
			37.5
		40	40
	40		42.5
		45	45
			47.5
40		50	50
	50		53
		56	56
			60
		63	63
	63		67
		71	71
			75
63		80	80
	80		85
		90	90
			95

available shirt or motor exceeds a particular customer's requirement will be minimized. The successive numbers in such a series are A, Ax, Ax^2, Ax^3, . . . , Ax^n. For example, if six steps in size of motor are to be made to cover the range from 1 to 10 horsepower, the ratio of one size to the next smaller should be $x = \sqrt[6]{10} = 1.4678$, and the successive sizes should be 1, 1.468, 2.154, 3.162, 4.642, 6.813, and 10.

For convenience and simplicity, the numbers are rounded-off, so the actual horsepower sizes used commercially are 1, 1.5, 2, 3, 5, 7.5, and 10. Such rounded-off values are called "preferred numbers."

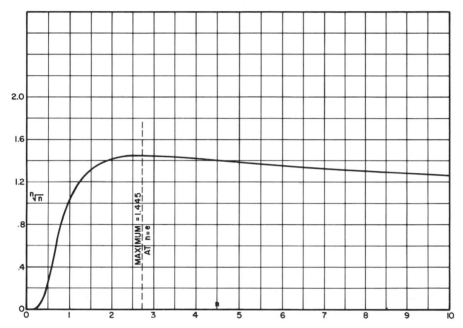

Fig. 5-9 Step ratio versus number of steps.

This principle of choosing a limited number of sizes in accord with a series of preferred numbers is followed throughout industry. It enables standard sizes of every sort of material, device, or part to be adopted, so that price bids will be comparable, products of different manufacturers can be interchanged, and the costs of maintaining stocks can be minimized.

The steps between sizes are chosen to give least overall cost, and so they are smaller when the production quantities are large. Since the demand may be small at first and then grow, the manufacturer may begin production with only a few sizes and add intermediate sizes later on. For this reason, it is customary to choose numbers that follow a preferred-number series with small steps and to omit some of the steps, rather than making all steps uniform. To facilitate this and to encourage the wide use of standard products, the United States of America Standards Institute has published tables of preferred numbers, such as Table 5.5, which gives rounded multiples of $\sqrt[40]{10}$. These are also called Renard numbers.

It is interesting to consider how the size of the steps changes if the number of steps is made proportional to the total range to be covered. If the smallest size is A, the largest is An, and there are n steps, the step ratio is $\sqrt[n]{n}$, which is plotted against n in Fig. 5.9. The maximum size of a step occurs when $n = e = 2.71828 \ldots$, and is equal to $\sqrt[e]{e} = 1.445.$[1] This may be shown by the methods explained in Sec. 11.1 and Eq. 11.2.

PROBLEMS

1. Write the nth term of the series:

  a. $S_n = 1 + \dfrac{1}{2} + \dfrac{1}{2^2} + \dfrac{1}{2^3} + \cdots + ?$

  b. Show by marking off successive terms on a straight line what the limit of S_n is.

Use the binomial theorem to find approximate values for the following numbers. Compare results when the number is divided in different ways, as $(60 - 7)^3$ vs. $(50 + 3)^3$ in Prob. 2.

2. $(53)^3$		**7.** $(372)^{2/5}$	
3. $\sqrt[4]{(17)^2}$		**8.** $(54)^7$	
4. $\sqrt[3]{630}$		**9.** $\sqrt[3]{5}$	
5. $\sqrt[5]{(45)^3 + (118)^2}$		**10.** $\sqrt{2}$	
6. $(98)^{1/2}$		**11.** $\sqrt[4]{3}$	

What are the limiting values of x for which the following series will converge?

  12. $x + x^4 + x^9 + x^{16} + \cdots$

  13. $1 - \dfrac{x^2}{2!} + \dfrac{x^4}{4!} - \dfrac{x^6}{6!} + \cdots$

---

[1] It is amusing to note that $\sqrt[\pi]{\pi} = 1.437$.

14. $x - \dfrac{x^3}{3!} + \dfrac{x^5}{5!} - \dfrac{x^7}{7!} + \cdots$

15. $\dfrac{x}{1 \cdot 2} - \dfrac{x^2}{2 \cdot 2^2} + \dfrac{x^3}{3 \cdot 2^3} - \dfrac{x^4}{4 \cdot 2^4} + \cdots$

16. $1 - x + \dfrac{x^2}{2^2} - \dfrac{x^3}{3^2} + \cdots$

17. Given that

$$\sin x = \frac{e^{jx} - e^{-jx}}{2j} \qquad \cos x = \frac{e^{jx} + e^{-jx}}{2}$$

and $\qquad e^x = 1 + x + \dfrac{x^2}{2!} + \dfrac{x^3}{3!} + \cdots + \dfrac{x^{n-1}}{(n-1)!}$

derive infinite series that will give approximate values for sin x and cos x, without any j terms.

Compute the values of the following functions by deriving and substituting directly in their power series expansions:

18. $e = 2.7182$

19. $\sqrt{e} = 1.6487$

22. $\tan 50° = 1.192$

20. $\sin 60° = 0.8660$

21. $\cos 10° = 0.9848$

23. Given that

$$\sin^{-1} x = x + \frac{x^3}{2 \cdot 3} + \frac{1 \cdot 3 \cdot x^5}{2 \cdot 4 \cdot 5} + \frac{1 \cdot 3 \cdot 5 \cdot x^7}{2 \cdot 4 \cdot 6 \cdot 7} + \cdots$$

Compute $\pi = 3.1415 \cdots$.

HINT: Let $x = \frac{1}{2}$, then

$$\sin^{-1}\left(\frac{1}{2}\right) = \frac{\pi}{6} = \frac{1}{2} + \frac{1 \cdot 1}{2 \cdot 3}\left(\frac{1}{2}\right)^3 + \cdots$$

24. At the birth of his son, a man deposits 1,000 dollars in a savings account at 4 per cent annual interest. If he neither deposits nor withdraws from this account, what will be the amount when the son begins college on his eighteenth birthday?

25. How much will an 18.75-dollar government war bond be worth after 10 years? The interest rate is 2.5 per cent.

26. A man buys a house for 14,000 dollars. The bank gives him a loan of 10,000 dollars at 5 per cent annual interest. Approximately, how much remains to pay on the principal at the end of 5 years, if the man pays 650 dollars each year?

27. A family needs 700 dollars immediately for hospital bills. How much would they have to borrow for 1 year at 6 per cent interest if the interest has to be paid in advance?

28. Expand the equation $\sin 5\alpha = \sin (\pi/2) = 1$, where $\alpha = 18°$, in terms of $\sin \alpha$ only. Show that the resulting equation is

$$5 \sin \alpha - 20 \sin^3 \alpha + 16 \sin^5 \alpha = 1$$

Thence show that $\sin 18° = (\sqrt{5} - 1)/4$.

Bibliography

1. American Standards Association: "American Standard Preferred Numbers," New York, 1958.
2. Bronwich, T. J.: "An Introduction to the Theory of Infinite Series," 2d ed., St. Martins's Press, Inc., New York, 1926.
3. Coxeter, H. S. M.: "Introduction to Geometry," John Wiley & Sons, New York, 1961.
4. Doherty, R. E., and E. G. Keller: "Mathematics of Modern Engineering," John Wiley & Sons, Inc., New York, 1936.
5. Mellor, J. W.: "Higher Mathematics," Longmans, Green, and Co., Ltd., London, 1922.
6. Newman, J. R.: "The World of Mathematics," pt. IV, Simon and Schuster, Inc., New York, 1956.
7. Pacioli, L.: "De Divina Proportione," Milan, 1956.
8. Perkins, L. R., and Ruth M. Perkins: "The Mathematics of Finance," John Wiley & Sons, Inc., New York, 1941.
9. Smail, L. L.: "Mathematics of Finance," McGraw-Hill Book Company, New York, 1953.
10. Thompson, D'Arcy W.: "On Growth and Form," Cambridge University Press, London, 1952.

Chapter 6 NUMERICAL CALCULATIONS

6-1 Reliability of Numerical Calculations. Absolute reliability is an essential requirement of engineering calculations. The most brilliant ability, theoretical knowledge, and practical experience of an engineer are made useless, and even worse than useless, by a single error in an important calculation.

Reliability of the numerical calculations is of greater importance in engineering than in any other field. In pure mathematics, an error in the numerical calculation of an example, which illustrates a general proposition, does not detract from the interest and value of the latter, which is the main purpose. In physics, the general law that is the subject of investigation remains true, even if in the numerical illustration of the law an error is made. With the most brilliant engineering design, however, if in the numerical calculation of a single structural member an error has been made, and its strength thereby been made inadequate, the rotor of the machine flies to pieces by centrifugal force, or the bridge collapses, and with it the reputation of the engineer.

Thus, rapidity of calculation, while by itself useful, is of no value whatever compared with reliability, that is, correctness.

The first requirements to secure reliability are neatness and care in the execution of the work. If the calculations are made on odd sheets of paper, with lead pencil, with frequent striking out and correcting of figures, it is practically hopeless to expect correct results in an extensive program of calculations. The work should be done in ink, on ruled paper. If changes are required, they should preferably be done by erasing, and not by striking out. The appearance of the work is a good indication of its reliability. A tabular arrangement of the calculated values is helpful.

A complete system of checking is essential in all extensive calculations. One way is to have the work done independently by two different calculators and then to compare the results. Or, a few points of the calculations may be checked by some one else. Neither of these ways is satisfactory, since an engineer should, and must, be able to make numerical calculations himself on whose correctness he can absolutely rely.

Important calculations should be performed twice, in different ways. Thus, when you multiply by the slide rule, the multiplication should be repeated mentally, approximately, as a check. A column of figures may be added first downward, then, as a check, upward. In all calculations, a mental estimate should first be made of the result, and then the exact calculation should be compared with the estimate. By employment of per unit quantities throughout (Sec. 3-10), the relative magnitudes of different quantities can be kept in mind and departures from normal proportions can be detected at their first appearance.

When a series of values is to be calculated, it is advisable first to calculate a few individual points, and then, entirely independently, to calculate in tabular form the series of values, and finally to check with the first calculated values. Since the different values in a series check each other, it is always advisable to calculate a number of points, that is, a short branch of a curve, even if only a single point is required. The points so calculated should be plotted to see whether they give a smooth curve. If the entire curve is irregular, the work should be thrown away, and it should all be done anew. If this happens repeatedly with the same calculator, the calculator may be advised to find another position more in agreement with his mental attributes. If a single point of the curve appears irregular, this indicates an error, which may be found by repeating the calculations for the one point.

Engineering calculations may be divided into three classes, depending on the accuracy required. In some problems, such as the effects of lightning, it is desired to find the order of magnitude only, since exact values cannot be predicted. In other cases, as in machine design, it is necessary to know that a definite requirement is met, but it is of no importance whether the margin is 30 or 40 per cent. In still other cases, an accuracy of a tenth of one per cent may be necessary, as in making close guarantees, or designing precise controls. Even for the most exact calculations, slide-rule accuracy is usually sufficient, if the rule is intelligently used. For instance, in dividing 297 by 283, the proper way is to divide $297 - 283 = 14$ by 283, and add the result to 1.

For simplicity, and to save time, the methods employed should not give more than the required accuracy. All calculations should be carried out to one more decimal than needed in the result, and in the

answer the last decimal may be dropped, so that the last figure re-
tained is probably correct within half a unit.

It follows from this that the values

$$2\tfrac{1}{2},\ 2.5,\ 2.50,\ 2.500$$

while mathematically equal, are not equivalent in their engineering
meanings:

> 2.5 means between 2.45 and 2.55
> 2.50 means between 2.495 and 2.505
> 2.500 means between 2.4995 and 2.5005

while $2\tfrac{1}{2}$ gives no clue to its accuracy.

Thus, it is not permissible to add zeros or to drop zeros at the end
of a number nor is it permissible to replace such a fraction as $\tfrac{1}{16}$ by
0.0625 without changing the meaning of the numerical value, as
regards its accuracy.

6-2 Simplified Formulas. The formal solution of apparently
simple engineering problems frequently leads to expressions so complicated as to make the numerical calculation of a series of values
quite impractical. Fortunately, in many such engineering problems,
and especially in the field of electrical engineering, the different
quantities that enter into the problem may be of very different magnitude. Thus, many complicated formulas can be greatly simplified
to such an extent that numerical values can be quickly and easily
calculated by neglecting terms so small that their omission does not
appreciably affect the result. This is possible because the accuracy
required in engineering, depending on the particular problem, usually is not greater than 0.1 to 1 per cent.

For instance, the voltage consumed by the resistance of an alternating-current transformer, at full load current, is only a small fraction of the supply voltage and the exciting current of the transformer
is only a small fraction of the full load current. Therefore the voltage
consumed by the exciting current flowing through the resistance is
only a small fraction of a fraction of the supply voltage; hence it is
negligible, and the transformer equations can be simplified by omitting it. The power loss in a large generator is a small fraction of the
input, the drop of speed under normal load in an induction motor is a
small fraction of the synchronous speed, etc., so that the squares of
these fractions can be omitted and the formulas simplified thereby.

Frequently, therefore, in engineering formulas, the products,
squares, and higher powers of many small quantities may be dropped;

or, if the quantities are not quite small enough to permit the neglect of their squares, at any rate their cubes and higher powers may be omitted.

The most convenient method of doing this is to develop the expressions in the form of infinite series of successive powers of the small quantities and then retain of these series only the first two or three terms, depending on the smallness of the terms and the desired accuracy.

6-3 Useful Approximations.   The forms most frequently used in simplifying expressions containing small quantities are multiplication and division, the binomial series, the exponential and logarithmic series, the sine and cosine series, etc.

Denoting a small quantity by s, and where several occur, by s_1, s_2, s_3, . . . , the following expression may be written:

$$(1 \pm s_1)(1 \pm s_2) = 1 \pm s_1 \pm s_2 \pm s_1 s_2 \qquad (6\text{-}1)$$

and, since $s_1 s_2$ is small compared with the small quantities s_1 and s_2, or as usually expressed, $s_1 s_2$ is a small quantity of higher order, it may be neglected, and the expression written

$$(1 \pm s_1)(1 \pm s_2) \cong 1 \pm s_1 \pm s_2 \qquad (6\text{-}2)$$

This is one of the most useful simplifications; the multiplication of terms containing small quantities is replaced by the simple addition of the small quantities.

If the small quantities s_1 and s_2 are not added to (or subtracted from) 1, but to other finite (that is, not small) quantities a and b, then a and b can be taken out as factors, thus:

$$(a \pm s_1)(b \pm s_2) = ab \left(1 \pm \frac{s_1}{a}\right)\left(1 \pm \frac{s_2}{b}\right) \cong ab \left(1 \pm \frac{s_1}{a} \pm \frac{s_2}{b}\right) \quad (6\text{-}3)$$

where s_1/a and s_2/b must be small quantities.

As seen, s_1 and s_2 need not be absolutely small quantities, but may be quite large, provided that a and b are still larger; that is, s_1 must be small compared with a, and s_2 small compared with b. For instance, in astronomical calculations, the mass of the earth (which no one but an astronomer would consider to be a small quantity) is neglected as small compared with the mass of the sun. Also, in considering the effect of a lightning stroke on a distribution circuit, the normal line voltage of 2,300 may be neglected as small compared with the voltage impressed by lightning.

Expressions containing a small quantity in the denominator are frequently simplified by bringing it into the numerator, by division, as in Eq. 5-2, that is, by the series

$$\frac{1}{1 \pm x} = 1 \mp x + x^2 \mp x^3 + x^4 \mp x^5 + \cdots \qquad (6\text{-}4)$$

which series, if x is a small quantity, s, can be approximated by

$$\frac{1}{1 \pm s} \cong 1 \mp s \qquad (6\text{-}5)$$

or where a greater accuracy is desired, by

$$\frac{1}{1 + s} \cong 1 - s + s^2 \qquad \text{or} \qquad \frac{1}{1 - s} \cong 1 + s + s^2 \qquad (6\text{-}6)$$

If we reverse the same expressions, a small quantity contained in the numerator may be brought into the denominator, where this is more convenient. In general, then, an expression like $b/(a + s)$, where s is small compared with a, may be replaced by

$$\frac{b}{a \pm s} = \frac{b}{a(1 \pm s/a)} \cong \frac{b}{a}\left(1 \mp \frac{s}{a} + \frac{s^2}{a^2}\right) \qquad (6\text{-}7)$$

the last term, s^2/a^2, being omitted, unless great exactness is desired.

6-4 Example—Power Output of an Electric Motor. In a direct-current shunt motor (Fig. 6-1) the impressed voltage is $e_0 = 125$ volts; the armature resistance is $r_0 = 0.02$ ohm; the field resistance is $r_1 = 50$ ohms; the power consumed by friction and windage is $p_f = 300$ watts; and the power consumed by iron loss is $p_i = 400$ watts. What is the power output of the motor at $i_0 = 50$, 100, and 150 amperes input?

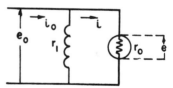

Fig. 6-1 Direct-current shunt motor.

The power produced at the armature conductors is the product of the voltage e generated in the armature conductors and the current i through the armature, and the power output at the motor shaft is

$$p = ei - p_f - p_i \qquad (6\text{-}8)$$

The current in the motor field is e_0/r_1, and the armature current, therefore, is

$$i = i_0 - \frac{e_0}{r_1} \qquad (6\text{-}9)$$

where e_0/r_1 is a small quantity compared with i_0.

The voltage consumed in the armature resistance is r_0i, and the voltage generated in the motor armature thus is

$$e = e_0 - r_0i \qquad (6\text{-}10)$$

where r_0i is a small quantity compared with e_0.

Substituting herein for i its value (Eq. 6-9) gives

$$e = e_0 - r_0\left(i_0 - \frac{e_0}{r_1}\right) \qquad (6\text{-}11)$$

Since the second term of Eq. 6-11 is small compared with e_0, and in this second term e_0/r_1 is small compared with i_0, this last can be neglected as small compared with a small term, and Eq. 6-11 becomes

$$e = e_0 - r_0i_0 \qquad (6\text{-}12)$$

Substituting Eqs. 6-9 and 6-12 into Eq. 6-8 gives

$$p = (e_0 - r_0i_0)\left(i_0 - \frac{e}{r_1}\right) - p_f - p_i$$

$$= e_0i_0\left(1 - \frac{r_0i_0}{e_0}\right)\left(1 - \frac{e}{r_1i_0}\right) - p_f - p_1 \qquad (6\text{-}13)$$

Equation 6-13 contains a product of two terms with small quantities, which can be multiplied as in Eq. 6-1, giving

$$p \cong e_0i_0\left(1 - \frac{r_0i_0}{e_0} - \frac{e_0}{r_1i_0}\right) - p_f - p_i = e_0i_0 - r_0i_0{}^2 - \frac{e_0{}^2}{r_1} - p_f - p_i$$

$$(6\text{-}14)$$

Substituting the numerical values gives

$$p = 125i_0 - 0.02i_0{}^2 - 312.5 - 300 - 400$$
$$= 125i_0 - 0.02i_0{}^2 - 1{,}012 \text{ approximately}$$

Thus, for $i_0 = 50$, 100, and 150 amperes, $p = 5{,}190$, 11,290, and 17,290 watts, respectively.

6-5   Use of the Binomial Series.   One of the most useful expressions for simplifying formulas is the binomial series (Eq. 5-22):

$$(1 \pm x)^n = 1 \pm nx + \frac{n(n-1)}{2}x^2 \pm \frac{n(n-1)(n-2)}{6}x^3$$

$$+ \frac{n(n-1)(n-2)(n-3)}{24}x^4 \pm \cdots \qquad (6\text{-}15)$$

If x is a small term, this gives the approximation:

$$(1 \pm s)^n \cong 1 \pm ns + \frac{n(n-1)}{2}s^2 \qquad (6\text{-}16)$$

the series being carried to one, two, or more terms, as accuracy may require.

By this means, higher powers and roots of terms containing small quantities can be eliminated. For instance,

$$\sqrt[n]{a \pm s} = (a \pm s)^{1/n} = \sqrt[n]{a}\left(1 \pm \frac{s}{na} + \cdots\right) \qquad (6\text{-}17)$$

$$\frac{1}{(a \pm s)^n} = \frac{1}{a^n(1 \pm s/a)^n} = \frac{1}{a^n}\left(1 \pm \frac{s}{a}\right)^{-n} = a^{-n}\left(1 \mp \frac{ns}{a} + \cdots\right) \qquad (6\text{-}18)$$

$$\frac{1}{\sqrt[n]{a \pm s}} = (a \pm s)^{-1/n} = a^{-1/n}\left(1 \pm \frac{s}{a}\right)^{-1/n}$$

$$= \frac{1}{\sqrt[n]{a}}\left(1 \mp \frac{s}{na} + \cdots\right) \qquad (6\text{-}19)$$

$$\sqrt[n]{(a \pm s)^m} = (a \pm s)^{m/n} = a^{m/n}\left(1 \pm \frac{s}{a}\right)^{m/n}$$

$$= \sqrt[n]{a^m}\left(1 \pm \frac{ms}{na} + \cdots\right) \qquad (6\text{-}20)$$

Squares and square roots are commonly eliminated in this way. The method is especially useful in numerical calculations, as, for instance,

$$(201)^2 = (200)^2(1 + \tfrac{1}{200})^2 \cong (200)^2(1 + \tfrac{1}{100}) = 40{,}400$$
$$(29.9)^2 = 30^2(1 - \tfrac{1}{300})^2 \cong 900(1 - \tfrac{1}{150})$$
$$= 900 - 6 = 894$$
$$\sqrt{97.8} = 10\sqrt{1 - 0.022} = 10(1 - 0.022)^{1/2}$$
$$\cong 10(1 - 0.011) = 9.89$$
$$\frac{1}{\sqrt{1.03}} \cong \frac{1}{1.015} = 0.985, \text{ etc.}$$

Equation 5-24 is an example of the use of this method in electric-circuit calculations.

6-6 Exponential Functions. Exponential, trigonometric, and hyperbolic functions (Sec. 9-5), as well as logarithms, frequently occur in engineering calculations. The exponential function is defined by the series (by Eq. 3-23):

$$\exp(\pm x) = e^{\pm x} = 1 \pm x + \frac{x^2}{2!} \pm \frac{x^3}{3!} + \frac{x^4}{4!} \pm \frac{x^5}{5!} + \cdots \quad (6\text{-}21)$$

and if x is a small quantity, s, this is

$$e^{\pm s} \cong 1 \pm s \quad (6\text{-}22)$$

or, more generally,

$$e^{\pm as} \cong 1 \pm as + \frac{a^2 s^2}{2} \pm \cdots \quad (6\text{-}23)$$

By Eq. 8-38, the natural logarithm is expressed by the infinite series

$$\ln(1 \pm x) = \pm x - \frac{x^2}{2} \pm \frac{x^3}{3} - \frac{x^4}{4} \pm \frac{x^5}{5} - \cdots \quad (6\text{-}24)$$

This leads to the approximation

$$\ln(1 \pm s) \cong \pm s - \frac{s^2}{2} \quad (6\text{-}25)$$

or, more generally,

$$\ln(a \pm s) = \ln a \left(1 \pm \frac{s}{a}\right) = \ln a + \ln\left(1 \pm \frac{s}{a}\right) \cong \ln a \pm \frac{s}{a} \quad (6\text{-}26)$$

and more accurately,

$$\ln(a \pm s) \cong \ln a \pm \frac{s}{a} - \frac{s^2}{2a^2} \quad (6\text{-}27)$$

Since $\log N = \log e (\ln N) = 0.4343 \ln N$, by Eq. 1-27, Eq. 6-27 may be written

$$\log(a \pm s) \cong \log a \pm 0.434 \frac{s}{a} \quad (6\text{-}28)$$

6-7 Other Functions. By Eqs. 3-25 and 3-26, the trigonometric functions are

$$\sin(\pm x) = \pm\left(x - \frac{x^3}{3!} + \frac{x^5}{5!} - \frac{x^7}{7!} + \cdots\right) \quad (6\text{-}29)$$

$$\cos(\pm x) = 1 - \frac{x^2}{2!} + \frac{x^4}{4!} - \frac{x^6}{6!} + \cdots \quad (6\text{-}30)$$

When x is a small quantity, s, these become

$$\sin \pm s \cong \pm s \mp \frac{s^3}{6} \quad (6\text{-}31)$$

$$\cos \pm s \cong 1 - \frac{s^2}{2} \quad (6\text{-}32)$$

Likewise, by Eqs. 9-24 and 9-25, the hyperbolic functions of a small angle, s, are approximated by

$$\sinh (\pm s) \cong \pm \left(s + \frac{s^3}{6} \right) \tag{6-33}$$

$$\cosh (\pm s) \cong 1 + \frac{s^2}{2} \tag{6-34}$$

6-8   Formulas Equivalent to $1 \pm s$.   It is interesting to note the large number of different-appearing expressions that are all approximately equal to either $1 + s$, or $1 - s$, when s is small compared with 1. Some of these are given in Table 6-1.

Table 6-1   Expressions Equal to $1 + s$ or $1 - s$

$1 + s \cong$		$1 - s \cong$	
$\dfrac{1}{1-s}$	e^s	$\dfrac{1}{1+s}$	e^{-s}
$\left(1 + \dfrac{s}{n}\right)^n$	$2 - e^{-s}$	$\left(1 - \dfrac{s}{n}\right)^n$	$2 - e^s$
$\left(1 + \dfrac{s}{2}\right)^2$	$1 + \ln(1+s)$	$\left(1 - \dfrac{s}{2}\right)^2$	$1 + \ln(1-s)$
$\dfrac{1}{\left(1 - \dfrac{s}{n}\right)^n}$	$1 - \ln(1-s)$	$\dfrac{1}{(1 + s/n)^n}$	$1 - \ln(1+s)$
$\left[\dfrac{1 + ms/n^2}{1 - (n-m)s/n^2}\right]^n$	$1 + n \ln\left(1 + \dfrac{s}{n}\right)$	$\left[\dfrac{1 - ms/n^2}{1 + (n-m)s/n^2}\right]^n$	$1 + n \ln\left(1 - \dfrac{s}{n}\right)$
$\sqrt{1 + 2s}$	$1 - n \ln\left(1 - \dfrac{s}{n}\right)$	$\sqrt{1 - 2s}$	$1 - n \ln\left(1 + \dfrac{s}{n}\right)$
$\dfrac{1}{\sqrt{1 - 2s}}$	$1 + \ln\sqrt{\dfrac{1+s}{1-s}}$	$\dfrac{1}{\sqrt{1 + 2s}}$	$1 + \ln\sqrt{\dfrac{1-s}{1+s}}$
$\sqrt{\dfrac{1+s}{1-s}}$	$1 - \ln\sqrt{\dfrac{1-s}{1+s}}$	$\sqrt{\dfrac{1-s}{1+s}}$	$1 - \ln\sqrt{\dfrac{1+s}{1-s}}$
$(1 + ns)^{1/n}$	$1 + \sin s$	$(1 - ns)^{1/n}$	$1 - \sin s$
$\dfrac{1}{(1 - ns)^{1/n}}$	$1 + n \sin\dfrac{s}{n}$	$\dfrac{1}{(1 + ns)^{1/n}}$	$1 - n \sin\dfrac{s}{n}$
$\left(\dfrac{1 + ns/2}{1 - ns/2}\right)^{1/n}$	$1 + \dfrac{1}{n}\sin ns$	$\left(\dfrac{1 - ns/2}{1 + ns/2}\right)^{1/n}$	$1 - \dfrac{1}{n}\sin ns$
$\left[\dfrac{1 + ms}{1 - (n-m)s}\right]^{1/n}$	$\cos\sqrt{-2s}$	$\left[\dfrac{1 - ms}{1 + (n-m)s}\right]^{1/n}$	$\cos\sqrt{2s}$
	etc.		etc.

6-9 Example. As an example, when s_1 and s_2 are both small, we may reduce to its simplest form the expression

$$F = \frac{\sqrt{a}\,\sqrt[4]{(a + s_1)^3}\,(4 - \sin 6s_2)\,\sqrt[4]{a}\,\exp(2s_1/a)\,\cos^2\sqrt{2s_1/a}}{\exp(-3s_2)(a + 2s_1)[1 - a\ln\sqrt{(a - s_2)/(a + s_2)}]\,\sqrt{a - 2s_1}}$$

Then

$$\sqrt[4]{(a + s_1)^3} = (a + s_1)^{3/4} = a^{3/4}\left(1 + \frac{s_1}{a}\right)^{3/4} \cong a^{3/4}\left(1 + \frac{3s_1}{4a}\right)$$

$$4 - \sin 6s_2 = 4\left(1 - \frac{1}{4}\sin 6s_2\right) \cong 4\left(1 - \frac{3s_2}{2}\right)$$

$$e^{2s_1/a} \cong 1 + \frac{2s_1}{a}$$

$$\cos^2\sqrt{\frac{2s_1}{a}} \cong \left(1 - \frac{s_1}{a}\right)^2 \cong 1 - \frac{2s_1}{a}$$

$$e^{-3s_2} \cong 1 - 3s_2$$

$$a + 2s_1 \cong a\left(1 + \frac{2s_1}{a}\right)$$

$$1 - a\ln\sqrt{\frac{a - s_2}{a + s_2}} = 1 - a\ln\sqrt{\frac{1 - s_2/a}{1 + s_2/a}} \cong 1 - a\ln\sqrt{1 - \frac{2s_2}{a}}$$

$$\cong 1 - a\ln\left(1 - \frac{s_2}{a}\right) \cong 1 + s_2$$

$$\sqrt{a - 2s_1} = a^{1/2}\left(1 - \frac{2s_1}{a}\right)^{1/2} \cong a^{1/2}\left(1 - \frac{s_1}{a}\right)$$

Therefore

$$F \cong \frac{(a^{1/2})(a^{3/4})(1 + 3s_1/4a)(4)(1 - 3s_2/2)(a^{1/4})(1 + 2s_1/a)(1 - 2s_1/a)}{(1 - 3s_2)(a)(1 + 2s_1/a)(1 + s_2)(a^{1/2})(1 - s_1/a)}$$

$$\cong \frac{4a^{3/2}(1 + 3s_1/4a - 3s_2/2 + 2s_1/a - 2s_1/a)}{a^{3/2}(1 - 3s_2 + 2s_1/a + s_2 - s_1/a)}$$

$$\cong 4\left(1 - \frac{s_1}{4a} + \frac{s_2}{2}\right) \text{ approximately}$$

PROBLEMS

Derive simple expressions for the following quantities when x is small and calculate them for the given values of x:

1. $\sin^3 x \cos x$ when $x = 0.02$
2. $e^x \tan x$ when $x = 0.04$

3. $(x + 2)^2 \sqrt{4 + x}$ when $x = 0.1$
4. $\sqrt[4]{x + 60}$ when $x = 5$
5. $e^{-\sin x}$ when $x = 0.007$
6. $e^{\cos x}$ when $x = 0.004$
7. $\ln (10 + x)$ when $x = 0.05$
8. $\cos (\pi + x) - \sin (\pi + x)$ when $x = 0.02$

Show by graphs of the following functions that for $0 < x < 0.10$ their values are nearly equal.

9. $y = 1 + s$

$$y = \frac{1}{1 - s}$$

$$y = e^s$$

$$y = 1 - \ln(1 - s)$$

10. $y = 1 - s$

$$y = 2 - e^s$$

$$y = \frac{1}{1 + s}$$

$$y = 1 - \sin s$$

Bibliography

1. Householder, A. S.: "Principles of Numerical Analysis," McGraw-Hill Book Company, New York, 1953.
2. Pipes, L. A.: "Applied Mathematics for Engineers and Physicists," McGraw-Hill Book Company, New York, 1946.
3. Schelkunoff, S. A.: "Applied Mathematics for Engineers and Scientists," D. Van Nostrand Company, Inc., Princeton, N.J., 1948.
4. Snyder, L. R.: "Essential Business Mathematics," 2d ed., McGraw-Hill Book Company, New York, 1953.

Chapter 7 EMPIRICAL CURVES

7-1   Curves to Represent Test Data.   The results of observations or tests usually are plotted in curve form. For instance, the core loss of an electric motor may be plotted as a function of voltage, or the temperature of a machine may be plotted against time elapsed after the load was applied. When plotted from numerical observations, the curves are said to be *empirical*. To make such curves widely useful, it is necessary to find equations for them, that is, to find a function $y = f(x)$ which represents the curve. While numerical values can be taken from the graph, no general conclusions can be derived from it, nor can it be used to derive expressions for related phenomena until its equation is known.

An illustration of this is afforded by the comparison of electric and magnetic circuit calculations. In the electric circuit, the relation between emf and current is given by Ohm's law, $i = e/r$, and calculations are universally and easily made. In the magnetic circuit, however, the reluctance, corresponding to r, is not constant, and the relation between mmf and magnetic flux cannot be expressed by any general law. As a result, magnetic circuit calculations cannot be made as conveniently or with as much generality as for electric circuits.

When a number of corresponding values of the independent variable x and the function y are found by test, the problem is to find an equation, $y = f(x)$, which represents these corresponding values: $x_1, x_2, x_3, \ldots, x_n$ and $y_1, y_2, y_3, \ldots, y_n$, approximately, that is, within the errors of observation.

The mathematical expression which represents an empirical curve may be a rational or an empirical equation. It is a rational equation if it expresses the properties of a curve such as one of the conic sections or if it can be derived theoretically as a conclusion from some general law of nature, but it is an empirical equation if no theoretical

[160]

reason can be given for the particular form of the equation. For instance, when representing the dying out of an electric current in an inductive circuit by an exponential function of time, we have a rational equation. The induced voltage, and, therefore, by Ohm's law, the current, varies in proportion to the rate of change of the current, or its derivative. As the exponential function is always proportional to its derivative, it rationally represents the dying out of the current in an inductive circuit. On the other hand, the relation between the loss by hysteresis and the magnetic density, $W = hB^{1.6}$, is an empirical equation, since no reason can be seen for this 1.6 power law, except that it agrees with the observations.

A rational equation, as a deduction from the laws of nature, applies over a much wider range than the range of the observations, while an empirical equation can be relied upon only within the range of the observations from which it was derived. For engineering purposes, a rational equation, therefore, is far preferable to an empirical one, even though an empirical equation frequently represents the observations with great accuracy. A rational equation usually does not represent observations precisely, for the reason that in Nature the conditions on which the rational law is based rarely are perfectly fulfilled. For instance, the representation of a decaying current by an exponential function is based on the assumptions that the resistance and inductance of the circuit are exactly constant, and capacitance is absent. None of these conditions can ever be perfectly satisfied, and thus a deviation occurs from the theory, owing to what are called *secondary effects*.

7-2 Derivation of Empirical Equations. To derive an equation to represent an empirical curve, careful consideration first should be given to the nature of the phenomenon to be expressed, since thereby the number of expressions which need to be tried on the empirical curve may be greatly reduced. Much help is obtained by considering the zero points of the curve and the points at infinity. For instance, if the observations represent the relation of the flow of air, y, produced by a fan to the speed x of the fan itself, the curve must go through the origin; that is, $y = 0$ for $x = 0$, and the mathematical expression of the curve $y = f(x)$ can contain no constant term. Also, in this case, with increasing x, y must continually increase also, so that for $x = \infty$, $y = \infty$. If the observations represent the dying out of an electric current as a function of the time, it is obvious that for $x = \infty$, $y = 0$. In representing the power consumed by a motor as a function of the voltage, when running without load, for $x = 0$, y cannot be zero, but must equal the loss due to the mechanical friction. An expression like

$y = Ax^n$ cannot represent the observations over the total range, for the equation must contain a constant term.

Thus, first, from the nature of the phenomenon to be represented by the empirical curve, it is determined:

(*a*) Whether the curve is periodic (repetitive) or nonperiodic.

(*b*) Whether the equation contains constant terms, that is, for $x = 0$, $y = a$, and inversely, or whether the curve passes through the origin, that is, $y = 0$ for $x = 0$, or whether it is hyperbolic; that is, $y = \infty$ for $x = 0$, or $x = \infty$ for $y = 0$.

(*c*) What values the expression reaches for ∞; that is, whether for $x = \infty$, $y = \infty$, or $y = 0$, and inversely.

(*d*) Whether the curve continuously increases or decreases, or reaches maxima and minima (see Chap. 11).

(*e*) Whether the law of the curve may change within the range of the observations, by some phenomenon appearing in some observations which does not occur in the others. For instance, in observations in which the magnetic density enters, as core loss, excitation curves, etc., frequently the curve law changes with the beginning of saturation, and in this case only the data below magnetic saturation would be used for deriving the theoretical equations, and the effect of saturation would be treated as a superposed secondary phenomenon. Thus, empirical curves can be represented by a single rational equation only when the physical conditions remain constant over the range of the observations.

From the shape of the empirical curve, with some experience, a guess can be made as to the probable form of an equation which may express it. For this purpose, it is of the greatest assistance to be familiar with the shapes of the more common forms of curves, as by plotting and studying various forms of equations $y = f(x)$.

By changing the scales on which observations are plotted, the apparent shape of the curve may be altered. It is desirable in plotting to use such a scale that the average slope of the curve will be about 45°, since in this way the accuracy of plotting and reading the curve will be about the same for y as for x.

7-3 Nonperiodic Curves—Power Series.

The commonest nonperiodic curves are the power series, parabolas, hyperbolas, and the exponential and logarithmic curves.

Usually, any set of observations can be represented exactly by a power series (Sec. 5-1) of one of the following forms if a sufficiently large number of terms is chosen:

$$y = a_0 + a_1x + a_2x^2 + a_3x^3 + \cdots \qquad (7\text{-}1)$$

$$y = a_1x + a_2x^2 + a_3x^3 + \cdots \qquad (7\text{-}2)$$

$$y = a_0 + \frac{a_1}{x} + \frac{a_2}{x^2} + \frac{a^3}{x^3} + \cdots \qquad (7\text{-}3)$$

$$y = \frac{a_1}{x} + \frac{a_2}{x^2} + \frac{a_3}{x^3} + \cdots \qquad (7\text{-}4)$$

For instance, if n corresponding numerical values of x and y are given, x_1,y_1; x_2,y_2; $\ldots$; x_n,y_n, they can be represented by the series Eq. 7-1, if we choose as many terms as required to determine the n coefficients:

$$y = a_0 + a_1x + a_2x^2 + a_3x^3 + \cdots + a_{n-1}x^{n-1} \qquad (7\text{-}5)$$

By substituting the n pairs of x,y values in Eq. 7-5, we obtain n simultaneous equations, which, when solved as in Sec. 4-5, give the n coefficients, $a_0, a_1, a_2, \ldots$.

Often, however, such an empirical representation turns out to be meaningless. For example, let the first column of Table 7-1 represent

Table 7-1   Coefficients of an Empirical Power Series

$\frac{e}{100} = x$	$P_h = y$	-0.5	$+2x$	$+2.5x^2$	$-1.5x^3$	$+1.5x^4$	$-2x^5$	$+x^6$	Sum
0.4	0.63	-0.5	$+0.8$	$+0.4$	-0.10	$+0.04$	-0.02	0	0.62
0.6	1.36	-0.5	$+1.2$	$+0.9$	-0.32	$+0.19$	-0.16	$+0.05$	1.36
0.8	2.18	-0.5	$+1.6$	$+1.6$	-0.77	$+0.61$	-0.65	$+0.26$	2.15
1.0	3.00	-0.5	$+2.0$	$+2.5$	-1.50	$+1.50$	-2.00	$+1.00$	3.00
1.2	4.03	-0.5	$+2.4$	$+3.6$	-2.59	$+3.11$	-4.98	$+2.99$	4.03
1.4	5.65	-0.5	$+2.8$	$+4.9$	-4.12	$+5.76$	-10.76	$+7.53$	5.61
1.6	8.59	-0.5	$+3.2$	$+6.4$	-6.14	$+9.83$	-20.97	$+16.78$	8.60

the voltage, $x = e/100$, in hundreds of volts, and the second column the no-load core losses, $y = P_h$ in kilowatts, of a 120-volt generator. As seven pairs of test values are given, we may represent them by a power series with seven terms, thus:

$$y = a_0 + a_1x + a_2x^2 + a_3x^3 + \cdots + a_6x^6 \qquad (7\text{-}6)$$

By substituting the test data in Eq. 7-6 and calculating the coefficients from the seven equations so derived, there is obtained to represent the core losses the equation

$$y = -0.5 + 2x + 2.5x^2 - 1.5x^3 + 1.5x^4 - 2x^5 + x^6 \qquad (7\text{-}7)$$

Summing the values of the terms for each value of x, as shown in Table 7-1, it is seen that the equation accurately represents the data.

By plotting the seven terms separately (Fig. 7-1), however, it is clear that the terms have no physical meaning, since they have no rational relation to each other. Further, if any one of the test observations is omitted and a new equation with only six terms is derived to represent the remaining six points, the new coefficients will have entirely different values from those in Eq. 7-7.

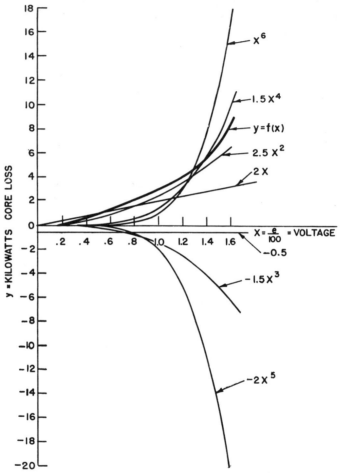

Fig. 7-1 Terms of empirical power series to represent core losses.

Therefore, a power series such as Eqs. 7-1 to 7-4 can be used to represent an empirical curve only under one of the following conditions:

(*a*) If the successive coefficients a_0, a_1, a_2, . . . decrease in value so rapidly that within the range of the observations the higher-order terms become very much smaller and appear as mere secondary adjustments.

(*b*) If the successive coefficients follow a definite law, indicating a convergent series which represents some function, such as an exponential, a sine, or log, etc.

(*c*) If all the coefficients, *a*, are very small, except for a very few, so that only these few need to be considered.

For example, let the numbers, *y*, in column 2 of Table 7-2 represent the torque required to drive a fan, for any fraction *x*, of the normal speed, as given by the values in column 1. These values can be represented by the equation

$$y = 0.5 + 0.02x + 2.5x^2 - 0.3x^3 + 0.015x^4 - 0.02x^5$$
$$+ 0.01x^6 \quad (7\text{-}8)$$

Here, only the constant term and the x^2 and x^3 terms have appreciable values, so that the remaining terms probably are merely the result of errors in measurement, or other secondary effects. The equation then takes the simple form

$$y = a_0 + a_2x^2 + a_3x^3 \quad (7\text{-}9)$$

Using the values of the coefficients from Eq. 7-8 gives

$$y' = 0.5 + 2.5x^2 - 0.3x^3 \quad (7\text{-}10)$$

The numerical values calculated from this are given in column 4 of Table 7-2 as y', and the differences between them and the observed values in column 2 are given in column 4, as y_1.

To adjust the coefficients to fit the data more exactly, we may represent the differences y_1 by a new equation of the same form. Since the x^3 term is small, we may lump all the corrections in the first two terms only. We have then to find *b* and *c* in the new equation of adjustment:

$$y_1 = b + cx^2 \quad (7\text{-}11)$$

This can be done by the method of least squares, as outlined in Sec. 13-9. We have seven equations:

$$
\begin{aligned}
b + 0.16c &= 0.01 \\
b + 0.36c &= 0.01 \\
b + 0.64c &= 0.01 \\
b + c &= 0.02 \qquad (7\text{-}12)\\
b + 1.44c &= 0.04 \\
b + 1.96c &= 0.05 \\
b + 2.56c &= 0.09
\end{aligned}
$$

Table 7-2   Data for Speed-Torque Curve of Fan

x	y	y'	y_1	y_2
0.4	0.89	0.88	0.01	0.01
0.6	1.35	1.34	0.01	0.00
0.8	1.96	1.95	0.01	−0.01
1.0	2.72	2.70	0.02	−0.01
1.2	3.62	3.58	0.04	0.00
1.4	4.63	4.58	0.05	−0.01
1.6	5.76	5.67	0.09	0.01

In accordance with Eq. 13-31, these may be combined into two equations that will determine the most probable values of b and c. The sum of the squares of the b coefficients in Eq. 7-12 is 7.00, the sum of the products of the seven pairs of b and c coefficients is 8.12, and the sum of the squares of the c coefficients is 13.94. Also, the sum of the products of the b coefficients by the constant term is 0.23, and that of the c coefficients by the constant term is 0.418. Therefore, the two new equations are

$$7.00b + 8.12c = 0.23$$
$$8.12b + 13.94c = 0.418 \qquad (7\text{-}13)$$

Solving these, we find $b = -0.006$ and $c = 0.033$, so that the adjusting equation is

$$y_1 = -0.006 + 0.033x^2 \qquad (7\text{-}14)$$

As a check, we may calculate the residual errors, or differences, y_2, between the actual values of y_1 and those given by Eq. 7-14. These are shown in column 5 of Table 7-2 and are seen to be evenly divided between $+$ and $-$, and all are 0.01 or less, within the limits of experimental error.

The final equation to represent the empirical data is the sum of Eqs. 7-10 and 7-14, or

$$y = 0.494 + 2.533x^2 - 0.300x^3 \qquad (7\text{-}15)$$

This Eq. 7-15 appears to be a rational one, since the first term, 0.494, represents the constant bearing-friction torque, and the large second term represents the work done by the fan in imparting a velocity to the air, requiring a torque proportional to the square of the fan speed. The third term approximates the decrease in air resistance due to the fact that the velocity of the air does not rise quite as fast as the speed does; i.e., the slip of the air with respect to the blades increases more rapidly than the speed.

In general, the power series has only limited usefulness for representing empirical curves and is employed mainly to approximate curves that follow very simple laws and to represent secondary corrections to curves of other forms. A power series may be convenient for temporary use, pending the derivation of a more rational law.

7-4 Parabolic and Hyperbolic Curves. One of the most useful classes of curves in engineering is that represented by the equation

$$y = ax^n \qquad (7\text{-}16)$$

or by the more general equation

$$y - b = a(x - c)^n \qquad (7\text{-}17)$$

These two equations represent exactly the same curve, the only difference being that Eq. 7-17 is referred to a different center of coordinates, displaced a distance c horizontally and b vertically. In discussion of curve shapes, only Eq. 7-16 need be considered.

If n is positive, the curves $y = ax^n$ are *parabolic curves* (Fig. 7-2) passing through the origin and increasing with increasing x. If $n > 1$, y increases with increasing rapidity as x grows larger. If $n < 1$, y increases less and less rapidly as x increases.

If the exponent is negative, the curves $y = ax^{-n} = a/x^n$ are *hyperbolic curves* (Fig. 7-3) starting from $y = \infty$ for $x = 0$ and decreasing to $y = 0$ for $x = \infty$. The equation $n = 1$ gives a straight line through the origin, while $n = 0$ and $n = \infty$ give straight horizontal and vertical lines, respectively.

Parabolic and hyperbolic curves may easily be recognized by the property that if x is changed by a constant factor, y also changes by a (different) constant factor. Thus, in the curve $y = ax^n$, multiplying x by a factor b will make $y = a(bx)^n = ab^nx^n$, that is, will multiply y by b^n.

If b is nearly equal to 1, we may put $b = 1 + s$, where s is a small quantity, and we have

$$y = a(1 + s)^nx^n \cong a(1 + ns)x^n \text{ approximately} \qquad (7\text{-}18)$$

That is, changing x by a small fraction, sx, changes y by a proportional small fraction, nsy.

This convenient way of recognizing parabolic and hyperbolic curves applies, however, only if the curve passes through the origin, that is, has no constant term. If constant terms exist, as in Eq. 7-17, then $(x - c)$ and $(y - b)$ follow the law of proportionate increases, instead of x and y. In such cases, various values of c and b may be tried to find those which give the proportionality, if possible.

Taking the logarithm of Eq. 7-16 gives

$$\log y = \log a + n \log x \qquad (7\text{-}19)$$

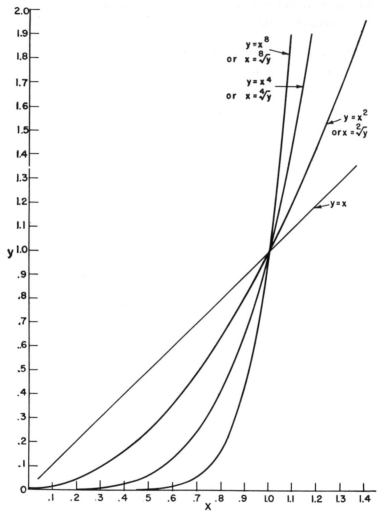

Fig. 7-2 Parabolic curves.

that is, a straight line. Hence a parabolic or hyperbolic curve can be recognized by plotting the logarithm of y against the logarithm of x (Fig. 1-6). If this gives a straight line, the curve is parabolic or hyperbolic, and the slope of the logarithmic curve, $\tan \theta = n$, is the exponent. This again applies only if the curve contains no constant term. If constant terms exist, the logarithmic line is curved. Therefore, by trying different constants, c and b, the curvature of the logarithmic line changes, and by interpolation constants may be found which make the line become straight. If one of the constants, c or b, is zero, the process is quite simple. It is always desirable to get some idea from the physical nature of the problem about the existence and the value of the c and b terms as a first step.

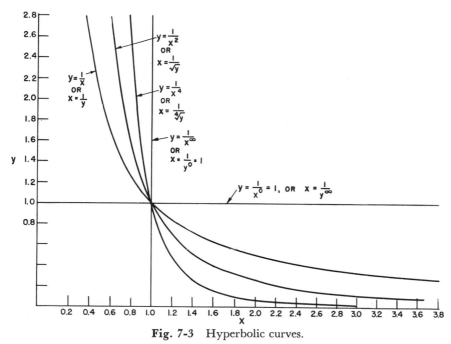

Fig. 7-3 Hyperbolic curves.

7-5 Exponential and Logarithmic Curves. An exponential function very frequently met with in engineering and physics is

$$y = ae^{nx} \tag{7-20}$$

or, in a more general form:

$$y - b = ae^{n(x-c)} \tag{7-21}$$

Usually, the exponent is negative, as in the form

$$y = ae^{-nx} \tag{7-22}$$

This expression is plotted in Fig. 7-4 for $a = 1$, $n = 1$, that is, $y = e^{-x}$. As seen, with increasing negative exponent, y decreases to-

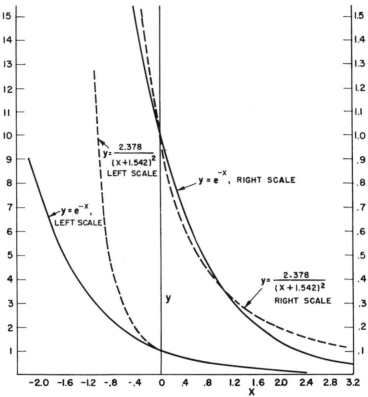

Fig. 7-4   Exponential function, $y = e^{-2x}$.

ward 0 at $x = \infty$, and with increasing positive exponent, y approaches ∞ at $x = -\infty$. The curve $y = e^{+x}$ has the same shape, except that the positive and negative branches are interchanged (mirror symmetry).

These equations may be written in inverted form:

$$nx = \ln \frac{y}{a} \qquad n(x - c) = \ln \frac{y - b}{a}$$

$$nx = -\ln \frac{y}{a} \qquad n(x - c) = -\ln \frac{y - b}{a} \qquad (7\text{-}23)$$

$$x = \ln y \qquad x = -\ln y$$

that is, as logarithmic curves.

The characteristic of the exponential function (Eq. 7-20) is that an increase of x by a constant term increases (or decreases) y by a constant factor. Thus, if an empirical curve, $y = f(x)$, has the property that

$$\frac{f(x + q)}{f(x)} = \text{a constant} \qquad \text{for constant } q \qquad (7\text{-}24)$$

the curve is an exponential function, and the following equation for it may be written:

$$\frac{f(x+q)}{f(x)} = \frac{ae^{n(x+q)}}{ae^{nx}} = e^{nq} \tag{7-25}$$

Hereby the exponential function can easily be recognized, and distinguished from the parabolic curve. In the former, a constant *term* added to x, in the latter a constant *factor* times x, causes a change of y by a constant *factor*.

The exponential function with negative exponent becomes vanishingly small as x increases, with far greater rapidity than the hyperbolic curve, and the exponential curve with positive exponent reaches practically infinite values far more rapidly as x increases than the parabolic curve. This is illustrated in Fig. 7-4 also, in which are shown superimposed the exponential curve, $y = e^{-x}$, and the hyperbolic curve, $y = 2.378/(x + 1.542)^2$, which coincides with the exponential curve at $x = 0$ and $x = 1$.

Taking the logarithm of Eq. 7-20 gives

$$\log y = \log a + nx \log e \tag{7-26}$$

That is, $\log y$ is a linear function of x, and plotting $\log y$ against x gives a straight line. This property gives a convenient way of recognizing exponential functions.

However, these properties apply only if there are no constant x and y terms. With a single exponential function, only the constant term of y needs consideration, as the constant x term can be eliminated. Equation 7-21 may be written

$$y - b = ae^{n(x-c)} = ae^{-nc}e^{nx} = Ae^{nx} \tag{7-27}$$

where $A = ae^{-nc}$ is a constant.

An exponential function that contains a constant y term will not give a straight line when plotting $\log y$ against x, but gives a curve. In such a case, we may plot $\log (y - b)$ against x for various trial values of b, and by interpolation that value of b may be found which makes the logarithmic curve become a straight line.

While the exponential function, appearing singly, is easily recognized, this becomes more difficult when there are combinations of two or more exponential functions with different exponents, thus:

$$y = a_1 e^{-bx} \pm a_2 e^{-cx} \tag{7-28}$$

For various values of a_1, a_2, b, c, quite a number of different forms of curve appear. As such combinations of exponential functions occur quite frequently in engineering, some typical forms are plotted in Figs. 7-5 and 7-6.

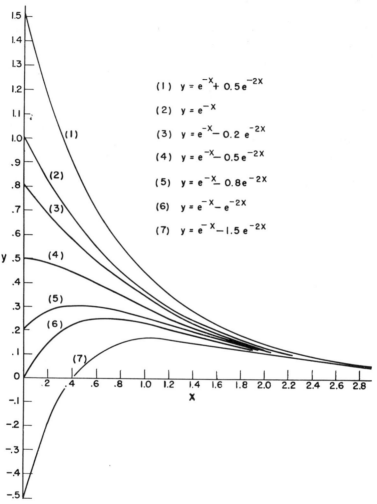

Fig. 7-5   Exponential functions, e^{-x} and e^{-2x}.

7-6   Example—Law of Air Resistance.   A classic example of the derivation of empirical formulas to represent test data is the following series of equations, which express the resistance offered by the air to the motion of artillery projectiles fired from rifled guns. The experimental data from which these equations were derived were originally obtained in a series of firings made by Krupp at Essen in

1881. General Mayevski formulated the data into equations, which were later extended by Colonel Zaboudski to include higher velocities. An American, Colonel James M. Ingalls, modified these and reduced them to English units about 1890.

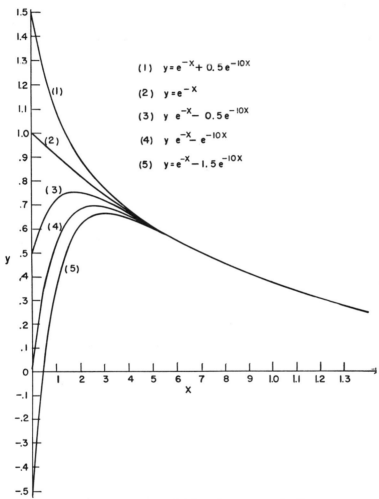

(1) $y = e^{-x} + 0.5 e^{-10x}$

(2) $y = e^{-x}$

(3) $y\ e^{-x} - 0.5 e^{-10x}$

(4) $y\ e^{-x} - e^{-10x}$

(5) $y = e^{-x} - 1.5 e^{-10x}$

Fig. 7-6 Exponential functions, e^{-x} and e^{-10x}.

It was found that the coefficient of air resistance, measured in pounds per square inch of projectile area, varies sharply as the projectile passes through the velocity of sound (about 1,100 feet per second under normal conditions). To allow for this, the range of velocities covered in the firings was divided into seven zones, and a separate formula was derived for the air resistance in each, with the results given in Table 7-3.

Table 7-3 Empirical Formulas for the Air Resistance to the Motion of Artillery Projectiles

Range of velocity, v, fps		Coefficient of resistance, lb/(in. of diam)^2 $R = C$ times retarding force
From	To	
0	790	$4.065v^{1.55} \times 10^{-3}$
790	970	$1.248v^{1.7} \times 10^{-3}$
970	1,230	$1.316v^2 \times 10^{-4}$
1,230	1,370	$9.57v^3 \times 10^{-8}$
1,370	1,800	$6.34v^5 \times 10^{-14}$
1,800	2,600	$5.934v^3 \times 10^{-8}$
2,600	3,600	$4.677v^2 \times 10^{-5}$

As shown by the plot of R vs. v in Fig. 7-7, the approximation, while not smooth, enabled extensive tables for the calculation of the range of artillery to be prepared, which were exclusively used for this purpose for more than twenty years. While the original firings were made with projectiles having a radius of the ogive equal to two calibers, the tables served very well for more modern shapes, when the coefficient was adjusted to suit, where

$$C = \frac{\text{(weight of projectile in pounds)(air density factor)}}{\text{(diameter in inches)}^2\text{(shape factor)}} \tag{7-29}$$

and the retarding force on the projectile is

$$r = \frac{R}{C} \quad \text{pounds} \tag{7-30}$$

where R is given by Table 7-3.

The shape factor varies from 1 for the original projectiles to about 0.6 for the most modern projectile shapes, but is considerably more than 1 for blunt or spherical projectiles.

Colonel Siacci succeeded in deriving a single formula to represent the entire range of velocity from 700 to 3,600 feet per second:

$$R = Cr = 0.896 \left[0.2847v - 224.2 + \sqrt{(0.2344v - 223.7)^2 + 209} \right.$$

$$\left. + \frac{0.01916v(v - 984.3)}{371 + (v/656.2)^{10}} \right] \tag{7-31}$$

While this equation gives a smooth curve, as shown in Fig. 7-7, it is far too involved for usual calculations, so that the separate formulas of Table 7-3 continued to be used until in 1918 the advent of high-angle fire, airplane spotting, and new mathematical methods for step-by-step range calculations brought in entirely new procedures.

The variable exponent of v in Table 7-3 and Eq. 7-31 makes these relations incorrect from a dimensional-analysis viewpoint. This is a fault common to all such purely empirical equations, which limits their validity to the narrow range of observations from which they were derived.

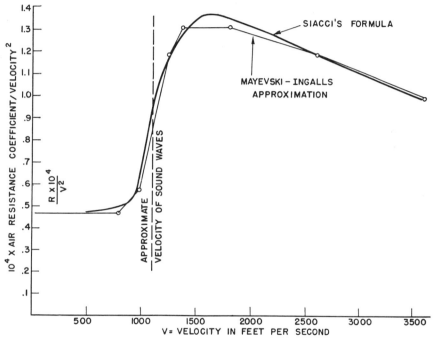

Fig. 7-7 Resistance of the air to artillery projectiles.

7-7 Exact Fitting of Tabulated Data. The growing use of digital computers for the "automation" of engineering calculations has created needs for new procedures in numerical techniques. One of these needs is the representation of a known curve in the form of a table of successive values—the inverse of the problem considered in Sec. 7-2.

The curve may be defined by an empirical equation found by the methods just cited, or by an exact equation such as a sine or exponential function. In either case, for a digital computer to make use of the data without actually calculating each value, it is necessary to provide a table of successive values of the function, which can be stored in the computer's "memory," for ready use in making the desired calculations. The tables for this purpose must be smooth; that is, the differences between successive, equally spaced values must themselves form smooth curves. To assure this, it is desirable to form tables of the first, second, and perhaps the third differences, as described in Sec. 1-16, and to adjust the tabulated values to correct any irregularities that occur. If this is not done, the discrepancies in the table may be magnified in the course of the calculations made by the computer.

By tabulating data in this way, and making calculations based on the sums and differences of the tabulated values, many problems can be solved that would ordinarily be thought to require use of the methods of calculus, which are considered in Chap. 8. The theory of such numerical procedures is called the calculus of finite differences.

PROBLEMS

Derive empirical formulas for y in terms of x from the sets of data given:

1.

y	−0.90	3.75	4.16	5.17	7.12	8.50	−4.9	−7.87	−10.8	−1.11	0.02
x	0.03	1.6	1.72	2.0	2.70	3.2	−1.3	−2.3	− 3.2	0	0.34

2.

y	1.05	0.98	1.17	1.16	1.65	1.55	2.0	2.50	2.80	3.30	6.30
x	0.21	0	0.43	0.51	0.77	0.80	0.98	1.2	1.35	1.50	2.3

3.

y	−0.10	−0.12	−0.18	−0.22	−0.26	−0.39	−0.50	−0.59	−0.70	−0.80	−0.84
x	0.10	0.12	0.20	0.25	0.30	0.50	0.70	0.90	1.2	1.6	1.8

4.

y	3.2	3.3	3.7	3.8	4.0	3.75	3.71	3.3	3.1	3.0	2.3
x	0.28	0.50	0.79	0.95	1.58	2.2	2.40	2.80	3.0	3.17	3.9

Bibliography

1. Bliss, G. A.: "Mathematics for Exterior Ballistics," John Wiley & Sons, Inc., New York, 1944.
2. Davis, Dale: "Empirical Equations and Monography," McGraw-Hill Book Company, New York, 1943.
3. Whitaker, E. T., and S. Robinson: "Calculus of Observations," 4th ed., Blackie & Son, Ltd., Glasgow, 1944.

Chapter 8 DIFFERENTIALS
AND INTEGRALS

8-1 The Nature of Differentials. In engineering, we are often concerned with the rate at which something changes or accelerates. We are interested in the velocity as well as the position of a moving piston or a projectile. To deal with these quantities and relate them in equations, we define them in terms of differentials, which are merely the values of the differences between successive values, when these latter are taken sufficiently close together.

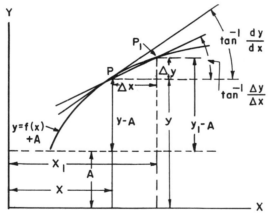

Fig. 8-1   Relation between dy/dx and $\Delta y/\Delta x$.

In Sec. 1-16, we tabulated the values of a continuous function, $y = f(x)$, for $x = 1, 2, 3$, etc., and we found that the differences $\Delta f(x)$ between successive values in the table could be used to calculate intermediate values, such as $f(x + \frac{1}{4})$. Thus, any value of $f(x)$ can be found by addition from a series of values of $\Delta f(x)$, just as any value of $\Delta f(x)$ can be found by subtraction from a series of values of $f(x)$.

In Fig. 8-1, two points P and P_1 on the curve $y = f(x) + A$ are shown at x,y and x_1,y_1. The line connecting the points is a chord of

[177]

the curve, which has a slope equal to the ratio of the difference in y to that in x:

$$\frac{y_1 - y}{x_1 - x} = \frac{\Delta y}{\Delta x} = \frac{\Delta f(x)}{\Delta x} \tag{8-1}$$

Suppose now that P_1 is brought continually nearer to P, so that Δx and Δy both become smaller. At the limit, when Δx and Δy are sensibly equal to zero and P_1 almost coincides with P, the slope of the chord becomes the same as that of the tangent to the curve at P and is equal to

$$\left(\frac{\Delta y}{\Delta x}\right)_{\Delta x \to 0} = \frac{dy}{dx} = \frac{df(x)}{dx} = f'(x) \tag{8-2}$$

When the difference between successive values of x and y is small,[1] we call it a *differential* instead of a difference and designate it by dx or dy instead of Δx or Δy. Even though dx and dy are themselves negligibly small or zero, their ratio is finite. Whereas there are many possible values of Δy at a point P on a curve, depending on how long a chord is considered and whether it is on the up or the down side of P, there is only one value of dy/dx at P. And it makes no difference what the value of the constant term A is.

By dealing with the ratios of these vanishingly small quantities, or differentials, we are considering perfectly definite relations between curves and their tangent lines, or between quantities and their rates of change. The ratio of dy to dx is called the *derivative* of y, with respect to x. For brevity, this is often written $f'(x)$, as in Eq. 8-2, or simply y'.

For example, if a car passes a point P at 3:00 o'clock and P_1, 30 miles away, at 4:00 o'clock, we have $\Delta y = 30$ miles and $\Delta x = 1$ hour, so the average speed (slope of the chord of the position-time curve) was 30 miles per hour. If the speed of the car was exactly the same all the time, the derivative of the distance with respect to time was also 30 miles per hour. If the speed varied from moment to moment, the derivative would be found by plotting a position-time curve, and measuring the slope at the moment considered. When the car is not moving, its position, or distance from P, does not change, so that the differential dy equals zero.

Just as the change in distance per unit of time, dy/dx, is the speed, so the change in speed per unit of time,

$$\frac{d}{dx}\left(\frac{dy}{dx}\right) = \frac{d^2y}{dx^2}$$

---

[1] That is, when the square of the difference between successive values of the function, $(\Delta x)^2$, is negligible compared with Δx.

is the acceleration. The nth derivative of any function is written $d^n f(x)/dx^n$, or simply $f^n(x)$. There is a close relationship between the nth-order difference in a table of successive values of y and the nth-order derivatives of y.

If the values of y are tabulated for smaller and smaller increments, Δx, the increments Δy will approach equality with the derivative times Δx, or $y' \Delta x$.

8-2   Differentiation.   To differentiate a function y, such as

$$y = f(x) + A \tag{8-3}$$

as shown in Fig. 8-1, we must find the slope of the tangent to the curve, in accordance with Eq. 8-2. When x increases by a small amount Δx, y changes to a new value, $y + \Delta y$, and Eq. 8-3 becomes

$$y + \Delta y = f(x + \Delta x) + A \tag{8-4}$$

Subtracting $y = f(x) + A$ from both sides gives

$$\Delta y = f(x + \Delta x) - f(x) \tag{8-5}$$

which is merely an expansion of Eq. 8-1, multiplied by Δx. When Δx is sensibly equal to zero, Eq. 8-5 divided by Δx reduces to Eq. 8-2.

To differentiate the function, $y = f(x) = x^n$, for example, the process indicated by Eq. 8-5 is carried through step by step:

$$\Delta y = (x + \Delta x)^n - x^n \tag{8-6}$$

Expanding this by Eq. 5-22, we have

$$\Delta y = x^n + nx^{n-1}\Delta x + \frac{n(n-1)}{2} x^{n-2}\Delta x^2 + \cdots - x^n$$

$$= nx^{n-1}\Delta x + \cdots$$

When Δx is very small, approaching zero as a limit, all the terms in Δx^2 and higher powers of Δx can be neglected, and $\Delta y/\Delta x$ becomes

$$\frac{\Delta y}{\Delta x} \rightarrow \frac{dy}{dx} = \frac{d(x^n)}{dx} = nx^{n-1} \tag{8-7}$$

The procedure indicated by Eq. 8-6 merely carries to the limit, as Δx approaches 0, the processes of interpolation considered in Sec. 1-16. The differential of a constant, or of any term that does not change when x changes, is zero:

$$\frac{da}{dx} = 0 \tag{8-8}$$

In general, if

$$f(x) = F_1(x)F_2(x),$$
$$\Delta f(x) = F_1(x + \Delta x)F_2(x + \Delta x) - F_1(x)F_2(x)$$
$$= [F_1(x) + \Delta x\, F_1'(x) + \cdots][F_2(x) + \Delta x\, F_2'(x) + \cdots\,]$$
$$\qquad\qquad\qquad\qquad\qquad - F_1(x)F_2(x)$$
$$= [F_1(x)F_2'(x) + F_2(x)F_1'(x)]\Delta x + \text{negligible terms in } \Delta x^2, \text{ etc.}$$

so that

$$f'(x) = \frac{d}{dx}[F_1(x)F_2(x)] = F_1(x)F_2'(x) + F_2(x)F_1'(x) \qquad (8\text{-}9)$$

Thus, the derivative of a product of n factors is the sum of n terms, each consisting of the product of $n - 1$ of the factors by the derivative of the remaining factor. Also, from Eq. 2-30,

$$\Delta \sin ax = \sin a(x + \Delta x) - \sin ax = \sin ax \cos a\Delta x$$
$$\qquad\qquad\qquad\qquad + \cos ax \sin a\Delta x - \sin ax \qquad (8\text{-}10)$$

When Δx is very small, Δx becomes dx, $\cos a\Delta x \cong 1$, and

$$\sin a\Delta x \cong a\, dx$$

by Eqs. 3-25 and 3-26, so that

$$\frac{d(\sin ax)}{dx} = a \cos ax \qquad (8\text{-}11)$$

Likewise, from Eq. 2-31,

$$\Delta \cos ax = \cos a(x + \Delta x) - \cos ax$$
$$= \cos ax \cos a\Delta x - \sin ax \sin a\Delta x - \cos ax \qquad (8\text{-}12)$$

so that, proceeding to the limit, we have

$$\frac{d}{dx}(\cos ax) = -a \sin ax \qquad (8\text{-}13)$$

From Eqs. 8-9, 8-10, and 8-13,

$$\frac{d}{dx}(\tan ax) = \frac{d[(\sin ax)(\cos ax)^{-1}]}{dx}$$
$$= a \cos ax(\cos ax)^{-1} + \sin ax\,(-1)(\cos ax)^{-2}(-a \sin ax)$$
$$= a + \frac{a \sin^2 ax}{\cos^2 ax} = a(1 + \tan^2 ax) = \frac{a}{\cos^2 ax}$$
$$= a \sec^2 ax \qquad (8\text{-}14)$$

To differentiate an exponential, a^x, we have

$$\Delta a^x = a^{x+\Delta x} - a^x = a^x(a^{\Delta x} - 1) \qquad (8\text{-}15)$$

To evaluate this, assume that a^x is represented by the infinite power series

$$a^x = a_0 + a_1 x + a_2 x^2 + a_3 x^3 + \cdots \qquad (8\text{-}16)$$

The first term of the series, a_0, must be 1, because we know by Eq. 1-8 that when $x = 0$, $a^x = a^0 = 1$. Then, from Eqs. 8-7, 8-8, and 8-16,

$$\frac{da^x}{dx} = a_1 + 2a_2 x + 3a_3 x^2 + 4a_4 x^3 + \cdots \qquad (8\text{-}17)$$

But, from Eqs. 8-15 and 8-16, at the limit, when $\Delta x = dx$ is indefinitely small

$$da^x = a^x(a^{dx} - 1) = a^x(a_1 \, dx + \cdots)$$

or $\qquad \dfrac{da^x}{dx} = a_1(1 + a_1 x + a_2 x^2 + a_3 x^3 + \cdots) = a_1 a^x \qquad (8\text{-}18)$

As Eqs. 8-17 and 8-18 are true for all values of x, they must be equal term by term. Therefore

$$2a_2 = a_1{}^2 \qquad \text{or} \qquad a_2 = \frac{a_1{}^2}{2}$$

$$3a_3 = a_1 a_2 \qquad \text{or} \qquad a_3 = \frac{a_1{}^3}{6}$$

$$4a_4 = a_1 a_3 \qquad \text{or} \qquad a_4 = \frac{a_1{}^4}{24} \cdots$$

and, finally

$$a^x = 1 + a_1 x + \frac{a_1{}^2 x^2}{2!} + \frac{a_1{}^3 x^3}{3!} + \frac{a_1{}^4 x^4}{4!} + \cdots \qquad (8\text{-}19)$$

and its derivative is

$$\frac{da^x}{dx} = a_1 a^x \qquad (8\text{-}20)$$

Equation 8-19 must be true for all values of x. We can find the value of a_1 most simply, therefore, by making $x = 1/a_1$, when a^x becomes

$$a^{1/a_1} = 1 + 1 + \tfrac{1}{2} + \tfrac{1}{6} + \tfrac{1}{24} + \cdots = 2.7182818 \cdots \qquad (8\text{-}21)$$

Comparing this with Eq. 3-24, we see that the two equations are identical, so that

$$a^{1/a_1} = e \qquad \text{or} \qquad a = e^{a_1} \qquad \text{or} \qquad a_1 = \log_e a = \ln a \qquad (8\text{-}22)$$

Hence from Eq. 8-20

$$\frac{da^x}{dx} = \ln a(a^x) \tag{8-23}$$

and from Eq. 8-19

$$e^x = \exp x = 1 + x + \frac{x^2}{2!} + \frac{x^3}{3!} + \frac{x^4}{4!} + \cdots \tag{8-24}$$

and

$$\frac{de^x}{dx} = e^x = \exp x \tag{8-25}$$

From this result, we can find the derivative of $\ln x$:

Let

$$y = \ln x \tag{8-26}$$

Then

$$x = e^y = \exp y \tag{8-27}$$

and by Eq. 8-25

$$\frac{dx}{dy} = \frac{de^y}{dy} = e^y = x \tag{8-28}$$

or

$$\frac{dy}{dx} = \frac{d(\ln x)}{dx} = \frac{1}{x} \tag{8-29}$$

In general, the derivative of any expression $f(x)$ is merely the coefficient of Δx in the infinite series formed by expanding $f(x + \Delta x)$ in powers of Δx, by such methods as those suggested in Chap. 6. That is,

$$f(x + \Delta x) = f(x) + f'(x)\Delta x + \cdots \tag{8-30}$$

Or, in graphic terms, the vertical distance between two nearby points on a curve is closely equal to the slope of the tangent line to the curve, multiplied by the horizontal distance between the points.

Continuing in this way, the derivatives, or slope functions, of all sorts of functions can be found, such as those tabulated in Appendix D.

8-3 Partial Derivatives. When an expression contains two or more independent variables, as

$$z = f(x,y) \tag{8-31}$$

it may be differentiated with respect to either variable separately. The symbol ∂ is used to indicate such partial differentiation. For example, if x varies in Eq. 8-31 without affecting the value of y, the partial derivative of z with respect to x is

$$\frac{\partial z}{\partial x} = \frac{\partial f(x,y)}{\partial x}$$

Thus, if $z = ax^2 + bxy + cy^2$,

$$\frac{\partial z}{\partial x} = 2ax + by$$

and $\qquad dz = \dfrac{\partial z}{\partial x} + \dfrac{\partial z}{\partial y} = (2ax + by)\,dx + (bx + 2cy)\,dy \qquad$ (8-32)

If x and y are related by another equation, and so are not independent, substituting this relation in Eq. 8-31 will reduce z to a function of one variable only. In this case, the partial derivative becomes identical with the derivative itself.

8-4 Integration. The inverse of differentiation is called *integration*. Thus, the inverse of Eq. 8-11, $d\,(\sin ax) = a \cos ax\,dx$, is

$$\int_0^x a \cos ax\,dx = \sin ax \qquad (8\text{-}33)$$

which is read "the integral of $a \cos ax\,dx$ between x and 0 is equal to $\sin ax$."

When we differentiate, we are taking the difference

$$\Delta y = f(x_1) - f(x)$$

as shown in Fig. 8-1. At the limit, when Δy approaches zero, the difference becomes $dy = f'(x)\,dx$, and the ratio $dy/dx = f'(x)$ is equal to the slope of the curve $y = f(x)$. The inverse of "taking the difference" is "taking the sum," or adding successive increments. If we plot a new curve,

$$z = \frac{dy}{dx} = f'(x)$$

as shown in Fig. 8-2, we see that the quantity $\Delta y = z\,\Delta x = f'(x)\,\Delta x$ represents the shaded increment of area between the z curve and the x axis. Therefore, the integral of $f'(x)\,dx$ between $x = x$ and $x = 0$ represents the whole area under the curve between these limits.

There is another major distinction between a differential and an integral. If a function contains a constant term A, the A term disappears when the function is differentiated:

$$\frac{d}{dx}\,[f(x) + A] = \frac{d}{dx}\,[f(x)] = f'(x) \qquad (8\text{-}34)$$

This is true because the differential of a constant term is zero; i.e., the slope of the tangent to a curve is the same no matter how far the curve is vertically displaced from the x axis. There is only one differential of a given function.

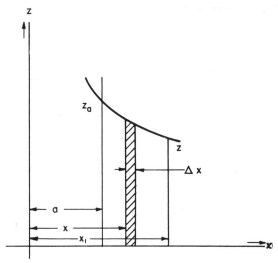

Fig. 8-2   Area under a curve is found by integration.

On the other hand, the integral of a function z is a summation of z times dx, and, therefore, represents the area under the curve $z = f(x)$. This is indefinite, unless the limits of the integration are specified. We make it a definite integral by setting upper and lower limits.

$$\int_a^x f'(x)\,dx = f(x) - f(a) \tag{8-35}$$

The area under the curve in Fig. 8-2 between $x = x_1$ and $x = a$ is the total area between $x = x_1$ and $x = 0$, less the area between $x = a$ and $x = 0$. For example,

$$\int_{-\pi/2}^x \cos x\,dx = \sin x \Big]_{-\pi/2}^x = \sin x - \sin\left(-\frac{\pi}{2}\right) = 1 + \sin x \tag{8-36}$$

The single bracket with super- and subscripts is used to show that the value of the definite integral is found by subtracting its value at the lower limit from that at the upper limit.

The result of an integration between limits is the difference of the expressions found by substituting first the upper and then the lower limit of integration in the indefinite integral and subtracting the second from the first. For example, Eq. 8-36 represents the area under the curve $y = \cos x$, between x and $-\pi/2$ (Fig. 8-3). To find the total area under the half-sinusoid, the limits may be taken from $x = -\pi/2$ to $x = \pi/2$, when the definite integral becomes

$$\int_{-\pi/2}^{\pi/2} \cos x\, dx = \sin x \bigg]_{-\pi/2}^{\pi/2} = 1 - (-1) = 2$$

Since the base length of the half-wave is π radians, its average height, the area divided by the base, is $2/\pi = 0.636 \ldots$.

Thus, the integral

$$\int_a^x f(x)\, dx$$

has a different value for every value of the lower limit a. There is a many-to-one correspondence between the integral of any function and the function itself.

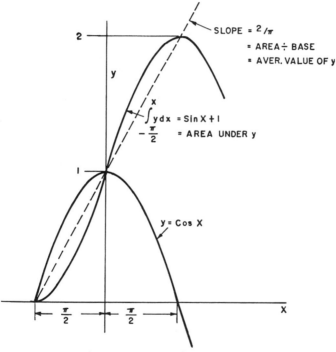

Fig. 8-3 Area under a sinusoid.

The value of any definite integral is found by subtracting the integration constant, or value of the integral at the lower limit of integration, from the value at the upper limit. What the lower limit of integration should be is determined by the conditions of the particular problem. For example, if we decide to measure the area under the curve $z = f(x)$ in Fig. 8-2, we must decide at what value of x to start the measurement. When we decide to start from $x = a$, the integral becomes definite and equal to

$$\int_a^x z \, dx$$

and the integration constant becomes

$$- \int z \, dx \Big]_{x=a}$$

The integral of any function, as $\int x^n \, dx$, is found by determining what function, when differentiated, will be equal to the expression that is to be integrated. In this case, by referring to Eq. 8-7, we note that if $f(x) = x^n$, then $f'(x) = nx^{n-1}$. Therefore, inversely, the function whose derivative is x^n must be

$$\int x^n \, dx = \frac{x^{n+1}}{n+1} \tag{8-37}$$

A table of integrals is given in Appendix D, together with the corresponding differentials.

By differentiating an expression, changing the result into an infinite series, and then integrating, a useful alternative form of the expression sometimes may be derived. For example, to find a simple expression for $\ln (1 + z)$, when z is small, we may substitute $1 + z$ for x in Eq. 8-29, and divide out, obtaining the infinite series expression

$$\frac{d[\ln (1 + z)]}{dz} = \frac{1}{1 + z} = 1 - z + z^2 - z^3 + \cdots$$

Integrating this by Eq. 8-37, we find

$$\ln (1 + z) = z - \frac{z^2}{2} + \frac{z^3}{3} - \frac{z^4}{4} + \cdots = z - \frac{z^2}{2} \text{ approximately}$$

$$\text{if } z < 0.1 \tag{8-38}$$

8-5 Simpson's Rules. It is helpful to note the close relation between the process of integrating a quantity $y = f(x)$ between x_0 and x_m and the equivalent process of measuring the successive ordinates, $y_0, y_1, y_2, \ldots, y_m$, and finding the area under the curve by multiplying the average ordinate by $(x_m - x_0)$.

In Sec. 1-16, we found that if $m + 1$ equally spaced ordinates of a curve $y = f(x)$ are $y_0, y_1, y_2, \ldots, y_m$, the value of any one ordinate y_n can be calculated from the known values of the preceding ordinates by Newton's interpolation formula (Eq. 1-36), which may be rewritten as

$$y_n = y_0 + n\,\Delta_1 + \frac{n(n-1)}{2}\,\Delta_2 + \frac{n(n-1)(n-2)}{6}\,\Delta_3 + \cdots \quad (8\text{-}39)$$

where Δ_1, Δ_2, Δ_3, . . . are the first-, second-, third-, etc., order differences between y_0, y_1, y_2, etc. By Eqs. 1-33 to 1-35, these differences are

$$\Delta_1 = y_1 - y_0 \qquad\qquad (8\text{-}40)$$
$$\Delta_2 = y_2 - 2y_1 + y_0 \qquad\qquad (8\text{-}41)$$
$$\Delta_3 = y_3 - 3y_2 + 3y_1 - y_0 \qquad\qquad (8\text{-}42)$$

It is assumed that the distance between successive ordinates, $x_1 - x_0 = x_2 - x_1$, . . . is equal to $h = (x_m - x_0)/n$ and that h is so small that the curve is sensibly a straight line over the length of each interval.

The process of integrating y from y_0 to y_m is simply that of calculating the area under the curve between x_0 and x_m. This area is equal to the average value of y times $x_m - x_0$ or is equal to the sum of all the m ordinates times h. The distance from x_0 to x_n is nh, so we may write $dx = h\,dn$ and from Eq. 8-39

$$\int_{x_0}^{x_m} y\,dx = h \int_0^m y_n\,dn$$

$$= h\left[y_0 \int_0^m dn + \Delta_1 \int_0^m n\,dn + \Delta_2 \int_0^m \frac{n(n-1)}{2}\,dn + \cdots \right]$$

$$= h\left[my_0 + \frac{m^2\,\Delta_1}{2} + \frac{m^2(2m-3)\,\Delta_2}{12} \right.$$

$$\left. + \frac{m^2(m-2)^2\,\Delta_3}{24} + \frac{m^2(6m^3 - 45m^2 + 110m - 90)\,\Delta_4}{120} + \cdots \right]$$

$$(8\text{-}43)$$

This equation enables us to find the area under the curve by direct calculation, knowing the values of $m + 1$ equally spaced ordinates, whatever the shape of the curve, without performing any further integrations. For example, suppose we measure only three ordinates of a curve, y_0, y_1, and y_2, spaced h apart. Then, from Eqs. 8-40, 8-41, and 8-43, we have $m = 2$, and

$$\text{Area} = h\left[2y_0 + 2(y_1 - y_0) + \frac{1}{3}(y_2 - 2y_1 + y_0) \right]$$

$$= \frac{h}{3}(y_0 + 4y_1 + y_2) \quad (8\text{-}44)$$

This is known as Simpson's "one-third rule."
If we use four ordinates instead of only three, $m = 3$, and

$$\text{Area} = h[3y_0 + \tfrac{9}{2}(y_1 - y_0) + \tfrac{9}{4}(y_2 - 2y_1 + y_0)$$
$$+ \tfrac{3}{8}(y_3 - 3y_2 + 3y_1 - y_0)]$$
$$= \frac{3h}{8}(y_0 + 3y_1 + 3y_2 + y_3) \qquad (8\text{-}45)$$

which is Simpson's "three-eighths rule."
And, for five ordinates, $m = 4$, so that Eq. 8-43 becomes

$$\text{Area} = h[4y_0 + 8(y_1 - y_0) + \tfrac{20}{3}(y_2 - 2y_1 + y_0)$$
$$+ \tfrac{8}{3}(y_3 - 3y_2 + 3y_1 - y_0) + \tfrac{7}{15}(y_4 - 4y_3 + 6y_2 - 4y_1 + y_0)]$$
$$= h\left(\frac{7y_0}{15} + \frac{4y_1}{5} + \frac{22y_2}{15} + \frac{4y_3}{5} + \frac{7y_4}{15}\right)$$
$$= \frac{h}{15}(7y_0 + 12y_1 + 22y_2 + 12y_3 + 7y_4) \qquad (8\text{-}46)$$

Finally, for seven ordinates, $m = 6$ and

$$\text{Area} = h[6y_0 + 18(y_1 - y_0) + 27(y_2 - 2y_1 + y_0)$$
$$+ 24(y_3 - 3y_2 + 3y_1 - y_0)$$
$$+ \tfrac{123}{10}(y_4 - 4y_3 + 6y_2 - 4y_1 + y_0)$$
$$+ \tfrac{33}{10}(y_5 - 5y_4 + 10y_3 - 10y_2 + 5y_1 - y_0)$$
$$+ \tfrac{41}{140}(y_6 - 6y_5 + 15y_4 - 20y_3 + 15y_2 - 6y_1 + y_0)]$$
$$= \frac{h}{140}(41y_0 + 216y_1 + 27y_2 + 272y_3 + 27y_4 + 216y_5 + 41y_6)$$
$$(8\text{-}47)$$

When fractions are rounded off slightly, this last equation reduces to

$$\text{Area} = \frac{3h}{10}(y_0 + 5y_1 + y_2 + 6y_3 + y_4 + 5y_5 + y_6) \qquad (8\text{-}48)$$

known as "Weddle's rule."
For example, we may apply these several rules to calculate the area under three curves:

$$\begin{aligned}
y &= \sin x &\quad &\text{from } x = 0 \text{ to } x = \pi/2 \\
y &= x^3 &\quad &\text{from } x = 1 \text{ to } x = 5 \\
y &= x^4 &\quad &\text{from } x = 1 \text{ to } x = 5
\end{aligned}$$

The exact areas in the three cases are

$$\int_0^{\pi/2} \sin x \, dx = -\cos x \Big]_0^{\pi/2} = 1$$

$$\int_1^5 x^3 \, dx = \frac{x^4}{4}\Big]_1^5 = \frac{625 - 1}{4} = 156$$

$$\int_1^5 x^4 \, dx = \frac{x^5}{5}\Big]_1^5 = \frac{3,125 - 1}{5} = 624.8$$

The areas given by the several rules are compared in Table 8-1.

Table 8-1   Area under the Curve

Number of ordinates used	Equation No.	sin x	x^3	x^4
	Exact	1.0000	156.00	624.80
3	8-44	1.0023	156.00	633.33
4	8-45	1.0010	156.00	628.59
5	8-46	1.0010	156.00	628.53
7	8-47	1.0000	156.00	624.795
7	8-48	1.0000	156.00	624.80

It is evident, therefore, that a remarkably accurate measure of the area under a curve, or of the average of any series of values, can be obtained by measuring a few equally spaced ordinates and applying Simpson's or Weddle's rule. In this way, the engineer can entirely dispense with any knowledge or use of integration formulas, as long as he is concerned merely with finding the area under a known curve, or the equivalent.

Simpson's rules are especially useful to civil engineers for calculating the amount of earth that must be moved to provide a level highway or supplied to fill a depression or make a dam. Profiles of the earth levels along different sections are prepared from surveys and contour maps, and the average height or depression is calculated by the one-third or three-eighths rule, with respect to the desired level. From these figures, it becomes a simple matter to calculate the total volume of earth to be moved.

8-6   Integration by Parts.   To simplify the integration of complicated functions, it is often useful to integrate by parts. Equation 8-9 may be written more simply as

$$d(xy) = x \, dy + y \, dx \tag{8-49}$$

whence we have

$$\int x \, dy = xy - \int y \, dx \tag{8-50}$$

For example, to find the integral of $z^2 \sin z$, we may first put $x = z^2$, $y = -\cos z$, in Eq. 8-50, giving

$$\int z^2 \sin z \, dz = -z^2 \cos z + 2 \int z \cos z \, dz \tag{8-51}$$

Next, put x_1 for $2z$, dy_1 for $\cos z \, dz$ in the last term of Eq. 8-51, whence by Eq. 8-50

$$\begin{aligned}
\int z^2 \sin z \, dz &= -z^2 \cos z + x_1 y_1 - \int y_1 \, dx_1 \\
&= -z^2 \cos z + 2z \sin z - \int 2 \sin z \, dz \\
&= (2 - z^2) \cos z + 2z \sin z
\end{aligned} \tag{8-52}$$

If the function to be integrated has a polynomial in the denominator, it is desirable to separate it into partial fractions before integrating. It may easily be verified by trial that a fraction $f(z)/F(z)$, whose denominator is an algebraic expression of nth order and whose numerator is an expression in the same variable but of lower order than n, can be resolved into a sum of n fractions, each having a first-order denominator, by means of the formula

$$\frac{f(z)}{F(z)} = \frac{f(z_1)}{(z - z_1)F'(z_1)} + \frac{f(z_2)}{(z - z_2)F'(z_2)} + \cdots \tag{8-53}$$

where z_1, z_2, . . . are the several roots of $F(z) = 0$ and $F'(z_1)$, $F'(z_2)$, . . . are the derivatives of $F(z)$ at the points where $z = z_1$, z_2, ...

If there are two or more equal roots, say $z_1 = z_2$, this equation does not hold true, as then $F'(z_1) = F'(z_2) = 0$. In this case, all but one of the multiple roots should be taken outside before the equation is applied. For example, if

$$F(z) = (z - z_1)^m (z - z_2)(z - z_3) \cdots = (z - z_1)^{m-1} F_1(z)$$

Then $\quad \dfrac{f(z)}{F(z)} = \dfrac{f(z)}{(z - z_1)^{m-1} F_1(z)}$

or

$$\begin{aligned}
\frac{f(z)}{F(z)} = \frac{f(z_1)}{(z - z_1)^m F_1'(z_1)} &+ \frac{1}{(z - z_1)^{m-1}} \left[\frac{f(z_2)}{(z - z_2)F_1'(z_2)} \right. \\
&\left. + \frac{f(z_3)}{(z - z_3)F_1'(z_3)} + \cdots \right]
\end{aligned} \tag{8-54}$$

Each of the terms except the first may then be expanded into partial fractions by repeated applications of Eq. 8-53 or 8-54, with denominators of the form $u(z - z_n)$.

As a simple example, consider the integral

$$\int_{x_1}^{x} \frac{(x^2 + 1)\, dx}{x^3 - 6x^2 + 11x - 6}$$

As the three roots of $x^3 - 6x^2 + 11x - 6 = 0$ are $x_1 = 1$, $x_2 = 2$, $x_3 = 3$ and as the first derivative of the denominator is $3x^2 - 12x + 11$, Eq. 8-53 gives the identity

$$\frac{x^2 + 1}{x^3 - 6x^2 + 11x - 6} = \frac{1 + 1}{(x - 1)(3 - 12 + 11)}$$
$$+ \frac{4 + 1}{(x - 2)(12 - 24 + 11)}$$
$$+ \frac{9 + 1}{(x - 3)(27 - 36 + 11)}$$
$$= \frac{1}{x - 1} - \frac{5}{x - 2} + \frac{5}{x - 3}$$

Thus the integral of the original expression is easily found by Eq. 8-29 to be

$$Z = \int_{x_1}^{x} \frac{(x^2 + 1)\, dx}{x^3 - 6x^2 + 11x - 6} = \int_{x_1}^{x} \frac{dx}{x - 1} - \int_{x_1}^{x} \frac{5\, dx}{x - 2} + \int_{x_1}^{x} \frac{5\, dx}{x - 3}$$
$$= \ln\left(\frac{x - 1}{x_1 - 1}\right) - 5\ln\left(\frac{x - 2}{x_1 - 2}\right) + 5\ln\left(\frac{x - 3}{x_1 - 3}\right)$$
$$= \ln \frac{(x - 1)(x_1 - 2)^5(x - 3)^5}{(x_1 - 1)(x - 2)^5(x_1 - 3)^5}$$

a result that was not apparent before the separation into parts.

A short table of derivatives and integrals is given in Appendix D. Tables are readily available that give the integrals of a large number of other functions. In general, however, the integral of almost any function can be found without reference to tables by separating it into parts, by transformation of variables, or by developing it into an infinite series and integrating term by term, as covered in the following section.

8-7 Taylor's Theorem. Many occasions arise in the solution of engineering problems, and especially in the solution of differential equations, in which it is desirable to express functions in the form of infinite power series. Such examples already considered as Eqs. 1-36, 3-23, and 5-22 have foreshadowed the usefulness of these power series. It is therefore important to have a simple method for their development that can be used for any sort of function. Taylor's theorem provides such a method.

What we are considering here is how to determine the coefficients of a power series in x that will accurately represent a function $f(x)$ already given in another form. In Sec. 1-16, "Interpolation," we saw that a *numerical value* of a function for any intermediate value of x can be calculated by Eq. 1-36 from a table of *numerical values* of the function for specific values of x. What we now have to do is to develop a series form of expression for a function, given a formula for the function. In the interpolation case, we calculated log 5.100, from known values of log 5, 5.2, 5.4, and 5.6. Now we wish to develop an infinite power series for sin x (for example), from the known properties of the sine, as a transcendental function.

To do this, we can employ the derivatives $f'(x)$, $f''(x)$, etc., of the given function $f(x)$, instead of the numerical differences between successive numbers in a table, as we did in interpolation. The first derivative measures the *slope*, or first difference between successive values, of the function. But it means the *level* difference, which would appear in a table of differences directly opposite the tabulated function, whereas in interpolation we are accustomed to using the *descending* differences that appear opposite successively lower values in Table 1-3. The question is, then, how can we construct a formula similar to Eq. 1-36, giving the values of $f(x)$ for any chosen values of x, that will be expressed in terms of the *level* differences, or derivatives, instead of the descending differences?

Assume that the infinite power series equal to $f(x)$ that we are seeking is

$$f(x) = f(x_0 + h) = A_0 + B_0 h + C_0 h^2 + D_0 h^3 + \cdots \quad (8\text{-}55)$$

where $h = x - x_0$ is the difference between any assigned value of x and a particular value, x_0.

If Eq. 8-55 is to be true for any value of h, it will be true for $h = 0$. Therefore, the first term of the series must be

$$A_0 = f(x_0)$$

Also, if Eq. 8-55 is to be true for all values of h, its first derivative must be equal to the first derivative of $f(x)$, or $f'(x)$. Hence

$$f'(x) = f'(x_0 + h) = B_0 + 2C_0 H + 3D_0 h^2 + \cdots \quad (8\text{-}56)$$

As Eq. 8-56 is true for any value of h, it will be true for $h = 0$. Therefore

$$B_0 = f'(x_0) \tag{8-57}$$

Proceeding in this way to differentiate Eq. 8-55 repeatedly, then make $h = 0$ and equate the results to the successive differentials of $f(x)$ at $x = x_0$, we find

$$C_0 = \frac{f''(x_0)}{2}, \; D_0 = \frac{f'''(x_0)}{6}, \; \cdots \;, N_0 = \frac{f^n(x_0)}{n!} \tag{8-58}$$

Thus Eq. 8-55 becomes

$$f(x) = f(x_0 + h) = f(x_0) + hf'(x_0) + \frac{h^2 f''(x_0)}{2!} + \frac{h^3 f'''(x_0)}{3!}$$

$$+ \frac{h^4 f''''(x_0)}{4!} + \cdots \tag{8-59}$$

which is known as Taylor's theorem.

Table 8-2   Comparison between Newton's Interpolation Formula and
Taylor's Theorem

	Interpolation formula, Eq. 1-36	Taylor's theorem, Eq. 8-59
Step between known and desired value of x	$x - x_0 = n$	$x - x_0 = h$
mth difference, or slope	$\Delta^m f(x)$	$f^m(x)$
Corresponding coefficient in series	$\dfrac{n(n - 1)(n - 2) \cdots (n - m + 1)}{m!}$	$\dfrac{h^m}{m!}$

In fact, if we use Eq. 1-37 to transform the successive terms of Eq. 1-36 from descending to level differences, so that

$$f(x + n) = f(x) + A \Delta' f(x - \tfrac{1}{2}) + B \Delta'' f(x - 1)$$
$$+ C \Delta''' f(x - \tfrac{3}{2}) \cdots \tag{8-60}$$

we shall find that the new coefficients A, B, C, etc., become approximately equal to n, $n^2/2!$, $n^3/3!$, . . . , or nearly the same as those of Eq. 8-59. The reason that the coefficients do not match exactly is that $\Delta' f(x_0 - \tfrac{1}{2})$ is not exactly equal to $f'(x_0)$, etc., since the slope of the curve $y = f(x)$ at a point midway between x_0 and $x_0 + h$ is not (necessarily) exactly equal to the slope of the chord connecting $y = f(x_0)$ with $y = f(x_0 + h)$.

8-8 Function Series Derived by Taylor's Theorem. As an example of the use of Taylor's theorem, we shall develop the series for $\sin x$. Taking $x_0 = 0$, we have for the successive derivatives of $\sin x$ at the point $x = 0$

$$f(x_0) = \sin 0 = 0,\ f'(x_0) = \cos 0 = 1,\ f''(x_0) = -\sin 0 = 0,$$
$$f'''(x_0) = -\cos 0 = -1,\ f^{iv}(x_0) = \sin 0 = 0,\ \text{etc.}$$

Substituting these values in Eq. 8-59 (putting 0 for x_0, and x for h), we find

$$f(x) = \sin x = 0 + x(1) + \frac{x^2}{2!}(0) + \frac{x^3}{3!}(-1) + \frac{x^4}{4!}(0) + \cdots \quad (8\text{-}61)$$

or

$$\sin x = x - \frac{x^3}{6} + \frac{x^5}{120} - \frac{x^7}{5,040} + \cdots \quad (3\text{-}25)$$

Similarly, if $f(x) = \cos x$, we have

$$f(x_0) = \cos 0 = 1,\ f'(x_0) = -\sin 0 = 0,\ f''(x_0) = -\cos 0 = -1,$$
$$f'''(x_0) = \sin 0 = 0,\ f^{iv}(x_0) = \cos 0 = 1,\ \text{etc.}$$

Putting these values in Eq. 8-59, we find

$$\cos x = 1 - \frac{x^2}{2} + \frac{x^4}{24} - \frac{x^6}{720} + \cdots \quad (3\text{-}26)$$

Thus, Taylor's theorem provides a method of generalizing the interpolation formula (Eq. 1-36) from numerical, or single-point, values to functional values, or complete curves.

In a similar way, for $f(x) = \tan x$, we have the values given in Table 8-3, so that from Eqs. 8-59 and 8-14.

$$\tan x = x + \frac{x^3}{3} + \frac{2x^5}{15} + \frac{17x^7}{315} + \cdots \quad (8\text{-}62)$$

Table 8-3   Data for Determining Tangent Series from Taylor's Theorem

$f(x) = \tan x$	$f(0) = 0$	$f(\pi/4) = 1$
$f'(x) = \sec^2 x = 1 + f^2$	$f'(0) = 1$	$f'(\pi/4) = 2$
$f''(x) = 2ff'$	$f''(0) = 0$	$f''(\pi/4) = 4$
$f'''(x) = 2ff'' + 2f'^2$	$f'''(0) = 2$	$f'''(\pi/4) = 16$
$f^{iv}(x) = 2ff''' = 6f'f''$	$f^{iv}(0) = 0$	$f^{iv}(\pi/4) = 80$
$f^{v}(x) = 2ff^{iv} + 8f'f''' + 6f''^2$	$f^{v}(0) = 16$	$f^{v}(\pi/4) = 512$
$f^{vi}(x) = 2ff^{v} + 10f'f^{iv} + 20f''f'''$	$f^{vi}(0) = 0$	$f^{vi}(\pi/4) = 3,904$
$f^{vii}(x) = 2ff^{vi} + 12f'f^{v} + 30f''f^{iv} + 20f'''^2$	$f^{vii}(0) = 272$	$f^{vii}(\pi/4) = 34,816$

Evidently, this series will converge rapidly when x is small, but will be slow in converging when x is large. To calculate tan x, for example, when x is in the neighborhood of 45°, or $\pi/4$, it is preferable to make $x_0 = \pi/4$ in Eq. 8-59 instead of zero. In this case, we have $h = x = \pi/4$ and all the derivatives must be evaluated at $x = \pi/4$, instead of $x = 0$. Hence from Eq. 8-59,

$$\tan x = \tan\left(\frac{\pi}{4} + h\right) = 1 + 2h + 2h^2 + \frac{8h^3}{3} + \frac{10h^4}{3} + \frac{64h^5}{15} + \frac{244x^6}{45}$$
$$+ \frac{2176x^7}{315} + \cdots \quad (8\text{-}63)$$

In such ways, an infinite power series can be developed quite readily for any function that has continuous derivatives. A table of such series is included in Appendix E.

8-9 Indeterminate Forms. It sometimes happens that when the value of a ratio is calculated, such as

$$R = \frac{f(x)}{F(x)} \quad (8\text{-}64)$$

the numerator and denominator are both found to be zero at a particular value of $x = x_0$, so that the value of R is indeterminate at this point. If so, the limiting value of R can be found by developing both numerator and denominator in infinite series by Taylor's theorem:

$$R = \frac{f(x_0) + hf'(x_0) + (h^2/2)f''(x_0) + \cdots}{F(x_0) + hF'(x_0) + (h^2/2)F''(x_0) + \cdots} \quad (8\text{-}65)$$

Evidently, if $f(x_0)$ and $F(x_0)$ are both equal to zero, and because h is small, the ratio becomes

$$R = \frac{f'(x_0)}{F'(x_0)} \quad (8\text{-}66)$$

And, if both the first derivatives, $f'(x_0)$ and $F'(x_0)$, are also equal to zero, the ratio becomes

$$R = \frac{f''(x_0)}{F''(x_0)} \quad (8\text{-}67)$$

For example, we may determine the limiting value of the ratio

$$R = \frac{x^3 - 6x^2 + 5x + 6}{2x^3 - 4x^2 + x - 2}$$

When $x = 2$,

$$R = \frac{8 - 24 + 10 + 6}{16 - 16 + 2 - 2} = \frac{0}{0}$$

Taking the derivatives of both numerator and denominator at $x = 2$, we find

$$R = \frac{3x^2 - 12x + 5}{6x^2 - 8x + 1} = \frac{12 - 24 + 5}{24 - 16 + 1} = -\frac{7}{9}$$

In this case, the factor $x - 2$ may be divided out of both numerator and denominator, giving at $x = 2$

$$R = \frac{(x - 2)(x^2 - 4x - 3)}{(x - 2)(2x^2 + 1)} = \frac{x^2 - 4x - 3}{2x^2 + 1} = -\frac{7}{9}$$

as before.

8-10   Finding Volumes by Integration.   A typical use of integration is to find the volume of some geometrical shape. The procedure is to imagine the volume sliced into thin parallel disks, each of thickness dz, and each disk to be cut into thin parallel strips, each of width dy, in such a way that the area of a typical disk can be expressed as the summation of the areas of its separate strips, expressed by an algebraic formula in terms of the chosen coordinates, and the total volume can be similarly expressed as the sum of the volumes of the separate disks. The summation process in each case is carried out by integration. Three integrations are required to find a volume in three dimensions, but usually the first integration, to find the length of each strip as the summation of short lines, each of length dx, is performed by inspection, and does not need to be formally stated. Instead of using rectangular coordinates, x, y, and z, as above indicated, cylindrical coordinates, r, θ, and z, or any other set of coordinates suitable for the problem, may be used.

For example, to find the volume of a cut-off sphere of radius R feet and height H feet (Fig. 8-4), we may consider the volume to be made up of a stack of horizontal (circular) disks, each of thickness dz, extending from $z = R - H$ to $z = R$, the origin being taken at the center of the sphere. Also, we may consider each disk to be made up of parallel strips, each of width dy, extending from $y = -R \cos \theta$ to $y = R \cos \theta$, as shown in Fig. 8-4B.

From the figure, the area of the disk at height $y = R \sin \theta$, which has a radius $R \cos \theta$, is found by summing the areas of the strips of width dy and length $2R \cos \theta \cos \phi$, from $\phi = -\pi/2$ to $\phi = \pi/2$.

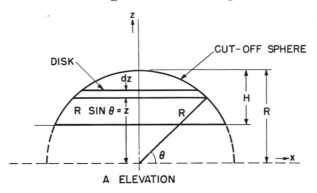

A ELEVATION

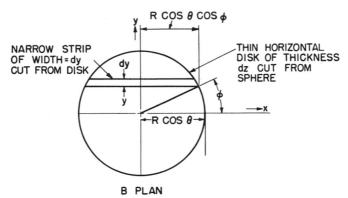

B PLAN

Fig. 8-4 Finding the volume of a cut-off sphere.

Since for a given value of θ

$$dy = d(R \cos \theta \sin \phi) = R \cos \theta \cos \phi \, d\phi \qquad (8\text{-}68)$$

the area of the disk is

$$A = \int_{-\pi/2}^{\pi/2} 2R \cos \theta \cos \phi \, (R \cos \theta \cos \phi) \, d\phi$$

or

$$A = 2R^2 \cos^2 \theta \int_{-\pi/2}^{\pi/2} \cos^2 \phi \, d\phi = R^2 \cos^2 \theta \int_{-\pi/2}^{\pi/2} (1 + \cos 2\phi) \, d\phi$$

or

$$A = R^2 \cos^2 \theta \left[\phi + \frac{\sin 2\phi}{2} \right]_{-\pi/2}^{\pi/2} = \pi R^2 \cos^2 \theta \qquad \text{square feet} \quad (8\text{-}69)$$

The volume of the cut-off sphere, V, is found by summing the volumes of the disks, each of area A and thickness

$$dz = d(R \sin \theta) = R \cos \theta \, d\theta \qquad (8\text{-}70)$$

from $z = R - H$ to $z = R$, that is, from $\theta_1 = \sin^{-1}\left[(R - H)/R\right]$ to

$\theta = \pi/2$. This gives

$$V = \int_{\theta_1}^{\pi/2} \pi R^2 \cos^2 \theta (R \cos \theta \, d\theta) = \pi R^3 \int_{\theta_1}^{\pi/2} (1 - \sin^2 \theta) \cos \theta \, d\theta$$

$$= \pi R^3 \left[\sin \theta - \frac{\sin^3 \theta}{3} \right]_{\theta_1}^{\pi/2}$$

$$= \pi R^3 \left[1 - \frac{1}{3} - \left(\frac{R - H}{R} \right) + \frac{1}{3} \left(\frac{R - H}{R} \right)^3 \right]$$

or $$V = \frac{\pi H^2}{3} (3R - H) \qquad \text{cubic feet} \qquad (8\text{-}71)$$

If $H = R$, the volume becomes a half-sphere, so that Eq. 8-71 gives $\tfrac{4}{3}\pi R^3$ for the volume of the complete sphere.

As a second problem, we shall find the volume that is common to two identical cylinders, of radius R feet, whose axes intersect each other at right angles (Fig. 8-5). As the simplest way to define the volume elements for this problem, we shall assume the volume to be made up of square slices, each of thickness dz, with sides equal to $2R \cos \theta$, as shown in the figure. The area of the square slice is evidently equal to $4R^2 \cos^2 \theta$, so that the total volume of the common portions of the two cylinders is

$$V = \int_{-R}^{R} 4R^2 \cos^2 \theta \, dz \qquad \text{cubic feet} \qquad (8\text{-}72)$$

From Fig. 8-5A, $z = R \sin \theta$ and $dz = R \cos \theta \, d\theta$, so that Eq. 8-72 becomes

$$V = \int_{-\pi/2}^{\pi/2} 4R^3 \cos^3 \theta \, d\theta = 4R^3 \int_{-\pi/2}^{\pi/2} (1 - \sin^2 \theta) \cos \theta \, d\theta$$

$$= 4R^3 \left[\sin \theta - \frac{\sin^3 \theta}{3} \right]_{-\pi/2}^{\pi/2} = \frac{16R^3}{3} \qquad \text{cubic feet} \qquad (8\text{-}73)$$

The volume can be visualized as that of a sphere enclosed in two circumscribed cylinders at right angles. The volume of the sphere enclosed in the intersection volume is $\tfrac{4}{3}\pi R^3$, by Eq. 8-71. The area of each of the square slices (Fig. 8-5B) is $4/\pi$ times the area of its inscribed circle. Therefore, the area of the volume common to the cylinders must be equal to

$$\frac{4}{\pi} \left(\frac{4}{3} \pi R^3 \right) = \frac{16R^3}{3}$$

which checks Eq. 8-73.

This example illustrates the point that it is all-important to select the volume elements used in the integration in such a way that they can be visualized easily. Often, in this way, the answer can be found by inspection, or by mental arithmetic.[1]

Simpson's one-third rule, Eq. 8-44, is very useful in calculating the volumes of regular geometric forms, such as cones, pyramids, spheres,

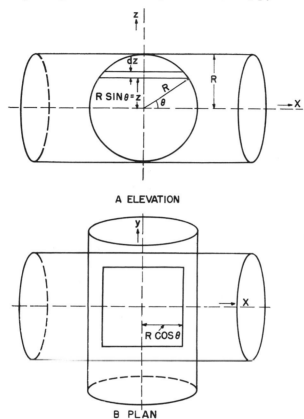

A ELEVATION

B PLAN

Fig. 8-5 Intersection of two equal cylinders.

etc. When used for this purpose, the rule is called the *prismoidal formula:*

$$\text{Volume} = \frac{T + 4M + B}{6} \times \text{height} \qquad (8\text{-}74)$$

where T = area of top section
M = area of center section
B = area of bottom section

---

[1] Dr. Steinmetz is said to have solved this problem in his head, in about two minutes, one evening at a dinner party.

One evening while waiting for a concert to begin, Professor R. M. Sutton and two of his friends also solved the problem, in their heads, by both of the above methods.

For example, the volume of a tapered right circular cylinder of height h, with top and bottom radii equal to a and b, respectively, is

$$V = \frac{\pi h}{6}\,[a^2 + (a + b)^2 + b^2] = \frac{\pi h}{3}\,(a^2 + ab + b^2)$$

and the volume of a sphere of radius R is

$$V = \frac{\pi(2R)}{6}\,(0 + 4\pi R^2 + 0) = \frac{4\pi R^3}{3}$$

which checks the values found above.

8-11 The Calculus. The procedures of taking derivatives, of integrating, and of dealing with the relations so found constitute the branch of mathematics called the *calculus*. The term has not been used up to this point because the procedures covered in this chapter are logical extensions of the arithmetic processes of taking sums and differences, so that any division between this chapter and the earlier ones is artificial.

The principal use for calculus in engineering comes from the fact that the equations which describe the performance of a great many machines and systems of apparatus, as well as natural phenomena, include differentials, integrals, or both among their terms. This comes about because speeds, accelerations, and other quantities that are needed to describe the behavior of rapidly moving bodies or changing events are most readily expressed in terms of differentials and integrals of the varying quantities. To solve such equations, it is necessary to employ the theory of differential equations and of integral equations, which have been developed in many mathematical books and treatises. The solution of such equations and the higher branches of the calculus are beyond the scope of this book, except for the brief treatment given in Chap. 12.

In Chap. 1 we dealt with arithmetic, in Chap. 2 trigonometry, in Chap. 3 complex quantities, and in Chap. 4 algebra; in this chapter we have covered the elements of calculus, and in Chap. 13 we shall consider probability. A little of what is called *vector analysis*, and also some analytic geometry, have been included in Chaps. 3, 4, and 7. Usually, these different mathematical disciplines are taught in separate courses, and are dealt with in independent books. In this book, the effort is made to unify these separate disciplines under the general title of *Mathematics, for Science and Engineering* since engineers and scientists use all, or nearly all, of them in their daily work and have no reason whatever to separate them into different categories. Whatever the

method may be of arriving at the relations between the several quantities that are pertinent to any problem, the final solution of the problem
will consist in a set of numbers, and, therefore, the final stage of the
problem solution is almost always an arithmetical process. Hence, it is
always necessary to look beyond and through the beauty, or the
elegance, or the logic of any mathematical process to its arithmetic
interpretation. It is for this reason that so much emphasis is placed in
this book on various ways of visualizing, approximating, and solving
numerically all the equations that are considered.

PROBLEMS

1. Show that the rate of change of the area of a circle with respect
to the radius is equal to the circumference of the circle.
Differentiate the following (find dy/dx):

2. $y = 2x^3 + 4x$

3. $y = \dfrac{1}{x}$

4. $y = \dfrac{x}{1 + x}$

5. $y = \sqrt{x^2 + 1}$

6. $y = 3x^3 + 2x^2 + x$

7. $y = \dfrac{1}{\sqrt{30 - x}}$

8. $y = \dfrac{1}{x} - \dfrac{3}{x^3}$

9. $y = \dfrac{x + \sqrt{x} + \sqrt{2}}{\sqrt{x^3}}$

10. $y = \sin(\ln x)$

11. $y = x^{\exp x}$

12. $y = \cos^4 2x$

13. $y = \dfrac{x}{2}\sqrt{x^2 + a^2} + \dfrac{a^2}{2}\ln(x + \sqrt{x^2 + a^2})$

Evaluate the following indefinite integrals:

14. $\displaystyle\int x^5(2 - x^{-2})\,dx$

15. $\displaystyle\int (3m - 2)^3\,dm$

16. $\displaystyle\int (2 - x)(\sqrt{x} + 3)\,dx$

17. $\displaystyle\int \dfrac{dx}{3x - 1}$

18. $\displaystyle\int \dfrac{7x^3}{2 - 7x^4}\,dx$

19. $\displaystyle\int \sin x \cos x\,dx$

20. $\displaystyle\int \sin^2 x \cos x\,dx$

21. $\displaystyle\int \dfrac{dx}{\sqrt{3 - 2x}}$

22. $\displaystyle\int \sin^2 \dfrac{x}{2} \cos \dfrac{x}{2}\,dx$

23. $\displaystyle\int \dfrac{x^2\,dx}{(3 + x^3)^2}$

24. $\int y^{\frac{2}{3}}(2y^{\frac{5}{3}} - 4)^{\frac{1}{3}} dy$

27. $\int \frac{dx}{\ln e^x}$

25. $\int \frac{\sin \phi}{\cos^4 \phi} d\phi$

28. $\int \frac{dx}{(1 + x^2) \tan^{-1} x}$

26. $\int \frac{\ln x \, dx}{x(1 - \ln^2 x)}$

29. Given

$$f(x) = 3 \frac{d^2y}{dx^2} - 2 \frac{dy}{dx} + y$$

Show that if $y = \cos x$, $f(\pi/4) = 0$.

Expand the functions in infinite series of powers of $(x - x_0)$:

30. $f(x) = e^{2x}$ $x_0 = 1$ **32.** $f(x) = xe^x$ $x_0 = 1$

31. $f(x) = \cos x$ $x_0 = -\frac{\pi}{3}$ **33.** $f(x) = \sin x$ $x_0 = \frac{\pi}{6}$

Evaluate the integrals using the appropriate Simpson rule:

34. $\int_0^{1.2} \frac{dx}{\sqrt{\cos x}}$ Use $h = 0.6$.

35. $\int_0^{1.6} \cos (\cos x) \, dx$ Use $h = 0.4$.

36. Find the volume in cubic feet of a vein of coal that is 12 miles long and has a cross-sectional area equal to the area between $y = 10 \sin x$ and $y = 3 \sin x$ for $0 \leq x \leq \pi$, where y is given in feet.

Bibliography

1. Bacon, H. M.: "Differential and Integral Calculus," 2d ed., McGraw-Hill Book Company, New York, 1955.
2. Dresden, Arnold: "Introduction to the Calculus," Holt, Rinehart and Winston, Inc., New York, 1940.
3. Franklin, Philip: "A Treatise on Advanced Calculus," John Wiley & Sons, Inc., New York, 1940.
4. Franklin, Philip: "Differential and Integral Calculus," McGraw-Hill Book Company, New York, 1950.
5. Nelson, Alfred L., et al.: "Calculus," D. C. Heath and Company, Boston, 1946.
6. Palmer, C. I., and C. E. Stewart: "Practical Calculus," McGraw-Hill Book Company, New York, 1955.
7. Phillips, H. B.: "Analytic Geometry and Calculus," 2d ed., John Wiley & Sons, Inc., New York, 1946.
8. Whitaker, E. T., and G. N. Watson: "A Course of Modern Analysis," The Macmillan Company, New York, 1943.
9. Wilson, E. B.: "Advanced Calculus," Ginn and Company, Boston, 1912.
10. Wylie, C. R., Jr.: "Calculus," McGraw-Hill Book Company, New York, 1953.

Chapter 9 FUNCTIONS

9-1 The Use of Functions. The steps in solving a typical problem of physics or engineering with two or more variables are:

1. Select and define the principal quantities with which the problem is concerned, such as x for distance, y for pressure, t for time, etc., preferably using per unit values throughout (Sec. 3-10).

2. Write down the known relations between x, y, t, etc., in the form of equations, $F(x,y,t, \ldots) = 0$, and check them by dimensional analysis (Sec. 3-9).

3. Solve these equations, reducing them finally to simple forms that enable any one quantity to be calculated in terms of the others, such as $y = f(x,t, \ldots)$.

Technical mathematics usually is required for the third step only. The relations obtained often take the form of functions such as $\sin x$, e^x, etc., which have characteristic properties and may be taken from published tables of numerical values. The engineer should be familiar with the most useful of these functions and should understand how other functions are derived.

The solutions found by the above procedure are *functions* (see Sec. 1-16), or general formulas, expressing y in terms of other quantities, whereas the solutions of algebraic equations considered in Chap. 4 are numerical values of y corresponding to a particular value of x. These formula solutions are general and may be represented by curves, whereas the *numerical solutions* are specific and represent single points on a graph.

The solution, or root, of an algebraic equation of any finite order, with rational coefficients, is called an *algebraic* number. Other numbers, such as e or π, which do not satisfy any algebraic equation with rational coefficients, are called *transcendental* numbers. Any non-algebraic equation containing such functions as $\sin x$, $\cos x$, e^x, etc., is called a *transcendental equation*. The formula solutions of differential equations considered in this chapter generally are *transcendental*

[203]

functions. In this book, they are usually expressed in the form of infinite power series and may be designated by special symbols or abbreviations.

While a great many functions, such as those named for Bessel, Legendre, Hankel, etc., are available in the form of tables and are widely used by mathematicians and physicists, the engineer has only occasional and limited use for them. The engineer can generally obtain the results that he needs by approximate methods, using only the familiar trigonometric and hyperbolic functions and infinite series expressions.

9-2 Algebraic Functions. The most general algebraic expression of the relations between two variables, as may be found in the second step of problem solution above,

$$\begin{aligned} F(x,y) = (a_{00} + a_{01}x + a_{02}x^2 + \cdots) \\ + (a_{10} + a_{11}x + a_{12}x^2 + \cdots)y + (a_{20} + a_{21}x + a_{22}x^2 + \cdots)y^2 \\ + \cdots + (+a_{n0} + a_{n1}x + a_{n2}x^2 + \cdots)y^n = 0 \quad (9\text{-}1) \end{aligned}$$

defines y as an *implicit algebraic function*. It relates y and x, so that to every value of x there correspond n values of y and to every value of y there correspond m values of x, if m is the exponent of the highest power of x in Eq. 9-1.

When Eq. 9-1 is solved for y (which usually cannot be carried out in finite form), the *explicit algebraic function*,

$$y = f(x) \qquad\qquad (9\text{-}2)$$

is obtained. Solving Eq. 9-1 for x expressed as a function of y gives the *inverse relation* of Eq. 9-2, that is,

$$x = f_1(y) \qquad\qquad (9\text{-}3)$$

In all these algebraic functions, x and y are assumed to be directed numbers, or complex quantities, that is

$$\begin{aligned} x = x_1 + jx_2 \\ y = y_1 + jy_2 \end{aligned} \qquad\qquad (9\text{-}4)$$

and likewise for the coefficients, $a_{00}, a_{01}, \ldots, a_{nm}$.

If all the coefficients a are real, and x is real, the corresponding n values of y either are real or are pairs of conjugate complex quantities: $y_1 + jy_2$ and $y_1 - jy_2$.

9-3 Rational Functions. If $n = 1$, Eq. 9-1 can be solved directly for y, giving the *rational function*,

$$y = \frac{a_{00} + a_{01}x + a_{02}x^2 + \cdots}{a_{10} + a_{11}x + a_{12}x^2 + \cdots} \qquad\qquad (9\text{-}5)$$

And, if a_{11}, a_{12}, . . . are all zero, so that the denominator of Eq. 9-5 contains no x, the *integer function*,

$$y = -a_0 + a_1x + a_2x^2 + \cdots + a_mx^m \qquad (9\text{-}6)$$

is obtained.

For $n = 2$, Eq. 9-1 can be solved for y as a quadratic equation, thereby giving, from Eq. 4-10,

$$y = -\frac{(a_{10}+a_{11}x+ \cdots)\pm \sqrt{\begin{aligned}&(a_{10} + a_{11}x + \cdots)^2\\&-4(a_{20}+a_{21}x+ \cdots)(a_{00}+a_{01}x+ \cdots)\end{aligned}}}{2(a_{20} + a_{21}x + a_{22}x^2 + \cdots)}$$

$$(9\text{-}7)$$

In this case, therefore, the explicit form, Eq. 9-2, of Eq. 9-1 contains a square root.

For $n > 2$, the explicit form $y = f(x)$ either becomes very complicated for $n = 3$, or 4, or cannot be expressed in finite form. However, y is still a function of x and can be calculated by successive approximations, as outlined in Sec. 4-3.

To find the numerical value y_1, which corresponds to a value of $x = x_1$, we may first substitute x_1 for x in Eq. 9-1, then estimate, or guess, the approximate value of the solution, y_1, and employ Taylor's theorem (Eq. 8-59) to find a second approximation. As an aid in making this first estimate of y_1, we may at first neglect all but the largest terms containing y, and find y by an equation such as Eq. 9-5 from this simplified form of the equation.

If $h = y_1 - y$ is the difference between the true value of the solution y_1 and the initially chosen value, or estimate, y, we have by Eq. 8-59

$$F(x_1,y_1) = F(x_1,y) + h\frac{dF(x_1,y)}{dy} + \frac{h^2}{2!}\frac{d^2F(x_1,y)}{dy^2} + \cdots = 0 \quad (9\text{-}8)$$

Since h is presumably small, we may neglect the higher orders of h in Eq. 9-8, and find

$$h = -\frac{F(x_1,y)}{dF(x_1,y)/dy} \qquad (9\text{-}9)$$

Adding this value of h to the assumed value of y, we obtain a new value $y_2 = y + h$. Putting y_2 in place of y in Eq. 9-8 and solving again for a new value h_1 by Eq. 9-9,

$$h_1 = -\frac{F(x_1,y_2)}{dF(x_1,y_2)/dy} \qquad (9\text{-}10)$$

we obtain a second approximation to the true value, $y_2 + h_1$. The process is repeated until sufficient accuracy is obtained, when h_1 is found to be negligibly small in comparison with y_2.

This process is practically the same as that outlined in Sec. 4-3 for the solution of algebraic equations. By Eq. 9-8, however, infinite series expressions can be developed to express $F(x_1,y_1)$ in the neighborhood of any chosen values of x_1 and y_1, so that it is a more general procedure.

9-4   Abelian Functions.   It is often desired to know the integrals of algebraic functions, such as in Eq. 9-2, that are found in solving Eq. 9-1. In the general case, these are called *Abelian integrals*, and the functions they give rise to are called *Abelian functions*. The trigonometric and exponential functions are included in the general class of Abelian functions.

Thus, from Eq. 9-2, we have, if $f(x)$ is an algebraic function,

$$z = \int f(x)\,dx \tag{9-11}$$

as the general Abelian integral, and its inverse function,

$$x = \phi(z) \tag{9-12}$$

as the general Abelian function.

If $n = 1$ in Eq. 9-1, the function $y = f(x)$ in Eq. 9-11 becomes the rational function, Eq. 9-5, or its special case, the integer function, Eq. 9-6.

The function in Eq. 9-6 can be integrated by powers of x. The right-hand member of Eq. 9-5 can be resolved into partial fractions (Eq. 8-53), thereby leading to integrals of such forms as

$$\int x^m\,dx \tag{9-13a}$$

$$\int \frac{dx}{x-a} \tag{9-13b}$$

$$\int \frac{dx}{(x-a)^m} \tag{9-13c}$$

$$\int \frac{dx}{x^2+a^2} \tag{9-13d}$$

Integrals 9-13a and c give rational functions, while b gives the logarithmic function $\log(x-a)$, and d gives the arc function $\tan^{-1}(x/a)$. Comparing b and d shows that the arc functions are logarithmic functions with quadrature (j) arguments. In its simplest form, the *logarithmic function*, or the logarithmic integral, is given by putting $a = 0$ in Eq. 9-13b:

$$z = \int \frac{dx}{x} = \ln x \tag{9-14}$$

and has for its inverse function the *exponential function,*

$$x = e^z = \exp z \qquad (9\text{-}15)$$

This last is expressed by the infinite series,

$$e^z = 1 + z + \frac{z^2}{2!} + \frac{z^3}{3!} + \frac{z^4}{4!} + \cdots \qquad (8\text{-}24)$$

as seen in Sec. 8-2.

9-5 Trigonometric and Hyperbolic Functions. If $n - 2$ in Eq. 9-1, the integral (Eq. 9-11) contains a square root of some power of x, as in Eq. 9-7. The first part of Eq. 9-7 is a rational function, already discussed. There remains the integral

$$z = \int \frac{\sqrt{b_0 + b_1 x + b_2 x^2 + \cdots + b_m x^m}}{c_0 + c_1 x + c_2 x^2 + \cdots} \, dx \qquad (9\text{-}16)$$

which leads to other important functions.

For $m = 1$ or 2, Eq. 9-16 becomes

$$z = \int \frac{\sqrt{b_0 + b_1 x + b_2 x^2}}{c_0 + c_1 x + c_2 x^2 + \cdots} \, dx \qquad (9\text{-}17)$$

By substituting new variables, resolving into partial fractions, and separating out the rational functions, Eq. 9-17 may be reduced to cases of the basic form

$$z = \int \frac{dx}{\sqrt{1 + x^2}} \qquad (9\text{-}18)$$

If the sign under the radical is minus, we have

$$z = \int \frac{dx}{\sqrt{1 - x^2}} = \text{arc sin } x \qquad (9\text{-}19)$$

and, for the inverse function, we obtain the familiar *trigonometric functions*

$$x = \sin z$$
$$\sqrt{1 - x^2} = \cos z \qquad (9\text{-}20)$$

The trigonometric functions may be expressed as infinite series:

$$\sin z = z - \frac{z^3}{3!} + \frac{z^5}{5!} - \frac{z^7}{7!} + \cdots \qquad (3\text{-}25)$$

$$\cos z = 1 - \frac{z^2}{2!} + \frac{z^4}{4!} - \frac{z^6}{6!} + \cdots \qquad (3\text{-}26)$$

as seen in Sec. 8-8.

If the sign under the radical in Eq. 9-18 is plus, we have

$$z = \int \frac{dx}{\sqrt{1 + x^2}} = -\ln\left(\sqrt{1 + x^2} - x\right) = \text{arc sinh } x \quad (9\text{-}21)$$

and for the inverse function we obtain the *hyperbolic functions*

$$x = \frac{e^z - e^{-z}}{2} = \sinh z \qquad \text{(hyperbolic sine)} \qquad (9\text{-}22)$$

$$\sqrt{1 + x^2} = \frac{e^z + e^{-z}}{2} = \cosh z \qquad \text{(hyperbolic cosine)} \quad (9\text{-}23)$$

When the series expansion given in Eq. 8-24 is substituted for e^z in Eqs. 9-22 and 9-23, the hyperbolic functions may be expressed in infinite series:

$$\sinh z = z + \frac{z^3}{3!} + \frac{z^5}{5!} + \frac{z^7}{7!} + \cdots \qquad (9\text{-}24)$$

$$\cosh z = 1 + \frac{z^2}{2!} + \frac{z^4}{4!} + \frac{z^6}{6!} + \cdots \qquad (9\text{-}25)$$

and, by the methods of Sec. 8-8,

$$\tanh x = x - \frac{x^3}{3} + \frac{2x^5}{15} - \frac{17x^5}{315} + \cdots \qquad (9\text{-}26)$$

A table of hyperbolic functions is given in Appendix F. The close similarity between the trigonometric and hyperbolic functions, indicated by comparing their infinite series forms (Eq. 3-25 with Eq. 9-24, 3-26 with 9-25, and 8-62 with 9-26), is illustrated by comparing Fig. 9-1 for the hyperbola with Fig. 2-1 for the circle.

In Fig. 9-1, the arc *APB* represents the rectangular hyperbola, whose equation is

$$x^2 - y^2 = a^2 \qquad (9\text{-}27)$$

where a is the shortest radius to the arc, or the value of r when $y = 0$. The hyperbolic angle, u, is the ratio of the length of the arc *AP* to the radius $r = OP$. The hyperbolic sine is the ratio of the vertical projection *PM* of the radius to the initial value a and the hyperbolic cosine is the ratio of the horizontal projection *OM* to a. The hyperbolic tangent is the ratio of *PM* to *OM*, or of the sinh to the cosh. Thus in Fig. 9-1

$$\sinh u = \frac{y}{a} \qquad \cosh u = \frac{x}{a} \qquad \tanh u = \frac{\sinh u}{\cosh u} = \frac{y}{x} \qquad (9\text{-}28)$$

From Eqs. 9-27 and 9-28, we find

$$a^2(\cosh^2 u - \sinh^2 u) = x^2 - y^2 = a^2$$

so that
$$\cosh^2 u - \sinh^2 u = 1 \tag{9-29}$$

Evidently, as the hyperbolic angle u increases indefinitely, x and y approach equality, so that $\sinh u$ becomes equal to $\cosh u$, and $\tanh u$ approaches unity.

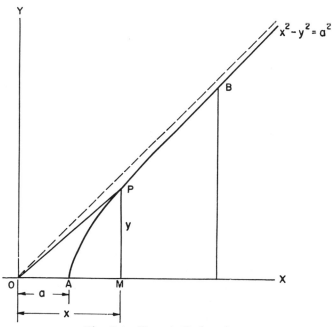

Fig. 9-1 Hyperbolic functions.

The length of the arc AP is the integral of the differential of the arc length from $x = a$ to $x = x$. The differential of the arc is

$$\sqrt{dx^2 + dy^2} = dx \sqrt{1 + \left(\frac{dy}{dx}\right)^2}$$

But from Eq. 9-27

$$2x\, dx - 2y\, dy = 0 \qquad \text{or} \qquad \frac{dy}{dx} = \frac{x}{y}$$

Therefore the differential arc length is

$$\frac{\sqrt{x^2 + y^2}}{y}\, dx$$

The radius OP is $\sqrt{x^2 + y^2}$, so that the ratio of the differential arc to the radius, or differential of the hyperbolic angle, is simply dx/y, and the hyperbolic angle u is the integral of this ratio from $x = a$ to $x = x$, or, from Eq. 9-27,

$$u = \int_a^x \frac{dx}{y} = \int_a^x \frac{dx}{\sqrt{x^2 - a^2}} = \ln \frac{x + \sqrt{x^2 - a^2}}{a} \qquad (9\text{-}30)$$

Therefore

$$e^u = \frac{x + \sqrt{x^2 - a^2}}{a} \qquad \text{or} \qquad \left(e^u - \frac{x}{a}\right)^2 = \frac{x^2}{a^2} - 1$$

giving

$$e^{2u} = \frac{2xe^u}{a} - 1$$

Dividing through by $2e^u$, we obtain the previously found equation for cosh u:

$$\frac{x}{a} = \frac{e^u + e^{-u}}{2} = \cosh u \qquad (9\text{-}23)$$

9-6 Relations between Exponential, Trigonometric, and Hyperbolic Functions. From the preceding, it follows that the three kinds of functions—exponential, trigonometric, and hyperbolic —are so related to each other that any one of them can be expressed in terms of any other. Thus, when complex variables, or a directed number $x + jy$, are used instead of merely x, one type of function is sufficient. For this purpose, the exponential function would naturally be chosen.

Since such functions of complex variables can be alternatively expressed as functions of real variables, tables of the functions of real variables only are sufficient for calculation purposes.

For convenience, and to show the analogies that exist, these functions are plotted in Fig. 9-2, and the relations between them are here tabulated:

$$\begin{aligned}
e^{\pm u} &= \cosh u \pm \sinh u = \cos ju \mp j \sin ju \\
e^{\pm jv} &= \cos v \pm j \sin v = \cosh jv \pm \sinh jv \\
e^{u \pm jv} &= e^u(\cos v \pm j \sin v) = e^u(\cosh jv \pm \sinh jv)
\end{aligned} \qquad (9\text{-}31)$$

$$\sin u = -j \sinh ju = -j \frac{e^{ju} - e^{-ju}}{2}$$

$$\sin jv = j \sinh v = j \frac{e^v - e^{-v}}{2} \qquad (9\text{-}32)$$

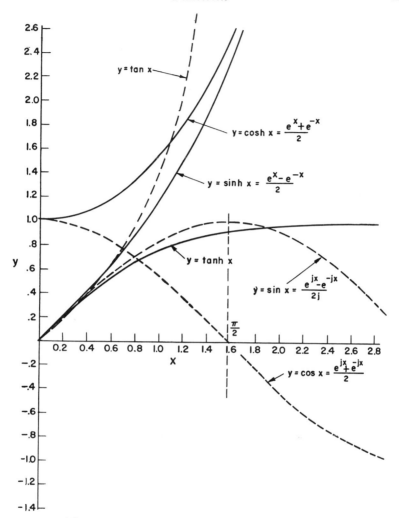

Fig. 9-2 Trigonometric and hyperbolic functions.

$$\sin (u \pm jv) = \sin u \cosh v \pm j \cos u \sinh v$$

$$= \left(\frac{e^v + e^{-v}}{2}\right) \sin u \pm j \left(\frac{e^v - e^{-v}}{2}\right) \cos u$$

$$\cos u = \cosh ju = \frac{e^{ju} + e^{-ju}}{2}$$

$$\cos jv = \cosh v = \frac{e^{jv} + e^{-jv}}{2} \tag{9-33}$$

$$\cos (u \pm jv) = \cos u \cosh v \mp j \sin u \sinh v$$

$$= \frac{e^v + e^{-v}}{2} \cos u \mp j \frac{e^v - e^{-v}}{2} \sin u$$

$$\sinh u = \frac{e^u - e^{-u}}{2} = -j \sin ju$$

$$\sinh jv = j \sin v = \frac{e^{jv} - e^{-jv}}{2} \tag{9-34}$$

$$\sinh (u \pm jv) = \sinh u \cos v \pm j \cosh u \sin v$$

$$= \frac{e^u - e^{-u}}{2} \cos v \pm j \frac{e^u + e^{-u}}{2} \sin v$$

$$\cosh u = \frac{e^u + e^{-u}}{2} = \cos ju$$

$$\cosh jv = \cos v = \frac{e^{jv} + e^{-jv}}{2} \tag{9-35}$$

$$\cosh (u \pm jv) = \cosh u \cos v \pm j \sinh u \sin v$$

$$= \frac{e^u + e^{-u}}{2} \cos v \pm j \frac{e^u - e^{-u}}{2} \sin v$$

$$\sinh (u \pm jv) = j \sin (\pm v - ju) = \pm j \sin (v \mp ju)$$
$$\cosh (u \pm jv) = \cos (v \mp ju) \tag{9-36}$$

$$\cos^2 u + \sin^2 u = 1 = \cosh^2 u - \sinh^2 u$$
$$\cos^2 u - \sin^2 u = \cos 2u \tag{9-37}$$
$$\cosh^2 u + \sinh^2 u = \cosh 2u$$

9-7   Elliptic Functions.   If $m = 3$ or 4 in Eq. 9-16, it becomes

$$z = \int \frac{\sqrt{b_0 + b_1 x + b_2 x^2 + b_3 x^3 + b_4 x^4}}{c_0 + c_1 x + c_2 x^2 + \cdots} dx \tag{9-38}$$

which, save for special cases, cannot be integrated by rational, logarithmic, or arc functions, but gives a new class of functions, the *elliptic integrals*, and their inverse forms, the *elliptic functions*. These bear relations to the ellipse similar to those which the trigonometric functions bear to the circle and the hyperbolic functions do to the equilateral hyperbola.

The general integral in Eq. 9-38 can be expressed as combinations of elementary functions and the three kinds of elliptic integrals·

$$u = \int \frac{dx}{\sqrt{x(1 - x)(1 - c^2x)}}$$

$$u_1 = \int \frac{x \, dx}{\sqrt{x(1 - x)(1 - c^2x)}} \qquad (9\text{-}39)$$

$$u_2 = \int \frac{dx}{(x - b) \sqrt{x(1 - x)(1 - c^2x)}}$$

(The three kinds may be expressed in several alternative forms.)

The inverse functions associated with the first of these elliptic integrals are the elliptic functions:

$$\sqrt{x} = \sin \operatorname{am} (u,c)$$
$$\sqrt{1 - x} = \cos \operatorname{am} (u,c) \qquad (9\text{-}40)$$
$$\sqrt{1 - c^2x} = \Delta \operatorname{am} (u,c)$$

known, respectively, as sine amplitude, cosine amplitude, and delta amplitude.

Elliptic functions are more general than the similar trigonometric functions, since they depend on two variables, x and c, instead of x alone. They are *doubly periodic*. The trigonometric functions repeat the same values after every change of the angle by 2π; that is, $\sin (x + 2\pi) = \sin x$, etc. The elliptic functions have two periods, p_1 and p_2 (not both real), that is,

$$\sin \operatorname{am} (u + mp_1 + np_2, c) = \sin \operatorname{am} (u,c), \text{ etc.} \qquad (9\text{-}41)$$

Hence, increasing the variable u by any multiple of either p_1 or p_2 gives the same function values.

The two periods are

$$p_1 = \int_0^1 \frac{dx}{2 \sqrt{x(1 - x)(1 - c^2x)}}$$

$$p_2 = \int_1^{1/c^2} \frac{dx}{2 \sqrt{x(1 - x)(1 - c^2x)}} \qquad (9\text{-}42)$$

If $m > 4$ in Eq. 9-17, similar integrals and their inverse functions appear, more complex than the elliptic functions, and with more than two periodicities. They are called *hyperelliptic integrals* and *hyperelliptic functions*.

Many problems in physics and engineering require elliptic functions for their formal solution. For instance, the time of each swing of a simple pendulum is not constant for different arcs, but only approximately so. If the arc of swing varies, or reaches large values, the time of swing can no longer be assumed constant, but must be calculated by elliptic functions.

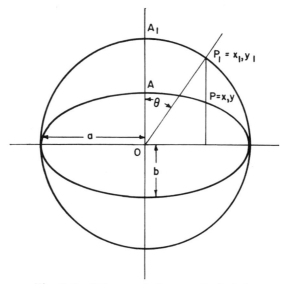

Fig. 9-3   Ellipse and circumscribed circle.

As an example of the use of elliptic integrals, we may determine the length of the arc of an ellipse. The equation of the ellipse in Fig. 9-3 is

$$\frac{x^2}{a^2} + \frac{y^2}{b^2} = 1 \tag{9-43}$$

and that of its circumscribed circle is

$$x^2 + y^2 = a^2 \tag{9-44}$$

The eccentricity, c or ϵ, of the ellipse is given by $c = \epsilon = \sqrt{1 - b^2/a^2}$, whence $b/a = \sqrt{1 - \epsilon^2}$.

To every point P at x,y there corresponds a point P_1 at x_1,y_1 on the circle that has the same abscissa x and angle $\theta = AOP_1$.

The arc of the ellipse from A to P is then

$$L = \int_0^\theta \sqrt{dx^2 + dy^2} = \int_0^\theta \sqrt{1 + \left(\frac{dy}{dx}\right)^2}\, dx \tag{9-45}$$

Let $z = \sin^2 \theta = x^2/a^2$, so that $x = a \sqrt{z}$. From Eq. 9-43

$$y^2 = b^2 \left(1 - \frac{x^2}{a^2}\right) = b^2(1 - z) \tag{9-46}$$

Differentiating Eq. 9-43, we find

$$2b^2 x \, dx + 2a^2 y \, dy = 0$$

or

$$\frac{dy}{dx} = \frac{-b^2 x}{a^2 y} = \frac{-b \sqrt{z}}{a \sqrt{1-z}} = \frac{-\sqrt{z(1-c^2)}}{\sqrt{1-z}} \tag{9-47}$$

Hence

$$L = \int_0^z \sqrt{1 + \frac{z(1-c^2)}{1-z}} \left(\frac{a \, dz}{2 \sqrt{z}}\right)$$

$$= \int_0^z \frac{a(1-c^2 z) \, dz}{2 \sqrt{z(1-z)(1-c^2 z)}} \tag{9-48}$$

This is the difference of two elliptic integrals, u and u_1, of the first and second kinds (Eq. 9-39). The exact solution of such a problem is beyond the scope of this book.

However, the problem can be solved approximately, if the eccentricity of the ellipse, c, is small. In this case, Eq. 9-48 reduces, by Eq. 5-22, to

$$L = a \int_0^z \frac{(2 - c^2 z) \, dz}{4 \sqrt{z(1-z)}} \tag{9-49}$$

Putting $\sin^2 \theta$ for z, we have

$$L = a \int_0^\theta \frac{(2 - c^2 \sin^2 \theta)(2 \sin \theta \cos \theta) \, d\theta}{4 \sin \theta \cos \theta}$$

$$= \frac{a}{2} \int_0^\theta (2 - c^2 \sin^2 \theta) \, d\theta$$

$$= a\theta - \frac{ac^2}{4} \int_0^\theta (1 - \cos 2\theta) \, d\theta$$

$$= a\theta - \frac{ac^2}{8} (2\theta - \sin 2\theta) \quad \text{approximately} \tag{9-50}$$

Elliptic and hyperelliptic functions are especially useful in the exact calculation of the magnetic and electrostatic fields across slotted air gaps. In nearly all practical engineering problems, however, sufficiently accurate solutions may be found by one or another method of approximation, such as that used above, without resorting to the use of these multiply periodic functions.

9-8 The Gamma Function. If, in Eq. 9-11, whether $f(x)$ is algebraic or not, we integrate between definite limits:

$$Z = \int_a^b f(x)\, dx \qquad (9\text{-}51)$$

the definite integral Z is no longer a function of x, but a constant:

$$Z = \phi(b) - \phi(a) \qquad (9\text{-}52)$$

For example, if $f(x) = c(x - n)^2$, then

$$z = \int c(x - n)^2\, dx = \frac{c(x - n)^3}{3} + \text{an integration constant} \qquad (9\text{-}53)$$

and the definite integral is

$$Z = \int_a^b c(x - n)^2\, dx = \frac{c}{3}\left[(b - n)^3 - (a - n)^3\right] \qquad (9\text{-}54)$$

This definite integral does not contain x, but it contains all the constants of the function $f(x)$ and thus is a function of the constants c and n, as well as of a and b.

In this manner, new functions may be derived by definite integrals. Thus, if

$$y = f(x,u,v,\ \dots) \qquad (9\text{-}55)$$

is a function of x, containing the constants u, v, $\dots$, then the definite integral

$$Z = \int_a^b f(x,u,v,\ \dots)\, dx \qquad (9\text{-}56)$$

is not a function of x, but is a function of u, v, $\dots$ and may be a new function.

For instance, let

$$y = e^{-x}x^{u-1} \qquad (9\text{-}57)$$

Then the integral

$$f(u) = \int_0^\infty e^{-x}x^{u-1}\, dx = \Gamma(u) \qquad (9\text{-}58)$$

is a new function of u, called the *gamma function*.

Some of its properties may be derived by partial integration. In Eq. 8-50, put $x = e^{-x}$, $y = x^u/u$, when it becomes the same as Eq. 9-58, or

$$\Gamma(u) = \int_0^\infty e^{-x}x^{u-1}\, dx = \left.\frac{e^{-x}x^u}{u}\right]_0^\infty + \int_0^\infty \frac{e^{-x}x^u\, dx}{u} \qquad (9\text{-}59)$$

Since the first term on the right side of the equation is zero at both limits, it drops out, and Eq. 9-59 reduces to

$$\Gamma(u) = \frac{1}{u}\Gamma(u + 1) \qquad \text{or} \qquad u\Gamma(u) = \Gamma(u + 1) \qquad (9\text{-}60)$$

If u and n are positive integers, and $n < u$, this gives

$$\Gamma(u) = (u - 1)(u - 2) \cdots (u - n)\Gamma(u - n) \qquad (9\text{-}61)$$

For $u = 1$, Eq. 9-58 reduces to

$$\Gamma(1) = \int_0^\infty e^{-x}\, dx = -e^{-x}\Big]_0^\infty = 1 \qquad (9\text{-}62)$$

Hence, for any positive integer, u,

$$\Gamma(u) = (u - 1)! \qquad (9\text{-}63)$$

so that the gamma function of an integer u is simply the factorial of $u - 1$, as given in Eq. 3-22.

Tables of the gamma function are available. It is interesting to note that $\Gamma(0) = \infty$ and $\Gamma(\tfrac{1}{2}) = \sqrt{\pi}$.

9-9 Other Functions. Numerous other functions have been derived for solving mathematical problems, of astronomy, acoustics, etc., such as the Bessel, Hankel, Legendre, theta, etc., functions. Tables of values of many such functions are available.

Unless the problems to be solved are of unusual extent or complexity, it is generally best for an engineer to seek the solution by developing the explicit analytic function (Eq. 9-2) in infinite series and performing any required integrations term by term.

For example, in the study of the propagation through space of the magnetic field of a current-carrying conductor, as in radio, lightning protection, etc., new functions are required, each of which can be derived by straightforward integration of an infinite power series.

Let $i = f(t)$ be the current in the conductor, as function of the time t. The magnetic field at a distance x from the conductor is proportional to the current, but lags behind it by the time $t_1 = x/c$, where c is the velocity of propagation of the field (speed of light). As the field intensity is inversely proportional to the distance, it is

$$H = \frac{f(t - x/c)}{x} \qquad (9\text{-}64)$$

and the total magnetic flux linking the conductor is proportional to

$$\phi = \int H\, dx = \int \frac{f(t - x/c)}{x}\, dx \qquad (9\text{-}65)$$

If the current is alternating, or varies sinusoidally in time, so that $f(t) = \sin at$, the numerator of Eq. 9-65 at a given instant takes a form such as

$$u = \int \frac{\sin x}{x}\, dx \qquad \text{or} \qquad v = \int \frac{\cos x}{x}\, dx \qquad (9\text{-}66)$$

If the current is unidirectional, rising as an exponential function of the time, Eq. 9-65 leads to the function

$$w = \int \frac{e^x\, dx}{x} \qquad (9\text{-}67)$$

To solve these equations, we substitute for $\sin x$, $\cos x$, and e^x the equivalent infinite series from Eqs. 3-23, 3-25, and 3-26 and integrate term by term. Thus

$$\int \frac{\sin x}{x}\, dx = x - \frac{x^3}{3(3!)} + \frac{x^5}{5(5!)} - \frac{x^7}{7(7!)} + \cdots \qquad (9\text{-}68a)$$

$$\int \frac{\cos x}{x}\, dx = \ln x - \frac{x^2}{2(2!)} + \frac{x^4}{4(4!)} - \frac{x^6}{6(6!)} + \cdots \qquad (9\text{-}68b)$$

$$\int \frac{e^x}{x}\, dx = \ln x + x + \frac{x^2}{2(2!)} + \frac{x^3}{3(3!)} + \frac{x^4}{4(4!)} + \cdots$$

$$(9\text{-}68c)$$

The function $\int_x^\infty (\cos t/t)\, dt$ frequently occurs in studies of the diffraction of sound and light. Tables of its values have been calculated under the name "integral cosine," or Ci x. The fact that this simple expression Ci x represents the unusual series (Eq. 9-68b) shows how slender the distinction is between such familiar functions as $\sin x$ or e^x and many other functions known in the form of series that are regarded as abstruse just because they have unfamiliar names.

It is often quicker and simpler to calculate the few values needed for a particular problem by such direct procedures as the above, rather than to "study up" on little-used mathematical functions.

9-10   The Unit Function.   Sudden changes, or discontinuities, must be considered in many engineering problems. When a bullet strikes the target, or a valve is opened, or a switch is closed, something new happens all of a sudden. The equations that described what was occurring before the change do not describe what happens afterward.

One way to treat such problems is to set up and solve the two sets of equations, before and after, quite independently, taking care to adjust the initial conditions of the later equations to match the terminal conditions of the earlier ones. For example, if we wish to determine the deformation of a spring when a weight is dropped on it from a height, we first consider the falling weight alone, and calculate the velocity it will have when it strikes the spring. Then, knowing the mass and initial velocity of the falling weight, we consider the motion of the spring and weight together, as an independent question.

Another way of treating such problems is to write equations that will be true before as well as after the sudden change, whose solutions describe what happens both before and afterward. For this purpose, it is convenient to make use of the unit function, **1**, or simply H, that was introduced by Oliver Heaviside. In its usual form, the unit function is a time-varying quantity equal to 0 before the time $t = 0$, and to 1 for all values of t greater than 0, as shown in Fig. 9-4a. This is the simplest possible form of expression for a sudden discontinuity, or shock:

$$H = 1 = 0 \qquad \text{if } t < 0$$
$$= 1 \qquad \text{if } t > 0 \tag{9-69}$$

If desired, the discontinuity can be introduced at a time t_0, in which case $H(t,t_0)$ is used instead of H. In this way, several different discontinuities can be taken account of in a single equation.

From the definition of H, its derivative is zero at all points except at $t = 0$, or

$$\frac{dH}{dt} = H' = 0 \qquad \text{if } t \neq 0 \tag{9-70}$$

We regard H' to be such that the integral of H' between ∞ and $- \infty$ is

$$\int_{-\infty}^{\infty} H' \, dt = \int_{-\epsilon}^{\epsilon} H' \, dt = 1 \tag{9-71}$$

where ϵ is a vanishingly small time interval.

However, the integral of H' between $- \infty$ and t (for $t \neq 0$) is to be such that

$$\int_{-\infty}^{t} H' \, dt = H \tag{9-72}$$

And, successive integrals of H are

$$\int_{-\infty}^{t} H \, dt = Ht \tag{9-73}$$

$$\int_{-\infty}^{t} dt \int_{-\infty}^{t} H \, dt = \frac{Ht^2}{2}$$

$$\int_{-\infty}^{t} dt \int_{-\infty}^{t} dt \int_{-\infty}^{t} H \, dt = \frac{Ht^3}{6}, \, \cdots \tag{9-74}$$

By use of the unit function, the separate equations $y = a$ when $0 < t < t_0$ (Fig. 9-4b) and $y = f(t)$ when $t > t_0$ (Fig. 9-4c) can be combined into the single equation (Fig. 9-4d) that is valid for all values of t:

$$y = a[H - H(t,t_0)] + f(t)H(t,t_0) \qquad -\infty < t < \infty \quad (9\text{-}75)$$

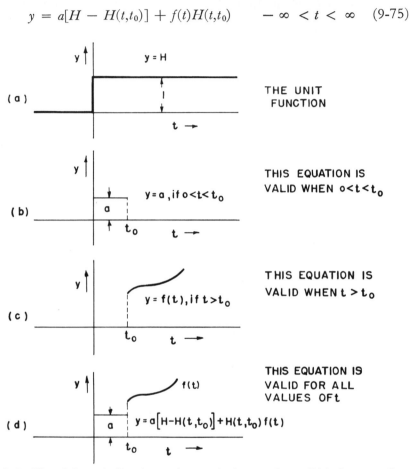

Fig. 9-4 Use of the unit function to form a single equation valid before as well as after a discontinuity.

A great advantage of this use of the unit function is that it eliminates the need for finding integration constants, as discussed in Sec. 8-4, since it makes differentiation and integration completely reversible. For example, if we differentiate Eq. 9-75, and divide by dt, we find

$$\frac{dy}{dt} = y' = a[H' - H'(t,t_0)] + f'(t)H(t,t_0) + f(t)H'(t,t_0) \quad (9\text{-}76)$$

In view of Eq. 9-70, the last term is zero except when $t = t_0$, so that Eq. 9-76 becomes

$$y' = a[H' - H'(t,t_0)] + f'(t)H(t,t_0) + f(t_0)H'(t,t_0) \qquad (9\text{-}77)$$

If we now multiply Eq. 9-77 by dt and integrate, we find

$$\int_{-\infty}^{t} y'\, dt = a \int_{0}^{t} H'\, dt + [f(t_0) - a] \int_{t_0}^{t} H'(t,t_0)\, dt + H(t,t_0) \int_{t_0}^{t} f'(t)\, dt$$
$$= aH + [f(t_0) - a]H(t,t_0) + [f(t) - f(t_0)]H(t,t_0)$$
$$= a[H - H(t,t_0)] + f(t)H(t,t_0) \qquad (9\text{-}78)$$

This is the same as Eq. 9-75, so that

$$\int_{-\infty}^{t} y'\, dt = y$$

contrary to what we found in Sec. 8-4, when H was not used.

H, or $\mathbf{1}$, may be considered to be a function of t, just as $\sin x$ is a function of x. However, the fact that H' becomes infinite at $t = 0$ limits its usefulness, or at any rate requires that quantities depending on H' be treated in accordance with special rules that are based on Eq. 9-71. One of these rules is that any function that is integrated from $-\infty$ must be zero at $-\infty$. Thus, if the first term of Eq. 9-75 were simply a, instead of aH, the value of y would be a, instead of 0, at $t = -\infty$ and the integration in Eq. 9-78 would not be the reverse of differentiation (Eq. 9-76).

The principal use of the unit function is in the solution of problems that involve transients, such as those due to switching of electrical circuits or to sudden impulses (see Sec. 12-6).

PROBLEMS

1. By substituting $y = e^{-x}$ in Eq. 9-58, obtain another form for $\Gamma(n)$:

$$\Gamma(n) = \int_{0}^{1} \left(\ln \frac{1}{y}\right)^{n-1} dy$$

2. Using the results of Prob. 1, show that $\Gamma(1) = 0! = 1$. Evaluate the following integrals in terms of $\Gamma(n)$, $1 < n \leq 2$.

3. $\displaystyle\int_{0}^{\infty} e^{-x^3}\, dx$ **4.** $\displaystyle\int_{0}^{\infty} xe^{-x^3}\, dx$ **5.** $\displaystyle\int_{0}^{\infty} e^{-3x}(x - 2)\, dx$

Perform the following integrations, express each result as an infinite series, and calculate the indicated numerical values.

6. $\displaystyle z = \int \frac{(2x + 8x^3 + 15x^4 + 6x^5)}{(x^2 + 2x^4 + 3x^5 + x^6)}\, dx$ Calculate x when $z = 0.1$.

7. $m = \displaystyle\int \frac{(2n - 2)\, dn}{(n^4 - 4n^3 + 4n^2 + 4)}$
   Calculate n when $m = 0.2$.

8. $y = \displaystyle\int \frac{\sin(-\phi)\, d\phi}{\cos \phi}$
   Calculate ϕ when $y = -0.4$.

9. $y = \displaystyle\int \frac{dm}{\sqrt{-m^2 - 2m}}$
   Calculate m when $y = 0.6$.

10. $y = \displaystyle\int \frac{dx}{\sqrt{x^2 + 2x + 2}}$
   Calculate x when $y = 1$.

11. Find the area that lies between $z = \sinh x$ and $z = \cosh x$, in the region between $x = 0$ and $x = \pi/2$.

12. Prove the identity

$$\frac{(1 + \tanh x)}{(1 - \tanh x)} = \cosh 2x + \sinh 2x$$

13. Find the distance from the origin to the point on the curve $y = \sinh^{-1} x$ at which $x = \frac{4}{3}$.

Calculate the length, $S = \int \sqrt{1 + y'^2}\, dx$, of each of the following curves, between the limits given:

14. $y^2 = x^3$ from $x = 0$ to $x = 4$
15. $y = \ln \cos x$ from $x = 0$ to $x = \pi/4$
16. $y = \ln x$ from $x = 1$ to $x = \sqrt{3}$
17. $y^2 = 4x$ from $y = 0$ to $y = 2$

18. Calculate the approximate value of

$$\int_0^{\pi/2} (\tan x + xe^{2x})\, dx$$

19. Write a single equation that will hold true before and after the following discontinuities:

$$y = 0 \qquad t \leq t_0$$
$$y = \frac{t}{2} - \frac{t_0}{2} \qquad t_0 < t < t_1$$
$$y = b + \sin^2 t \qquad t_1 < t$$

Bibliography

1. Allen, E. S.: "Six-place Tables," 7th ed., McGraw-Hill Book Company, New York, 1947.

2. Allendoerfer, C. B., and C. O. Oakley: "Principles of Mathematics," McGraw-Hill Book Company, New York, 1955.
3. Beckenbach, Edwin F., ed.: "Modern Mathematics for the Engineer," McGraw-Hill Book Company, New York, 1956.
4. Doherty, R. E., and E. G. Keller: "Mathematics of Modern Engineering," vol. I, and vol. II by E. G. Keller, John Wiley & Sons, Inc., New York, 1936 and 1942.
5. Flügge, W.: "Four-place Tables of Transcendental Functions," McGraw-Hill Book Company, New York, 1954.
6. Jahnke, E., and F. Emde: "Tables of Functions with Formulae and Curves," Hafner Publishing Company, Inc., New York, 1938.
7. Lighthill, M. J.: "An Introduction to Fourier Analysis and Generalized Functions," Cambridge University Press, New York, 1958.
8. Smith, J. J., and P. L. Alger: A Derivation of Heaviside's Operational Calculus Based on the Generalized Functions of Schwartz, *Trans. Am. Inst. Elec. Eng.*, vol. 68, pt. 2, pp. 939–944, 1949.
9. Smith, J. J., and P. L. Alger: The Use of the Null-Unit Function in Generalized Integration, *Proc. Intl. Cong. Math.*, vol. 1, 1950, and *Franklin Inst.*, vol. 25, pp. 235–250, March, 1952.
10. Smith, J. J.: Tables of Green's Functions, Fourier Series, and Impulse Functions for Rectangular Coordinate Systems, *Trans. Am. Inst. Elec. Eng.*, vol. 70, pt. 1, pp. 22–30, 1951.
11. Temple, G.: The Theory of Generalized Functions, *Proc. Roy. Soc. (London)*, series A, vol. 228, pp. 175–190, 1955.

Chapter *10* TRIGONOMETRIC SERIES

10-1 Periodic Phenomena. Things that can be measured, such as temperature, distance, speed, voltage, etc., may be considered in three general categories, constant, transient, or periodic. Constant, for instance, is the height of the Empire State Building (over a period of many years) or the terminal voltage of a storage battery (over a period of many hours or days). Transient phenomena occur during a change in conditions, such as a change of current when load is applied to an electric motor or a change of sound level when a whistle is blown. Periodic phenomena, or events that continually repeat themselves, are the rise and fall of the tides, the motion to and fro of the piston in a gasoline engine, the variation of mean daily temperature with the seasons of the year, or the distribution of magnetic flux from the successive poles around the air-gap periphery of an electric generator.

The characteristic of a periodic function $y = f(x)$ is that at constant intervals of the independent variable x, called *cycles* or *periods*, the same values of the function recur. For example, in a 60-cycle alternating-current household supply circuit, the instantaneous value of the voltage at any moment is the same as it will be $\frac{1}{60}$ of a second later and at every like interval thereafter. That is, the voltage is represented by an expression such as $e = E \sin (120\pi t + \theta)$, where t is the time in seconds. Each time t increases by $\frac{1}{60}$ second, the value of $120\pi t$ increases by 2π, and the same value of e recurs.

Most periodic quantities in engineering are functions of time or of space, and as such are single-valued, or *univalent*. That is, for any value of the independent variable, there can be only one value of the function. Or, at any given instant in time, and any given point in space, any physical quantity can have only one numerical value.

The trigonometric functions $\sin \theta$ and $\cos \theta$ also are periodic, having the same values for each 2π increase in θ. By adding together a series of sine and cosine waves, $\sin \theta$, $\sin 2\theta$, $\sin 3\theta$, . . . , we can construct

[224]

new periodic functions. The method for determining the coefficients and frequencies of the sine and cosine functions to form any desired waveshape is called the method of *Fourier series*.

This approximate representation of a given, arbitrary, waveshape, or curve, by the sum of a series of sine and cosine terms, may be compared with the corresponding representation of a curve as the sum of a power series, by means of Taylor's theorem (Eq. 8-59). The Taylor series provides a good fit for a curve over a narrow range, while the Fourier series allows a good fit to be obtained over a much wider range.

10-2 Fourier Series. Any ordinary single-valued (univalent) periodic function

$$y = f(x) \tag{10-1}$$

can be expressed by a Fourier series, or as the sum of an infinite number of sine waves of successively higher orders. Substituting $n\theta$ for x, since we are now dealing with circular functions, this gives

$$y = a_0 + a_1 \cos \theta + a_2 \cos 2\theta + a_3 \cos 3\theta + \cdots + b_1 \sin \theta$$
$$+ b_2 \sin 2\theta + b_3 \sin 3\theta + \cdots \tag{10-2}$$

The sine and cosine terms may be combined by use of Eq. 2-46 or 2-47:

$$y = a_0 + c_1 \cos (\theta - \beta_1) + c_2 \cos (2\theta - \beta_2) + c_3 \cos (3\theta - \beta_3)$$
$$+ \cdots \tag{10-3}$$

or

$$y = a_0 + c_1 \sin (\theta + \gamma_1) + c_2 \sin (2\theta + \gamma_2) + c_3 \sin (3\theta + \gamma_3)$$
$$+ \cdots \tag{10-4}$$

where $c_n = \sqrt{a_n{}^2 + b_n{}^2}$
$\tan \beta_n = b_n/a_n$
$\tan \gamma_n = a_n/b_n$

Equation 10-2 is true because the coefficients a_n and b_n can be uniquely determined by equating Eq. 10-2 to Eq. 10-1 point by point for successive values of x and solving the simultaneous equations so found, or an equivalent procedure. For example, suppose we wish to represent an alternating rectangular wave (Fig. 10-1) by a trigonometric series. The height of the wave is M, and its values repeat for each 2π increase in the independent variable θ. Thus the wave is represented by the discontinuous series

$$\begin{aligned}
y &= M && \text{from } \theta = 0 \text{ to } \theta = \pi \\
y &= -M && \text{from } \theta = \pi \text{ to } \theta = 2\pi \\
y &= M && \text{from } \theta = 2\pi \text{ to } \theta = 3\pi \\
y &= -M && \text{from } \theta = 3\pi \text{ to } \theta = 4\pi, \text{ etc.}
\end{aligned} \tag{10-5}$$

Comparing Eq. 10-5 with its assumed equivalent, Eq. 10-2, it is evident that a_0 is zero because the average height of the wave is zero. Also, all the values of a_n are zero, because y changes sign when θ passes through zero (for each y at θ there is a numerically equal $-y$ at

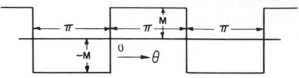

Fig. 10-1   Alternating rectangular wave.

$-\theta$), whereas the cosine terms do not change sign $[\cos \theta = \cos (-\theta)]$. Hence Eq. 10-2 for the rectangular wave of Fig. 10-1 reduces to

$$y = b_1 \sin \theta + b_2 \sin 2\theta + b_3 \sin 3\theta + b_4 \sin 4\theta + \cdots$$
$$+ b_n \sin n\theta + \cdots \quad (10\text{-}6)$$

To evaluate any particular coefficient b_n, we first multiply both sides of Eq. 10-6 by $\sin n\theta \, d\theta$ and then integrate over a half-cycle from 0 to π:

$$\int_0^\pi y \sin n\theta \, d\theta = \int_0^\pi (b_1 \sin \theta \sin n\theta + b_2 \sin 2\theta \sin n\theta + \cdots$$
$$+ b_n \sin^2 n\theta + \cdots) \, d\theta \quad (10\text{-}7)$$

Substituting Eq. 10-5 in the left side of Eq. 10-7 gives

$$\int_0^\pi y \sin n\theta \, d\theta = M \int_0^\pi \sin n\theta \, d\theta = -\frac{M}{n} \cos n\theta \Big]_0^\pi$$
$$= -\frac{M}{n}(-1-1) = \frac{2M}{n} \quad (10\text{-}8)$$

if n is an odd integer. If n is even, however, Eq. 10-8 is equal to zero, since in this case

$$\cos n\theta \Big]_0^\pi = 1 - 1 = 0$$

To evaluate the right side of Eq. 10-7, we make use of Eq. 2-35:

$$\int_0^\pi b_n \sin m\theta \sin n\theta \, d\theta = \frac{b_n}{2} \int_0^\pi [\cos (m-n)\theta - \cos (m+n)\theta] \, d\theta$$
$$= \frac{b_n}{2}\left[\frac{\sin (m-n)\theta}{m-n} - \frac{\sin (m+n)\theta}{m+n} \right]_0^\pi = 0$$
$$\text{if } m \neq n \quad (10\text{-}9)$$

So long as m and n are unequal integers, each term of Eq. 10-9 at each of the limits is the sine of a whole multiple of π and therefore is zero. Hence all the terms on the right side of Eq. 10-7 are zero except the term for which $m = n$. This is, from Eq. 2.44,

$$\int_0^\pi b_n \sin^2 n\theta \, d\theta = \frac{b_n}{2} \int_0^\pi (1 - \cos 2n\theta) \, d\theta$$

$$= \frac{b_n}{2} \left[\theta - \frac{\sin 2n\theta}{2n} \right]_0^\pi = \frac{b_n \pi}{2} \qquad (10\text{-}10)$$

Finally, equating Eqs. 10-10 and 10-8, we find

$$\frac{2M}{n} = \frac{b_n \pi}{2} \qquad \text{or} \qquad b_n = \frac{4M}{n\pi} \qquad (10\text{-}11)$$

where n is any odd integer.

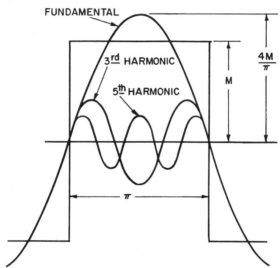

Fig. 10-2 Principal harmonics of alternating rectangular wave.

Substituting this in Eq. 10-6, we find that the Fourier series that represents the alternating rectangular wave of Fig. 10-1 becomes

$$y = \frac{4M}{\pi} \left(\sin \theta + \frac{\sin 3\theta}{3} + \frac{\sin 5\theta}{5} + \frac{\sin 7\theta}{7} + \cdots \right) \qquad (10\text{-}12)$$

| Funda-mental | Third harmonic | Fifth harmonic | Seventh harmonic |

Figure 10-2 shows the separate terms of Eq. 10-12 and shows how their sum approaches a true rectangular wave as more and more terms are included.

As another example, we may find the Fourier series to represent a triangular alternating wave (Fig. 10-3). Here, again, the wave has reverse symmetry about $\theta = 0$, so that the constant term and all the cosine terms are zero and Eqs. 10-6 and 10-7 correctly represent the function. If the origin of θ were taken at the peak of the triangle, the trigonometric series would contain only cosine terms, and for any other location of the zero point of θ, both sine and cosine terms would be included.

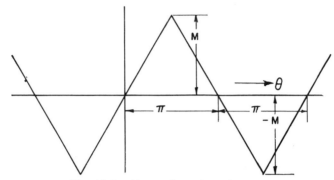

Fig. 10-3   Alternating triangular wave.

The triangular wave is represented by the discontinuous series

$$y = \frac{2M\theta}{\pi} \qquad\qquad \text{from } \theta = -\frac{\pi}{2} \text{ to } \theta = \frac{\pi}{2}$$

$$y = \frac{2M}{\pi}(\pi - \theta) \qquad \text{from } \theta = \frac{\pi}{2} \text{ to } \theta = \frac{3\pi}{2} \qquad\qquad (10\text{-}13)$$

$$y = \frac{2M}{\pi}(\theta - 2\pi) \qquad \text{from } \theta = \frac{3\pi}{2} \text{ to } \theta = \frac{5\pi}{2}$$

$$y = \frac{2M}{\pi}(3\pi - \theta) \qquad \text{from } \theta = \frac{5\pi}{2} \text{ to } \theta = \frac{7\pi}{2}, \text{ etc.}$$

Substituting Eq. 10-13 in the left side of Eq. 10-7, we have

$$\int_0^\pi y \sin n\theta \, d\theta = \frac{2M}{\pi} \int_0^{\pi/2} \theta \sin n\theta \, d\theta$$

$$+ \frac{2M}{\pi} \int_{\pi/2}^\pi (\pi - \theta) \sin n\theta \, d\theta \qquad (10\text{-}14)$$

To evaluate this, we make use of the identity (Eq. 8-50)

$$\int y \, dx = xy - \int x \, dy$$

putting $y = \theta$, $dx = \sin n\theta \, d\theta$, whence

$$\int \theta \sin n\theta \, d\theta = -\frac{\theta \cos n\theta}{n} + \int \frac{\cos n\theta}{n} \, d\theta$$

$$= -\frac{\theta \cos n\theta}{n} + \frac{\sin n\theta}{n^2} \qquad (10\text{-}15)$$

From Eq. 10-15, Eq. 10-14 becomes:

$$\int_0^\pi y \sin n\theta \, d\theta = \frac{2M}{\pi}\left[\left(-\frac{\theta \cos n\theta}{n} + \frac{\sin n\theta}{n^2}\right)_0^{\pi/2} - \left(\frac{\pi}{n}\cos n\theta\right)_{\pi/2}^\pi \right.$$
$$\left. + \left(\frac{\theta \cos n\theta}{n} - \frac{\sin n\theta}{n^2}\right)_{\pi/2}^\pi\right] = \frac{4M}{\pi n^2}\sin\frac{n\pi}{2} \qquad (10\text{-}16)$$

If n is an even integer, this is equal to zero. If n is odd, it becomes

$$\int_0^\pi y \sin n\theta \, d\theta = \frac{4M}{\pi n^2}(-1)^{(n+3)/2} \qquad (10\text{-}17)$$

The right side of Eq. 10-7 is equal to Eq. 10-10, as before. Equating Eq. 10-10 to Eq. 10-17, we find for the value of b_n

$$b_n = \frac{8M}{\pi^2 n^2}(-1)^{(n+3)/2} \qquad (10\text{-}18)$$

where n is any odd integer.

Substituting this in Eq. 10-6, we find the Fourier series for the alternating triangular wave of Fig. 10-3 to be

$$y = \frac{8M}{\pi^2}\left(\sin\theta - \frac{\sin 3\theta}{9} + \frac{\sin 5\theta}{25} - \frac{\sin 7\theta}{49} + \cdots\right) \qquad (10\text{-}19)$$

Useful numerical series can be derived in this way, such as are given in Appendix C. For example, for $\theta = \dfrac{\pi}{2}$ and $M = 1$ in Eq. 10-19,

$$\frac{\pi^2}{8} = 1 + \frac{1}{3^2} + \frac{1}{5^2} + \frac{1}{7^2} + \cdots \qquad (10\text{-}20)$$

And, multiplying this by

$$\frac{4}{3} = \frac{1}{1 - \frac14} = 1 + \frac{1}{4} + \frac{1}{16} + \frac{1}{64} + \cdots$$

gives

$$\frac{\pi^2}{6} = 1 + \frac{1}{2^2} + \frac{1}{3^2} + \frac{1}{4^2} + \frac{1}{5^2} + \cdots \qquad (10\text{-}21)$$

The first term of a trigonometric series such as Eq. 10-12 or Eq. 10-19 is called the *fundamental* wave and the other terms are called the *harmonics*. By analyzing a periodic function in this way we can consider its component frequencies separately, for example, the overtones of a violin or the slot ripples of the magnetic field of an induction motor. Thus, the engineer can convert a complex phenomenon into the sum of several simple phenomena that can be readily understood and dealt with independently.

The most important periodic functions in electrical engineering are the alternating currents and voltages. Usually, as a first approximation, they are represented by a single trigonometric function, as

$$i = i_0 \cos (\theta - \beta) \qquad \text{or} \qquad e = e_0 \sin (\theta - \delta)$$

that is, they are assumed to be pure sine waves.

In practice, this ideal condition is never attained perfectly. Sometimes the deviations from a sine wave are sufficiently large to require consideration. This is especially true for electric circuits containing electrostatic capacitance, as, for instance, long-distance transmission lines or underground cable systems. In such cases, the actual voltage or current waveshape may be measured by an oscillograph, and it may then be desirable to analyze this empirical waveform into a fundamental and a series of higher periodic waves, or harmonics. The procedure in such an analysis is similar to the foregoing, except that the left side of Eq. 10-7 must be evaluated by summation of a series of values taken from the empirical curve, instead of by formal integration.

10-3   General Method of Analysis.   To determine the successive coefficients of a trigonometric series, Eq. 10-2, to represent any empirical periodic wave, the procedure can be mapped out as follows:

To find the first coefficient, a_0, the equation is integrated over a complete period:

$$\int_0^{2\pi} y \, d\theta = \int_0^{2\pi} a_0 \, d\theta + \int_0^{2\pi} (a_1 \cos \theta + \cdots + b_1 \sin \theta + \cdots) \, d\theta$$
$$= 2\pi a_0$$

so that

$$a_0 = \frac{1}{2\pi} \int_0^{2\pi} y \, d\theta = \text{average of } y \Big]_0^{2\pi} \qquad (10\text{-}22)$$

All the sine and cosine terms drop out because their average values are zero over a complete cycle. The constant term, a_0, thus is the total area of the periodic curve over one cycle, divided by the width of the base, 2π, or is the average value of y.

To find the nth cosine coefficient, a_n, the equation is multiplied by $\cos n\theta$ and integrated over a complete period:

$$\int_0^{2\pi} y \cos n\theta \, d\theta = \int_0^{2\pi} a_n \cos^2 n\theta \, d\theta = \pi a_n \qquad (10\text{-}23)$$

so that

$$a_n = \frac{1}{\pi} \int_0^{2\pi} y \cos n\theta \; d\theta = \text{average of } 2y \cos n\theta \Big]_0^{2\pi}$$

(10-24)

Equation 10-24 follows from Eqs. 10-9 and 10-10. The value of a_n is twice the average of $y \cos n\theta$ over a complete cycle. Similarly, the nth sine coefficient is found by multiplying by $\sin n\theta$ and integrating over a complete period:

$$\int_0^{2\pi} y \sin n\theta \; d\theta = \int_0^{2\pi} b_n \sin^2 n\theta \; d\theta = \pi b_n$$

(10-25)

so that

$$b_n = \frac{1}{\pi} \int_0^{2\pi} y \sin n\theta \; d\theta = \text{average of } 2y \sin n\theta \Big]_0^{2\pi}$$

(10-26)

Hereby any individual harmonic can be calculated, without calculating any preceding harmonic.

In general, the higher harmonics become smaller and smaller. When the complete series of coefficients is to be calculated, it is preferable not to use the complete periodic function, y, but only the residual left after subtracting the harmonics which have already been calculated. That is, after a_0 has been calculated, it is subtracted from y, and the difference, $y_0 = y - a_0$, is used to calculate a_1 and b_1.

Then, $a_1 \cos \theta + b_1 \sin \theta$ is subtracted from y_0, and the difference,

$$y_1 = y_0 - (a_1 \cos \theta + b_1 \sin \theta) = y - (a_0 + a_1 \cos \theta + b_1 \sin \theta)$$

(10-27)

is used for the calculation of a_2 and b_2, etc.

In this manner, a higher accuracy is derived, and the calculations are simplified by having the successive values of the function of the same magnitude as the coefficients a_n and b_n at each stage.

The procedure is further simplified by separating the odd harmonics (n an odd number) from the even harmonics, and the sine from the cosine terms, before finding the individual coefficients.

All the even harmonics, $\sin 2\theta$, $\cos 2\theta$, etc., have the same values at $\theta + \pi$ as at θ, whereas all the odd harmonics, $\sin \theta$, $\sin 3\theta$, $\cos \theta$, etc., have values at $\theta + \pi$ numerically equal to the values at θ, but negative. Hence the sum of all the odd harmonics at any value of θ is

$$y_1(\theta) = \tfrac{1}{2}[y_0(\theta) - y_0(\theta + \pi)]$$

(10-28)

where $y_0 = y - a_0$; and the sum of all the even harmonics is

$$y_2(\theta) = \tfrac{1}{2}[y_0(\theta) + y_0(\theta + \pi)] \qquad (10\text{-}29)$$

Likewise, the sine and cosine series terms can be separated by noting that $\sin \theta = -\sin(-\theta)$, whereas $\cos \theta = \cos(-\theta)$. Thus the cosine terms, u, are

$$u_1(\theta) = \tfrac{1}{2}[y_1(\theta) + y_1(-\theta)]$$
$$u_2(\theta) = \tfrac{1}{2}[y_2(\theta) + y_2(-\theta)] \qquad (10\text{-}30)$$

and the sine terms, v, are

$$v_1(\theta) = \tfrac{1}{2}[y_1(\theta) - y_1(-\theta)]$$
$$v_2(\theta) = \tfrac{1}{2}[y_2(\theta) - y_2(-\theta)] \qquad (10\text{-}31)$$

After these preliminary calculations, the individual coefficients, $a_1, a_2, a_3, \ldots$; $b_1, b_2, b_3, \ldots$ can be quickly determined by the averages:

$$a_n = 2 \times \text{average of } u_n \cos n\theta \Big]_0^{\pi/2}$$
$$b_n = 2 \times \text{average of } v_n \sin n\theta \Big]_0^{\pi/2} \qquad (10\text{-}32)$$

Many periodic functions contain no even harmonics; that is, they are symmetrical alternating waves (Fig. 10-2), in which case $y_0, y_2, u_2,$ and v_0 are all zero.

As in most engineering calculations, it is most important to arrange the work so as to derive the results simply and rapidly and at the same time accurately. If we proceed immediately to use Eqs. 10-24 and 10-26, the work may become so extensive as to be a serious waste of time. By the systematic resolution of the work into simpler functions, with Eqs. 10-22 and 10-28 to 10-32, the actual work and the chances of error can be greatly reduced.

10-4   Example—Analysis of Annual Cycle of Mean Daily Temperatures.

As an example of the resolution of a periodic wave into its harmonics, we shall analyze the observed mean daily temperatures, in degrees centigrade, in Schenectady throughout the year, as shown in Fig. 10-4. The numerical work should be carried through in tabular form.

Table 10-1 gives the exact daily temperatures and the resolution of the periodic temperature function into its constant term a_0, the odd series y_1, and the even series y_2. The resolution of the cosine and sine series, u_1, v_1, u_2, v_2, is carried through in similar tables, and a final table is calculated that determines the constants a_n and b_n from the u_1, v_1, u_2, v_2 series. By means of Eqs. 10-22 and 10-28 to 10-32, the above calculations can be performed.

Table 10-1   Resolution of the Daily Periodic Temperature Function into Its Constant Term, Odd and Even Series

(1) θ	(2) y	(3) $y - a_0 = y_0$	(4) y_1	(5) y_2
Jan. 0	− 4.2	−12.95	−13.10	+0.15
10	− 4.7	−13.45	−13.55	+0.10
20	− 5.2	−13.95	−13.65	−0.30
Feb. 30	− 5.4	−14.15	−13.55	−0.60
40	− 3.8	−12.55	−12.35	−0.20
50	− 2.6	−11.35	−11.20	−0.15
Mar. 60	− 1.6	−10.35	− 9.75	−0.60
70	+ 0.2	− 8.55	− 7.65	−0.90
80	+ 1.8	− 6.95	− 6.05	−0.90
Apr. 90	+ 5.1	− 3.65	− 3.35	−0.30
100	+ 9.1	+ 0.35	− 0.35	+0.70
110	+11.5	+ 2.75	+ 1.75	+1.00
May 120	+13.3	+ 4.55	+ 3.90	+0.65
130	+15.2	+ 6.45	+ 5.85	+0.60
140	+17.7	+ 8.95	+ 8.15	+0.80
June 150	+19.2	+10.45	+10.10	+0.35
160	+19.5	+10.75	+10.80	−0.05
170	+20.6	+11.85	+12.15	−0.30
July 180	+22.0	+13.25		
190	+22.4	+13.65		
200	+22.1	+13.35		
Aug. 210	+21.7	+12.95		
220	+20.9	+12.15		
230	+19.8	+11.05		
Sept. 240	+17.9	+ 9.15		
250	+15.5	+ 6.75		
260	+13.8	+ 5.15		
Oct. 270	+11.8	+ 3.05		
280	+ 9.8	+ 1.05		
290	+ 8.0	− 0.75		
Nov. 300	+ 5.5	− 3.25		
310	+ 3.5	− 5.25		
320	+ 1.4	− 7.35		
Dec. 330	− 1.0	− 9.75		
340	− 2.1	−10.85		
350	− 3.7	−12.45		
Total:	315.1			
Divided by 36:	8.75 = a_0			

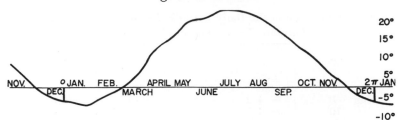

Fig. 10-4 Mean daily temperature at Schenectady.

This resolution of the temperature wave of Fig. 10-4 gives the coefficients in Table 10-2 for the fundamental and the harmonics through the seventh.

Table 10-2 Cosine and Sine Coefficients for Temperature Wave of Fig. 10-4

Cosine coefficients	Sine coefficients
$a_0 = +8.75$	
$a_1 = -13.28$	$b_1 = -3.33$
$a_2 = -0.001$	$b_2 = -0.602$
$a_3 = -0.33$	$b_3 = -0.14$
$a_4 = -0.154$	$b_4 = +0.386$
$a_5 = +0.014$	$b_5 = -0.090$
$a_6 = +0.100$	$b_6 = -0.154$
$a_7 = -0.222$	$b_7 = -0.082$

Transforming by the binomial,

$$a_n \cos n\theta + b_n \sin n\theta = c_n \cos (n\theta - \gamma_n)$$

by substituting $c_n = \sqrt{a_n{}^2 + b_n{}^2}$ and $\tan \gamma_n = b_n/a_n$ gives the values shown in Table 10-3,

Table 10-3 Numerical Values for Cosine Series of Temperature Function

$a_0 = +8.75$

$c_1 = -13.69$	$\gamma_1 = +14.2°$	or	$\gamma_1 = +14.2°$	
$c_2 = -0.602$	$\gamma_2 = +89.9°$	or	$\dfrac{\gamma_2}{2} = +44.95° + 180n$	
$c_3 = +0.359$	$\gamma_3 = -23.0°$	or	$\dfrac{\gamma_3}{3} = -7.7° + 120n = +112.3° + 120m$	
$c_4 = -0.416$	$\gamma_4 = -68.2°$	or	$\dfrac{\gamma_4}{4} = -17.05° + 90n = +72.95° + 90m$	
$c_5 = +0.091$	$\gamma_5 = -81.15°$	or	$\dfrac{\gamma_5}{5} = -16.23° + 72n = +55.77° + 72m$	
$c_6 = +0.184$	$\gamma_6 = -57.0°$	or	$\dfrac{\gamma_6}{6} = -9.5° + 60n = +50.5° + 60m$	
$c_7 = -0.085$	$\gamma_7 = +75.0°$	or	$\dfrac{\gamma_7}{7} = +10.7° + 51.4n$	

where n and m may be any integers.

Since any multiple of 2π or $360°$ may be added to an angle γ_n, any multiple of $360/n$ may be added to the angle γ_n/n, and thus the angle γ_n/n may be made positive, etc.

The equation of the temperature wave then becomes

$$
\begin{aligned}
y = 8.75 \;-\; & 13.69 \cos (\theta - 14.2°) - 0.602 \cos 2(\theta - 45.0°) \\
& - 0.359 \cos 3(\theta - 52.3°) - 0.416 \cos 4(\theta - 73.0°) \\
& - 0.091 \cos 5(\theta - 19.8°) - 0.184 \cos 6(\theta - 20.5°) \\
& - 0.085 \cos 7(\theta - 10.7°) \quad \text{(a)}
\end{aligned}
$$

or, transformed to sine functions by the substitution,

$$\cos \omega = -\sin (\omega - 90°)$$

$$
\begin{aligned}
y = 8.75 \;+\; & 13.69 \sin (\theta - 104.2°) + 0.602 \sin 2(\theta - 90.0°) \\
& + 0.359 \sin 3(\theta - 82.3°) + 0.416 \sin 4(\theta - 95.5°) \\
& + 0.091 \sin 5(\theta - 109.8°) + 0.184 \sin 6(\theta - 95.5°) \\
& + 0.085 \sin 7(\theta - 75.0°) \quad \text{(b)}
\end{aligned}
$$

The cosine form is more convenient for some purposes, the sine form for other purposes.

Substituting $\beta = \theta - 14.2°$; or $\delta = \theta - 104.2°$, these two equations, (a) and (b), can be transformed into the form

$$
\begin{aligned}
y = 8.75 \;-\; & 13.69 \cos \beta - 0.62 \cos 2(\beta - 30.8°) \\
& - 0.359 \cos 3(\beta - 38.1°) - 0.416 \cos 4(\beta - 58.8°) \\
& - 0.091 \cos 5(\beta - 5.6°) - 0.184 \cos 6(\beta - 6.3°) \\
& - 0.085 \cos 7(\beta - 47.9°) \quad \text{(c)}
\end{aligned}
$$

and

$$
\begin{aligned}
y = 8.75 \;+\; & 13.69 \sin \delta + 0.602 \sin 2(\delta + 14.2°) \\
& + 0.359 \sin 3(\delta + 21.9°) + 0.416 \sin 4(\delta + 8.7°) \\
& + 0.91 \sin 5(\delta - 5.6°) + 0.184 \sin 6(\delta + 8.7°) \\
& + 0.085 \sin 7(\delta + 29.2°) \quad \text{(d)}
\end{aligned}
$$

The periodic variation of the temperature y, as expressed by these equations, is a result of the periodic variation of the thermomotive force, that is, the solar radiation. This latter is a minimum on December 22, that is, 9 time-degrees before the zero of θ, and hence may be expressed approximately by

$$z = c - h \cos (\theta + 9°)$$

or substituting for θ its value in terms of β and δ, respectively,

$$z = c - h \cos (\beta + 23.2°) = c + h \sin (\delta + 23.2°)$$

This means that the maximum of y occurs $23.2°$ after the maximum of z; in other words, the temperature lags $23.2°$, or about $\frac{1}{16}$ period, behind the thermomotive force.

Near $\delta = 0°$, all the sine functions in (d) are increasing; that is, the temperature wave rises steeply in spring.

Near $\delta = 180°$, the sine functions of the odd angles are decreasing and of the even angles are increasing, and the decrease of the temperature wave in fall thus is smaller than the increase in spring.

The fundamental wave greatly preponderates, with amplitude $c_1 = 13.69$.

In the spring, for $\delta = -14.5°$, all the higher harmonics rise in the same direction and give the sum 1.74, or 12.7 per cent of the fundamental. In the fall, for $\delta = -14.5 + \pi$, the even harmonics decrease and the odd harmonics increase the steepness and give the sum -0.67, or -4.9 per cent.

Therefore, in the spring, the temperature rises 12.7 per cent faster, and in autumn it falls 4.9 per cent more slowly than corresponds to a sine wave; the difference in the rate of temperature rise in spring and temperature fall in autumn thus is $12.7 + 4.9 = 17.6$ per cent.

The maximum rate of temperature rise is $90 - 14.5 = 75.5°$ behind the temperature minimum and $23.2 + 75.5 = 98.7°$ behind the minimum of the thermomotive force.

As most periodic functions met by the electrical engineer are symmetrical alternating functions, that is, contain only the odd harmonics, in general the work of resolution into a trigonometric series is very much less than in the above example. Where such reduction has to be carried out frequently, it is advisable to memorize the trigonometric functions for each 10° up to 3 decimals; that is, within the accuracy of the slide rule, as thereby the necessity of looking up tables is eliminated, and the work, therefore, is done much more expeditiously. In general, the slide rule can be used for the calculations.

10-5 Analysis of Trigonometric Series by Polyphase Relations.

In some cases, the reduction of a periodic function, or complex wave, into harmonics can be carried out more quickly by use of polyphase relations, such as Eq. 2-49. Especially is this true if the complete trigonometric series, which represents the periodic function, is not required, but the existence and amount of certain harmonics are to be determined. It is often desired, for instance, to know whether the function contains even, or third-order, harmonics and how large they may be.

This method does not give the coefficients, a_n and b_n, of the individual harmonics, but derives from the numerical values of the complete wave the numerical value of any desired harmonic, together with its multiples. That is, when the third harmonic is separated out, the value obtained includes also the sixth, ninth, twelfth, etc., harmonics.

This polyphase method has already been used in separating the even harmonics from the general wave (Eq. 10-29) by taking the average of the values of y for the angle θ and for $\theta + \pi$.

Assume that to an angle θ there is successively added a **constant** quantity a, thus:

$$\theta; \; \theta + a; \; \theta + 2a; \; \theta + 3a; \; \theta + 4a; \; \text{etc.}$$

until the same angle θ plus a multiple of 2π is reached,

$$\theta + na = \theta + 2m\pi$$

that is, $a = 2m\pi/n$, or, in other words, a is $1/n$ of a multiple of 2π. Then the sum of the cosine as well as the sine functions of all these angles is zero:

$$\cos\theta + \cos(\theta + a) + \cos(\theta + 2a) + \cos(\theta + 3a) + \cdots$$
$$+ \cos[\theta + (n-1)a] = 0 \cdots \quad (10\text{-}33)$$

$$\sin\theta + \sin(\theta + a) + \sin(\theta + 2a) + \sin(\theta + 3a) + \cdots$$
$$+ \sin[\theta + (n-1)a] = 0 \cdots \quad (10\text{-}34)$$

where

$$na = 2m\pi \cdots \quad (10\text{-}35)$$

Equations 10-33 and 10-34 hold for all values of a, except for $a = 2\pi$, or a multiple thereof. For $a = 2\pi$, obviously all the terms of Eq. 10-33 or 10-34 become equal, and the sums become $n\cos\theta$ and $n\sin\theta$, respectively.

Thus, if the series of numerical values of y is divided into n successive sections, each covering $2\pi/n$ degrees, and these sections added together, we have

$$(\theta) + y\left(\theta + \frac{2\pi}{n}\right) + y\left(\theta + 2\frac{2\pi}{n}\right) + y\left(\theta + 3\frac{2\pi}{n}\right) + \cdots$$
$$+ y\left[\theta + (n-1)\frac{2\pi}{n}\right] \cdots \quad (10\text{-}36)$$

In this sum, all the harmonics of the wave y cancel, by Eqs. 10-33 and 10-34, except the nth harmonic and its multiples,

$$a_n\cos n\theta + b_n\sin n\theta, \; a_{2n}\cos 2n\theta + b_{2n}\sin 2n\theta, \; \text{etc.}$$

In the latter, all the terms of the sum (Eq. 10-36) are equal; that is, Eq. 10-36 equals n times the nth harmonic and its multiples. Therefore, the nth harmonic of the periodic function y together with its multiples is given by

$$y_n(\theta) = \frac{1}{n}\left\{y(\theta) + y\left(\theta + \frac{2\pi}{n}\right) + y\left(\theta + 2\frac{2\pi}{n}\right) + \cdots \right.$$
$$\left. + y\left[\theta + (n-1)\frac{2\pi}{n}\right]\right\} \quad (10\text{-}37)$$

For instance, for $n = 2$,

$$y_2 = \tfrac{1}{2}[y(\theta) + y(\theta + \pi)]$$

gives the sum of all the even harmonics, that is, gives the second harmonic together with its multiples, the fourth, sixth, etc., as seen in Eq. 10-29, and for $n = 3$,

$$y_3 = \frac{1}{3}\left[y(\theta) + y\left(\theta + \frac{2\pi}{3}\right) + y\left(\theta + \frac{4\pi}{3}\right)\right]$$

gives the third harmonic, together with its multiples, the sixth, ninth, etc.

This method does not give the mathematical expression of the harmonics, but their numerical values. Thus, if the mathematical expressions are required, each of the component harmonics has to be reduced from its numerical values to the mathematical equation, and the method then usually offers no advantage.

It is especially suitable, however, where certain classes of harmonics are desired, as the third together with its multiples. In this case, from the numerical values, the effective value, that is, the equivalent sine wave, may be calculated.

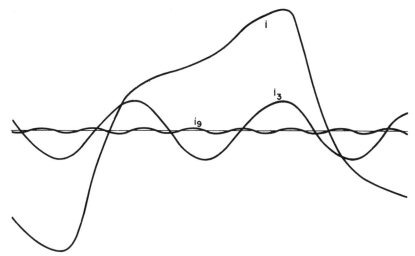

Fig. 10-5 Exciting current waveform of a transformer.

As illustration may be investigated the separation of the third harmonics from the exciting current of a transformer.

In Table 10-4 are given, in columns 1, 3, and 5, the angles θ, in $10°$ steps, and in columns 2, 4, and 6, the corresponding values of the exciting current i, as derived by calculation from the hysteresis cycle of the iron or by measuring from the photographic film of an oscillograph. Column 7 then gives one-third the sum of columns 2, 4, and 6, that is, the third harmonic with its overtones, i_3.

Table 10-4   Analysis of Exciting Current Waveform for Third Harmonic

(1)	(2)	(3)	(4)	(5)	(6)	(7)
θ	i	θ	i	θ	i	i_3
0	+24.0	120	−15.1	240	+ 8.5	+5.8
10	+20.0	130	−16.5	250	+10	+4.5
20	+12	140	−18.5	260	+11	+1.5
30	+ 4	150	−21	270	+12	−1.7
40	− 1.5	160	−22.7	280	+13	−3.7
50	− 6.5	170	−23.7	290	+14	−5.4
60	− 8.5	180	−24	300	+15.1	−5.8

To find the ninth harmonic and its overtones, i_9, the same method is now applied to i_3, for angle 3θ. This is recorded in Table 10-5.

Table 10-5   Analysis of Exciting Current Waveform for Ninth Harmonic

(1)	(2)	(3)	(4)	(5)	(6)	(7)
3θ	i_3	3θ	i_3	3θ	i_3	i_9
0	+5.8	120	−3.7	240	−1.5	+0.2
30	+4.5	150	−5.4	270	+1.7	+0.3
60	+1.5	180	−5.8	300	+3.7	−0.2

In Fig. 10-5 are plotted the total exciting current i, its third harmonic i_3, and the ninth harmonic i_9.

This method has the advantage of showing the limitation of the exactness of the results resulting from the limited number of numerical values of i, on which the calculation is based. Thus, in the example, Table 10-4, in which the values of i are given for every 10°, values of the third harmonic are derived for every 30°, and for the ninth harmonic for every 90°. For the latter, only two points per half-wave are determinable from the numerical data, and as the two points per half-wave are just sufficient to locate a sine wave, it follows that within the accuracy of the given numerical values of i, the ninth harmonic is a sine wave, or in other words, to determine whether still higher harmonics than the ninth exist, more numerical values for i are required than for every 10°.

10-6   Empirical Waveshapes. As periodic functions are of the greatest importance in electrical engineering, a familiarity with the waveshapes produced by the different harmonics is desirable. After a little study or experience, it is readily possible to tell immediately from the shape of an alternating wave, as given by an oscillograph, what harmonics are present, or at least which predominate.

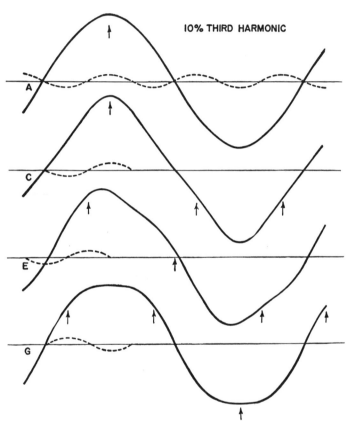

Fig. 10-6   Effect of small third harmonic.

The effect of the lower harmonics, such as the second to fifth, is to change the shape of the wave from a sine curve, giving it such features as a flat top, or one to three peaks, or a steep or flat approach to the zero point, etc. The higher harmonics superimpose ripples on the wave, without much change in its general shape.

To illustrate the variation in shape of the alternating waves caused by various lower harmonics, superimposed upon the fundamental at different relative positions, that is, different phase angles, in Figs.

10-6 and 10-7 are shown the effect of a third harmonic of 10 and 30 per cent of the fundamental, respectively. *A* gives the fundamental and *C, D, E, F, G* the waves resulting from the superposition of the triple harmonic in phase with the fundamental (*C*), under 45° lead (*D*), 90° lead or quadrature (*E*), 135° lead (*F*), and opposition (*G*).

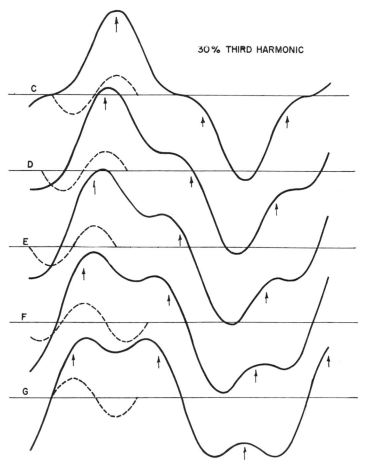

Fig. 10-7 Effect of large third harmonic.

(The phase differences here are referred to the maximum of the fundamental: with waves of different frequencies, the phase differences naturally change from point to point, and in speaking of phase difference, the reference point on the wave must thus be given. For instance, in *C* the third harmonic is in phase with the fundamental at the maximum point of the latter, but in opposition at its zero point.)

The equations of these waves are

A: $y = 100 \cos \beta$
C: $y = 100 \cos \beta + 10 \cos 3\beta$
E: $y = 100 \cos \beta + 10 \cos (3\beta + 90°)$
G: $y = 100 \cos \beta + 10 \cos (3\beta + 180°) = 100 \cos \beta - 10 \cos 3\beta$
C: $y = 100 \cos \beta + 30 \cos 3\beta$
D: $y = 100 \cos \beta + 30 \cos (3\beta + 45°)$
E: $y = 100 \cos \beta + 30 \cos (3\beta + 90°)$
F: $y = 100 \cos \beta + 30 \cos (3\beta + 135°)$
G: $y = 100 \cos \beta + 30 \cos (3\beta + 180°) = 100 \cos \beta - 30 \cos 3\beta$

In all these waves, one cycle of the triple harmonic is given in dotted lines, to indicate its relative position and intensity, and the maxima of the harmonics are indicated by the arrows.

As seen, with the harmonic in phase or in opposition (C and G), the waves are symmetrical; with the harmonic out of phase, the waves are unsymmetrical, of the so-called "saw-tooth" type, and the saw tooth is on the rising side of the wave with a lagging, on the decreasing side with a leading triple harmonic. The latter are shown in D, E, F; the former have the same shape but reversed, that is, rising and decreasing sides of the wave interchanged, and therefore are not shown.

The triple harmonic in phase with the fundamental, C, gives a peaked wave with flat zero, and the peak and the flat zero become the more pronounced, the higher the third harmonic, until finally the flat zero becomes a double reversal of voltages, as shown in Fig. 10-8D.

Figure 10-8 shows the effect of a gradual increase of an in-phase triple harmonic: A is the fundamental, B contains a 10 per cent, C a 38.5 per cent, and D a 50 per cent triple harmonic, as given by the equations:

A: $\qquad\qquad y = 100 \cos \beta$
B: $\qquad\qquad y = 100 \cos \beta + 10 \cos 3\beta$
C: $\qquad\qquad y = 100 \cos \beta + 38.5 \cos 3\beta$
D: $\qquad\qquad y = 100 \cos \beta + 50 \cos 3\beta$

At C, the wave is horizontal at the zero, that is, remains zero for an appreciable time at the reversal. In this figure, the three harmonics are shown separately in dotted lines, in their relative intensities.

A triple harmonic in opposition to the fundamental (Figs. 10-6G and 10-7G) is characterized by a flat top and steep zero, and with the increase of the third harmonic, the flat top develops into a double peak (Fig. 10-8G), while steepness at the point of reversal increases.

The simple saw tooth, produced by a triple harmonic in quadrature with the fundamental, is shown in Fig. 10-6*E*. With increasing triple harmonic, the hump of the saw tooth becomes more pronounced and changes to a second and lower peak, as shown in Fig. 10-7. This figure gives the variation of the saw-tooth shape in steps of phase difference: with the phase of the third harmonic shifting from in phase to 45° lead, the flat zero, by moving up on the wave, has formed a hump or saw

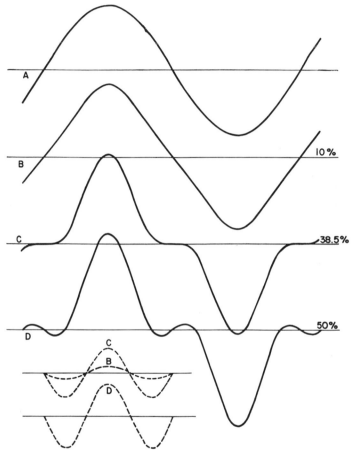

Fig. 10-8 Flat zero and reversal by third harmonic.

tooth low down on the decreasing (and with 45° lag on the increasing) side of the wave. At 90° lead, the saw tooth has moved up to the middle of the down branch of the wave, and with 135° lead, has moved still further up, forming practically a second, lower, peak. With 180° lead—or opposition of phase—the hump of the saw tooth has moved up to the top, and formed the second peak—or the flat top, with a lower third harmonic, as in Fig. 10-7*G*.

Figures 10-9 and 10-10 give the effect of the fifth harmonic, super-imposed on the fundamental, of 5 per cent in Fig. 10-9 and of 20 per cent in Fig. 10-10. Again A gives the fundamental sine wave, C the effect of the fifth harmonic in opposition with the fundamental, E in quadrature (lagging), and G in phase. One cycle of the fifth harmonic is shown in dotted lines, and the maxima of the harmonics are indicated by the arrows.

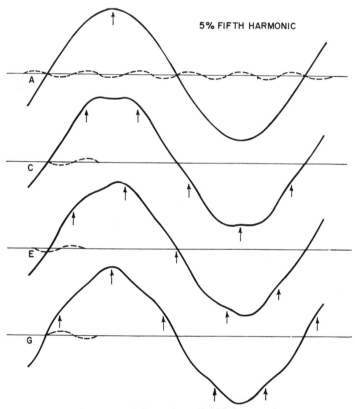

Fig. 10-9   Effect of small fifth harmonic.

The equations of these waves are given by

A:	$y = 100 \cos \beta$
C:	$y = 100 \cos \beta - 5 \cos 5\beta$
E:	$y = 100 \cos \beta - 5 \cos (5\beta + 90°)$
G:	$y = 100 \cos \beta + 5 \cos 5\beta$
A:	$y = 100 \cos \beta$
C:	$y = 100 \cos \beta - 20 \cos 5\beta$
E:	$y = 100 \cos \beta - 20 \cos (5\beta + 90°)$
G:	$y = 100 \cos \beta + 20 \cos 5\beta$

In the distortion caused by the fifth harmonic (in opposition to the fundamental), the flat top (Fig. 10-9*C*) or double peak (at higher values of the harmonic, Fig. 10-10*C*) is accompanied by flat zero (or, at very high values of the fifth harmonic, double reversal at the zero, similar to Fig. 10-8*D*), while in the distortion by the third harmonic it is accompanied by sharp zero.

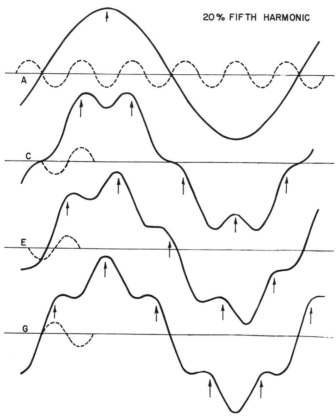

20% FIFTH HARMONIC

Fig. 10-10 Effect of large fifth harmonic.

With the fifth harmonic in phase with the fundamental, a peaked wave results with steep zero, Fig. 10-9*G*, and the transition from the steep zero to the peak, with larger values of the fifth harmonic, then develops into two additional peaks, thus giving a treble peaked wave, Fig. 10-10*G*, with steep zero. The beginning of treble peakedness is noticeable already in Fig. 10-9*G*, with only 5 per cent of fifth harmonic.

By combining third and fifth harmonics of proper values, they can be made to neutralize each other's effects in any one of their characteristics, but they will then accentuate each other in other characteristics. Generally, as in flux or voltage waves exhibiting the effects of magnetic saturation, the largest harmonic is the third, and the fifth is next largest and these are opposed at the peak of the wave. In a symmetrical wave, the third harmonic is zero at the 60° point, and the (smaller) fifth is zero at the 36° point. Hence, the sum of the two harmonics will be zero somewhere between 50 and 60°. This provides us with a simple rule for finding the fundamental component of a symmetrical alternating wave (Fig. 10-11):

The maximum of the fundamental component is roughly equal to 1.25 times the height of the wave at the 53.2° point.

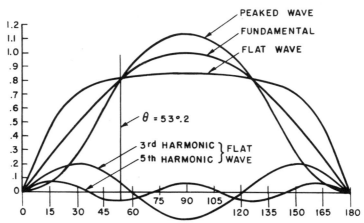

Fig. 10-11 Crossing point of actual and fundamental waves.

This rule is exact if only third and fifth harmonics are present, and if the ratio of the fifth to the third is 0.35, since the actual wave will then cross the fundamental at 53.2°, and since

$$\sin 53.2° = 0.8 = \frac{1}{1.25}$$

PROBLEMS

Obtain the Fourier expansions and sketch the graphs of the following described functions:

1. $F(t) = +1$ from $t = 0$ to $t = \dfrac{\pi}{4}$ $\left[\text{Period of } F(t) \text{ is } \dfrac{\pi}{2}. \right]$

$F(t) = -1$ from $t = \dfrac{\pi}{4}$ to $t = \dfrac{\pi}{2}$

2. $F(x) = 1 - x^2$ from $x = -1$ to $x = +1$

3. $F(\phi) = \phi(e^{-\phi} - e^{-\pi})$ from $\phi = 0$ to $\phi = \pi$

4. $F(t) = \sin 2t$ from $t = 0$ to $t = \dfrac{\pi}{2}$

5. $F(x) = 1 - e^{-x}$ from $x = 0$ to $x = \dfrac{3\pi}{2}$

6. Given:

$$F(t) = \frac{8}{\pi^2}\left(\sin t - \frac{1}{3^2}\sin 3t + \frac{1}{5^2}\sin 5t - \cdots\right)$$

and $F(\pi/2) = 1$. Obtain an infinite series to approximate $(\pi/4)^2$.

7. Obtain the Fourier series for the function $f(x) = x^2$ from $x = -\pi$ to $x = \pi$. Derive the relations:

$$\frac{\pi^2}{6} = \left(1 + \frac{1}{2^2} + \frac{1}{3^2} + \frac{1}{4^2} + \cdots\right)$$

$$\frac{\pi^2}{12} = \left(1 - \frac{1}{2^2} + \frac{1}{3^2} - \frac{1}{4^2} + \cdots\right)$$

8. Given that the curve of a simply supported beam L feet in length with a concentrated load P pounds at $x = c$ is represented by the sine series

$$y = \frac{2L^3 P}{k\pi^4} \sum_{n=1,2,\,\ldots}^{\infty} \frac{\sin(n\pi c/L)}{n^4} \sin\frac{n\pi x}{L}$$

(k is a constant determined by the shape and material of the beam), find the maximum deflection under the following conditions. Take the origin at the left end of the beam.

   a. $P = 500$ pounds, $k = 2 \times 10^6$, $L = 30$ feet, and $c = 15$ feet
   b. $P = 4,000$ pounds, $k = 6 \times 10^7$, $L = 100$ feet, and $c = 25$ feet

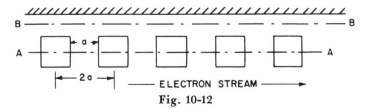

Fig. 10-12

9. An electron stream passes along a row of vertical conductors in a certain "traveling-wave" amplifier (see Fig. 10-12). Write Fourier series representations for the electric field caused by the electron stream;

a. Along *A-A*. The electric field may be assumed to be represented by Fig. 10-13, where

$$y = 0 \qquad \text{from } x = 0 \text{ to } x = a$$
$$y = k \qquad \text{from } x = a \text{ to } x = 2a$$

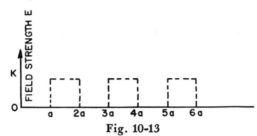

Fig. 10-13

b. Along *B-B*. The electric field may be assumed to be represented by

$$y = c_2 - \frac{1}{c_1} \sin x \qquad \text{from } x = 0 \text{ to } x = \pi$$

$$y = c_2 = c_3 \sin x \qquad \text{from } x = \quad \text{to } x = 2\pi$$

In "traveling-wave" theory, the components of the resulting Fourier series are known as "space harmonics," since the representation is for space instead of time.

Bibliography

1. Churchill, R. V.: "Fourier Series and Boundary Value Problems," McGraw-Hill Book Company, New York, 1941.
2. Mellor, J. W.: "Higher Mathematics," Longmans, Green & Co. Inc., New York, 1922.

Chapter 11   MAXIMA AND MINIMA

11-1   Extreme Values of a Function.   In engineering studies, the problem frequently occurs of determining the maxima and minima, that is, the highest and lowest values of some quantity. For instance, the output of a machine is to be found at which its efficiency is a maximum, or the voltage is to be chosen that will make the total cost of electric power transmission a minimum, or it is desired to find the maximum power that can be delivered by an induction motor.

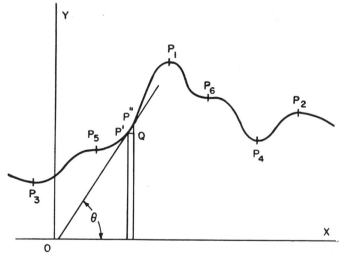

Fig. 11-1   Graphic determination of maxima and minima.

The maximum and minimum values of a known function, $y = f(x)$, can be found by plotting it as a curve, and reading from the graph the values of y at the extreme upper and lower limits of the curve. In Fig. 11-1, maxima occur at P_1 and P_2 and minima at P_3 and P_4. This graphical method of finding the extremes is necessary if the mathematical relation between x and y is unknown, or is so complex that their calculation is impractical.

[249]

As an example of the graphical method, suppose it is desired to know the magnetic flux density, B, at which the permeability of a sample of steel is a maximum. By measurement of B at successive values of the magnetizing force, H, the magnetization curve of Fig. 11-2 is found. The permeability, defined as the ratio of B to H, is then calculated for a series of points on this curve, and plotted in Fig. 11-3 against H. By inspection, it is evident that the maximum permeability occurs at $H = 1.5$ and is equal to 4,600.

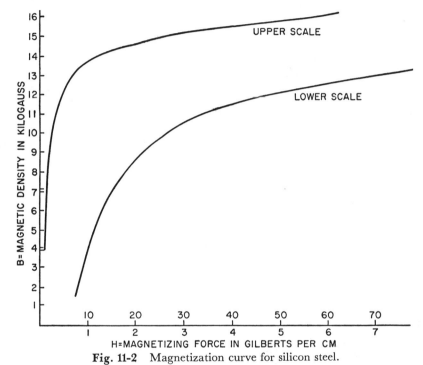

Fig. 11-2 Magnetization curve for silicon steel.

A maximum or minimum point on the curve

$$y = f(x) \tag{11-1}$$

is defined in mathematical terms by the condition that the value at this point is either greater or less than at the adjacent points on each side. This usually means that the slope of the tangent to the curve is zero, giving the equation

$$\frac{dy}{dx} = f'(x) = 0 \tag{11-2}$$

For, as seen in Fig. 11-1, the angle θ that the tangent to the curve makes with the horizontal axis is between 0 and 90° on the ascending branch of the curve, it decreases to zero (or becomes 180°) when the highest value of y is reached (the tangent is then horizontal), and it remains between 180 and 90° on the descending branch. At a point of inflection, P_6, the inclination of the tangent may fall to zero (or rise to 180°), and then reverse its direction of turning, in which case the point will not be a maximum or minimum.

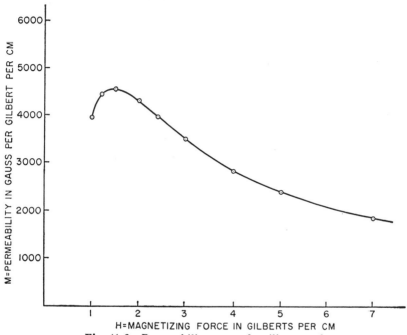

Fig. 11-3 Permeability curve for silicon steel.

Therefore, besides Eq. 11-2, there is a further necessary condition for a maximum or a minimum of y. For the curve of Eq. 11-1 to have a maximum at a point x, and not merely a point of inflection, the second derivative at x must be negative. That is

$$\frac{d^2y}{dx^2} < 0 \qquad \text{if } y \text{ is a maximum} \qquad (11\text{-}3)$$

Likewise, for a minimum value of y the second derivative must be positive:

$$\frac{d^2y}{dx^2} > 0 \qquad \text{if } y \text{ is a minimum} \qquad (11\text{-}4)$$

These equations merely state that the inclination of the tangent of the curve continues to turn in the same direction when the curve recedes from the extreme value of y, as it did when approaching it.

11-2   Engineering Problems of Maxima and Minima.   In engineering problems, the question whether the solution of Eq. 11-2 represents a maximum or a minimum rarely need be asked, as it is generally obvious from the nature of the problem whether a maximum or a minimum occurs, or neither.

As an example of this formal method of finding the extreme value of a function, suppose we wish to know at what peripheral speed the output of a jet turbine (steam or water) is a maximum. Let the speed of the incoming jet be S_1 feet per second and the peripheral speed of the wheel be S_2.

The impulse force on the turbine blades is proportional to the relative speed of the jet and the wheel, that is, to $S_1 - S_2$. The power P produced is force times speed S_2; hence

$$P = kS_2(S_1 - S_2) \tag{11-5}$$

This is an extreme when dP/dS_2 is zero, or when

$$\frac{dP}{dS_2} = kS_1 - 2kS_2 = 0 \tag{11-6}$$

or
$$S_2 = \frac{S_1}{2} \tag{11-7}$$

that is, when the peripheral speed of the wheel equals half the jet velocity. Taking the derivative of Eq. 11-6 gives

$$\frac{d^2P}{dS_2{}^2} = -2k \tag{11-8}$$

Since this is negative, the relation (Eq. 11-7) represents a maximum value of P, as desired.

As another example of a familiar engineering problem (see Sec. 3-13), suppose a constant current i_0 flows through a circuit containing the resistor r_0. If this resistor is shunted by another one, r ohms, what must the value of r be to make the power consumed in the shunting resistor a maximum (Fig. 11-4)?

Let i be the current in the shunting resistor. The power consumed in r is then

$$P = ri^2 \tag{11-9}$$

The current in the fixed resistor is $i_0 - i$. The voltage is the same across both resistors, since they are connected in shunt (in parallel).

Each product of current by resistance must, therefore, be the same:

$$e = ir = (i_0 - i)r_0 \tag{11-10}$$

whence

$$i = \frac{r_0 i_0}{r + r_0} \tag{11-11}$$

Substituting this in Eq. 11-9 gives

$$P = \frac{r r_0^2 i_0^2}{(r + r_0)^2} \tag{11-12}$$

and this power is a maximum when dP/dr equals zero, or

$$\frac{(r + r_0)r_0^2 i_0^2 - 2r r_0^2 i_0^2}{(r + r_0)^3} = 0 \tag{11-13}$$

giving

$$r = r_0 \tag{11-14}$$

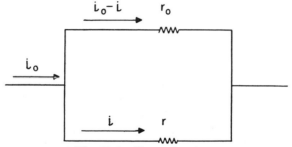

Fig. 11-4   Shunted resistor.

That is, the power consumed in r is a maximum if the resistance r of the shunt is equal to the fixed resistance r_0.

The current in r then is, by Eq. 11-11,

$$i = \frac{i_0}{2} \tag{11-15}$$

and the power in r is

$$P = \frac{r_0 i_0^2}{4} \tag{11-16}$$

If the function $y = f(x)$ is differentiated directly, as in Eq. 11-13, the calculation is frequently much more complicated than necessary. It is therefore desirable to simplify the function as much as possible before differentiating.

If y is an extreme, any expression differing therefrom by a constant term or constant factor also is an extreme. So also is the reciprocal of y, or its square, or any power of it. Thus, before differentiating, constant terms and constant factors can be dropped, fractions inverted, the expression raised to any power, etc.

For instance, in the preceding example, in Eq. 11-12, the value of r is to be found which makes P a maximum. If P is an extreme,

$$y_1 = \frac{r}{(r + r_0)^2} \tag{11-17}$$

also is an extreme. The reciprocal of y_1,

$$y_2 = \frac{(r + r_0)^2}{r} = r + 2r_0 + \frac{r_0^2}{r} \tag{11-18}$$

is also an extreme (y_2 is a minimum when y_1 is a maximum, and inversely). Therefore, Eq. 11-12 can be simplified to the form, omitting the constant term,

$$y_3 = r + \frac{r_0^2}{r} \tag{11-19}$$

This differentiated gives

$$\frac{dy_3}{dr} = 1 - \frac{r_0^2}{r^2} = 0 \tag{11-20}$$

Hence $r = r_0$ as before (Eq. 11-14).

In the calculation of maxima and minima by differentiating the function $y = f(x)$, it must be kept in mind that this method gives the values of x for which y becomes an extreme; but whether this extreme has a physical reality or not requires further investigation. That is, the range of values for x and y may be much wider mathematically than in an engineering application.

Suppose it is desired to find the maximum noninductive load that can be delivered over a transmission line whose sending end voltage is E, resistance is r_0, and reactance x_0. Let the resistance of the noninductive load be r. Then the problem is to find the maximum value of i^2r (see Eq. 3-21):

$$i^2r = \frac{E^2r}{(r + r_0)^2 + x_0^2} \tag{11-21}$$

when r is varied. Inverting and omitting the constant term makes this equivalent to finding the value of r that makes y a minimum, where

$$y = r + \frac{r_0^2 + x_0^2}{r} \tag{11-22}$$

The derivative of this is

$$\frac{dy}{dr} = 1 - \frac{r_0^2 + x_0^2}{r^2} \tag{11-23}$$

When this is zero, we have

$$r = \sqrt{r_0{}^2 + x_0{}^2} \tag{11-24}$$

as the condition for maximum delivered power. The corresponding current is

$$i = \frac{E}{\sqrt{2}\sqrt{r_0{}^2 + x_0{}^2}\,(r_0 + \sqrt{r_0{}^2 + x_0{}^2})}$$

and the delivered power is

$$P = i^2 \sqrt{r_0{}^2 + x_0{}^2} = \frac{E^2}{2(r_0 + \sqrt{r_0{}^2 + x_0{}^2})}$$

This problem can be solved graphically by means of the well-known circle diagram (Fig. 11-5). In the diagram, the applied voltage E is

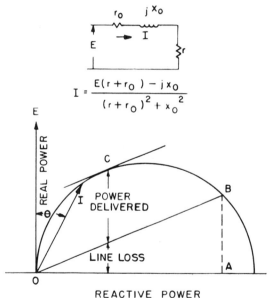

Fig. 11-5 Circle diagram showing maximum power delivered over reactive line.

taken as the vertical axis, and the current phasor lags the voltage by the power factor angle θ. The vertical (in-phase) component of current times E is the real power, and the horizontal component is the reactive power. The locus of the current phasor is a semicircle whose diameter is E/x_0. When the load resistance is very large, the current is small, and nearly vertical; when $r = 0$, the current is

$$OB = \frac{E}{\sqrt{r_0{}^2 + x_0{}^2}}$$

Maximum power is delivered when the current phasor (see Sec. 3-4) is at C, where the tangent to the circle is parallel to the short-circuit current OB.

11-3   Maxima and Minima Depending on Two Variables.   In engineering calculations, it is often required to determine extremes of quantities that are functions of two or more variables. For instance, there may be required the maximum power that can be delivered over a circuit, in which the resistance and reactance can be varied independently. That is, if

$$y = f(u,v) \tag{11-25}$$

a pair of values u,v is to be found that will make y a maximum or a minimum.

Choosing any value u_0 of the independent variable u, a value of v can be found that gives the maximum (or minimum) value of y that can be attained for $u = u_0$. This is done by differentiating $y = f(u_0,v)$ with respect to v and equating the result to zero, thus:

$$\frac{d_f(u_0,v)}{dv} = 0 \tag{11-26}$$

From this equation, a value

$$v = f_1(u_0) \tag{11-27}$$

is found that gives the maximum value of y for the given value u_0. Then, by substituting this expression for v in Eq. 11-25, we obtain an equation that gives the relation between the extreme values of y and the values of u_0:

$$y = f(u_0,f_1(u_0)) = f_2(u_0) \tag{11-28}$$

The value of u_0 that gives the most extreme value of y_1 (the maximum of the maxima, or minimum of the minima) is now found by differentiating Eq. 11-28 with respect to u_0 and equating to zero:

$$\frac{df_2(u_0)}{du_0} = 0 \tag{11-29}$$

Geometrically, $y = f(u,v)$ represents a surface in space with the coordinates y,u,v and $y = f(u_0,v)$ represents the curve of intersection of this surface with the plane $u_0 = $ constant. Differentiation (Eq. 11-26) gives the maximum (or minimum) value of y on this intersection curve, and $y = f_2(u_0)$ gives the curve in space that connects all the extremes of the various intersections with the u_0 planes; differentiating this (Eq. 11-29) determines the value of u_0 at which the most extreme of all the values of y occurs.

It is equally possible to differentiate Eq. 11-25, first with respect to

u, holding v constant, thus:

$$\frac{df(u,v_0)}{du} = 0 \tag{11-30}$$

and thereby get

$$u = f_3(v_0) \tag{11-31}$$

as the value of u which makes y an extreme for the chosen value of $v = v_0$. Substituting Eq. 11-31 into Eq. 11-25, we obtain

$$y = f_4(v_0) \tag{11-32}$$

as the equation of extremes. Differentiating this with respect to v_0 gives

$$\frac{df_4(v_0)}{dv_0} = 0 \tag{11-33}$$

which determines the value of v_0 at which the most extreme value of y occurs.

Geometrically, this alternative procedure determines the intersection curves of the surface with the plane $v_0 = $ constant.

If both Eqs. 11-26 and 11-29 (or Eqs. 11-30 and 11-33) represent maxima, or minima, they determine a true extreme value of y. However, if one represents a maximum and the other a minimum, they determine a saddle point (or point of inflection) instead of an extreme value of y.

The procedure will be made plain by an example:

An alternating voltage $e = 30,000$ is impressed on a circuit of resistance $r_0 = 20$ ohms and reactance $x_0 = 50$ ohms. What are the values of r and x for the load at the far end that will allow maximum power to be delivered over the circuit? Let $i = $ the current. The total resistance is $r + r_0$, the total reactance $x + x_0$; hence, the current is (Eq. 3-21)

$$i = \frac{e}{\sqrt{(r + r_0)^2 + (x + x_0)^2}} \tag{11-34}$$

The power delivered is

$$P = i^2 r = \frac{re^2}{(r + r_0)^2 + (x + x_0)^2} \tag{11-35}$$

For any given value of r, the reactance that gives maximum power is determined by

$$\frac{dP}{dx} = 0 \tag{11-36}$$

P is a maximum when $(x + x_0)^2$ is a minimum; hence, Eq. 11-36 gives

$$\frac{d(x + x_0)^2}{dx} = 2(x + x_0) = 0 \quad \text{or} \quad x = -x_0 \quad (11\text{-}37)$$

That is, for any chosen load resistance r, the power delivered will be a maximum when the load reactance is chosen equal to that of the line, but of opposite sign (is an equal capacitance). Substituting Eq. 11-37 in Eq. 11-35 gives the maximum power for a chosen value of r:

$$P_0 = \frac{re^2}{(r + r_0)^2} \quad (11\text{-}38)$$

Inverting and simplifying, the maximum value of P_0 will occur when $(r + r_0)^2/r$, or $r + r_0^2/r$, is a minimum. Hence

$$\frac{d(r + r_0^2/r)}{dr} = 1 - \frac{r_0^2}{r^2} = 0 \quad \text{or} \quad r = r_0 \quad (11\text{-}39)$$

will give the maximum possible power, and this extreme value of power is, putting $r = r_0$ in Eq. 11-38,

$$P_{\text{max}} = \frac{r_0 e^2}{(2r_0)^2} = \frac{e^2}{4r_0} \quad (11\text{-}40)$$

Alternatively, differentiating Eq. 11-35 with respect to r first,

$$\frac{dP}{dr} = 0 \quad (11\text{-}41)$$

will give the value of r that gives maximum power for any chosen value of x.

Inverting and simplifying Eq. 11-35, this leads to

$$\frac{d}{dr}\left[r + \frac{r_0^2 + (x + x_0)^2}{r}\right] = 1 - \frac{r_0^2 + (x + x_0)^2}{r^2} = 0$$

or

$$r = \sqrt{r_0^2 + (x + x_0)^2} \quad (11\text{-}42)$$

Substituting this in Eq. 11-35 gives for the maximum power

$$P_0 = \frac{e^2}{2[r_0 + \sqrt{r_0^2 + (x + x_0)^2}]} \quad (11\text{-}43)$$

The value of x which makes the maximum power P_0 the highest possible value is given by $dP_0/dx = 0$.

Evidently, P_0 will be a maximum when $(x + x_0)^2$ is a minimum, that is, when $x = -x_0$. Putting this in Eq. 11-43, the maximum possible power is

$$P_{max} = \frac{e^2}{4r_0}$$

as before.

With the values of e, r_0, and x_0 given, the maximum power that can be delivered occurs when $r = 20$ and $x = -50$ ohms and is

$$P_{max} = \frac{(30,000)^2}{4(20)} = 11.25 \times 10^6 \text{ watts, or } 11,250 \text{ kilowatts}$$

The corresponding current is $i = e/2r_0 = 30,000 = 750$ amperes, and the load voltage is

$$e' = i\sqrt{r^2 + x^2} = 750\sqrt{(20)^2 + (5)^2} = 40,400 \text{ volts}$$

At this maximum condition, the efficiency of transmission is only 50 per cent, since half the total power is consumed in r_0 and the receiving end voltage is excessively high. In practice, therefore, a smaller value of load capacitance, and a considerably higher value of load resistance, will be employed with this circuit, thus obtaining a higher efficiency and better voltage regulation. Conversely, if a larger amount of power is required, steps would be taken to decrease the line impedance or to raise the sending end voltage.

11-4 Calculus of Variations. A great many problems in engineering and physics require for their solution that some quantity be made a maximum or a minimum. For example, the contour of a soap film is such that its surface area is a minimum. To find the shape of the brachistochrone, or curve of most rapid descent (see Sec. 4-10), it is necessary to derive an expression for the time taken by a ball to roll down an arbitrary curve drawn from a point A to a lower point B and then determine what shape the curve must have to make the time a minimum.

The law of conservation of energy states that the sum of the kinetic and potential energies of any physical system remains constant aside from friction or heat losses. Hamilton's principle of least action states that, in addition, the motion will occur in such a way that the integral of the kinetic energy T times the elapsed time shall be a minimum, or

$$\int_{t_1}^{t_2} T\, dt = \text{a minimum} \tag{11-44}$$

The name *calculus of variations* is given to the general theory that makes use of these principles. Heretofore, we have found specific values of x, y, etc., that will make a given function a maximum or a minimum. Now the problem is to find the shape of an entire curve, $y = f(x)$, that will cause an integral such as Eq. 11-44 to have an extreme value. The usual problem is to make a function $F(x,y,y')$ a minimum when the integration is carried out along a curve $y = f(x)$ between two points x_0,y_0 and x_1,y_1: ·

$$I = \int_{x_0}^{x_1} F(x,y,y') \, dx = \text{a minimum} \tag{11-45}$$

We shall first imagine that the integration is performed along some other nearby curve, $y = f(x) + \Delta y$, where Δy represents a small departure *away from* the curve $y = f(x)$, just as dy represents a small distance *along* the curve. Then, if we differentiate Eq. 11-45 with respect to Δy, the new integral resulting will be the total change in I due to performing the integration along the new curve instead of along $y = f(x)$. If $y = f(x)$ is to have the form that makes I a minimum, this new integral must be zero. Since both y and $y' = dy/dx$ change with Δy, the differential of I with respect to Δy is

$$\Delta I = \int_{x_0}^{x_1} \left(\frac{\partial F}{\partial y} \Delta y + \frac{\partial F}{\partial y'} \Delta y' \right) dx = 0 \tag{11-46}$$

The second term of Eq. 11-46 may be integrated by parts, giving

$$\int_{x_0}^{x_1} \frac{\partial F}{\partial y'} \Delta y' \, dx = \left[\frac{\partial F}{\partial y'} \Delta y \right]_{x_0}^{x_1} - \int_{x_0}^{x_1} \Delta y \frac{d}{dx} \frac{\partial F}{\partial y'} \, dx \tag{11-47}$$

The first term of Eq. 11-47 is zero, because both the old and the new curves must pass through the same end points; i.e., $\Delta y = 0$ when $x = x_0$ and $x = x_1$, and Eq. 11-47 must vanish at every point of the interval between, if I is to be zero as the conditions require.

Carrying out the differentiation in the second term of Eq. 11-47, and combining it with Eq. 11-46, we obtain

$$\Delta I = \int_{x_0}^{x_1} \left[\frac{\partial F}{\partial y} - \frac{\partial^2 F}{\partial x \, \partial y'} - \frac{\partial^2 F}{\partial y \, \partial y'} y' - \frac{\partial^2 F}{\partial y'^2} y'' \right] dx \, \Delta y = 0 \tag{11-48}$$

For this to be zero, the expression in brackets must be zero. Therefore, by carrying out the indicated differentiations and solving the resulting second-order differential equation, the form of $y = f(x)$ can be found, and the problem is solved.

The simplest problem of this kind is to show that the shortest distance between two points is a straight line. The length of an element of an arc of the curve $y = f(x)$ is

$$\sqrt{dx^2 + dy^2} = \sqrt{1 + y'^2} \, dx$$

For this to be a minimum, the bracketed expression in Eq. 11-48 must be zero when this expression is substituted for $F(x,y,y')$. We have

$$\frac{\partial F}{\partial y} = \frac{\partial}{\partial y} \sqrt{1 + y'^2} = 0$$

$$\frac{\partial F}{\partial y'} = \frac{y'}{\sqrt{1 + y'^2}}$$

$$\frac{\partial^2 F}{\partial x \, \partial y'} = 0$$

$$\frac{\partial^2 F}{\partial y \, \partial y'} = 0$$

and

$$\frac{\partial^2 F}{dy'^2} = \frac{1}{(1 + y'^2)^{\frac{1}{2}}} - \frac{y'^2}{(1 + y'^2)^{\frac{3}{2}}} = \frac{1}{(1 + y'^2)^{\frac{3}{2}}}$$

Substituting in the bracketed expression in Eq. 11-48 and equating to zero, we have

$$-\frac{y''}{(1 + y'^2)^{\frac{3}{2}}} = 0 \qquad \text{or} \qquad y'' = 0$$

Integrating twice, we find

$$y = ax + b$$

which is the equation of a straight line, the constants a and b being determined by the condition that the line must pass through the two points x_0, y_0 and x_1, y_1.

PROBLEMS

1. Divide 36 into the sum of two parts such that the product of one part and the square of the other is a maximum.
2. A rectangular area is to be enclosed by a fence 500 yards long. Find the dimensions of the rectangle if the area is a maximum.
3. If 110 volts is maintained at one end of a direct-current line whose resistance is 2.2 ohms, what is the maximum power in watts that can be transmitted over the line?
4. Find the depth of the stiffest beam that can be cut from a cylindrical tree 12 inches in diameter and of length L. Stiffness is proportional to the width and to the cube of the depth.
5. Find the cylinder with maximum volume that may be inscribed in a hemisphere of radius r.
6. Show that $ae^{kx} + be^{-kx}$ has a minimum value equal to $2\sqrt{ab}$.
7. Find the height of the flame of a lamp standing at the center of a round table 4 feet in diameter, so that a given horizontal area at

its edge may receive the greatest illumination from the flame. The intensity of light varies directly as the sine of the angle which a ray makes with the plane of the table, and inversely as the square of the distance.

8. Two trains are running uniformly at the rates of 30 and 40 miles per hour, respectively, along lines at right angles. Show that if their distances at one time from the point of crossing of the lines are 30 miles and 20 miles, the distance between them can never be less than 12 miles.

9. Prove that the shortest distance between two fixed points in a plane is a straight line. HINT: Use $ds^2 = dx^2 + dy^2$ and assume that the axis may be rotated and translated until the two points lie on the x axis.

10. A buoy is to be made by cutting sectors from two circular plates of radius 8 feet. It will be composed of two equal right circular cones with a common base. If the volume of the buoy is to be a maximum, find its dimensions.

11. Neglecting air resistance, what is the angle of projection that will give maximum horizontal range, R, to a shell shot from a gun which has a muzzle velocity equal to v, given that

$$R = \frac{v^2 \sin 2\alpha}{32.2}$$

Bibliography

1. Kimball, W. S.: "Calculus of Variations," Butterworth & Co. (Publishers), Ltd., London, 1952.
2. Newman, J. R.: "The World of Mathematics," pt. 5, Simon and Schuster, Inc., New York, 1956.
3. Weinstock, R.: "Calculus of Variations with Applications to Physics and Engineering," McGraw-Hill Book Company, New York, 1952.

Chapter 12 DIFFERENTIAL EQUATIONS

12-1 The Usefulness of Differential Equations. The easiest way to solve an engineering problem is to ask some one who knows how and then to make the necessary calculations in accordance with his instructions. After some experience acquired in this way, the beginner may learn to select and use correctly the appropriate formulas from a handbook or reference manual. The mathematics he will use in so doing will be chiefly arithmetic and trigonometry, when the quantities to be determined are calculated independently. Some algebra and analytic geometry will be required when the interrelations between two or more quantities need to be considered. In this way, and in due time, one may become a good "handbook engineer," though having little or no knowledge of calculus.

To become an engineer in a higher sense, one must also learn how to extend and modify available formulas and to solve entirely new problems with some degree of facility. This requires, first, that the appropriate equations to fit the problem be derived, and, second, that these equations be solved, after which the resulting formulas may be turned over to a handbook engineer, or an assistant, to make the numerical calculations.

A large proportion of the practical problems that an engineer must deal with are concerned with rapidly changing events, such as the motion of a projectile, the vibrations of a structure, the decay of current in an electric circuit, the flow of liquids, or the transmission of heat. A typical problem of this character is that of determining the motions of an elastic structure, such as a fabricated steel beam, when a load is suddenly applied to it. In this example, the motion of each particle, or element of the beam, is in accord with Newton's second law of motion, which states that the velocity (speed of movement) of any object will change at a rate proportional to the applied force per unit of mass. The equation of motion for each element of the beam,

[263]

therefore, will have the form

$$\frac{M \, dv}{dt} = F_1 + F_2 + F_3 + \cdots \tag{12-1}$$

where $M =$ mass of the element

$s =$ displacement from the initial, undisturbed, position

$t =$ elapsed time

$ds/dt = v =$ velocity of the element = rate of change of the displacement

$d^2s/dt^2 = dv/dt =$ acceleration, or rate of change of the velocity

$F_1, F_2, F_3 =$ forces acting on the element

The letter in each case stands for the numeral representing the number of units of the quantity, measured in a consistent system of units (see Sec. 3-10).

Each element of the beam is restrained from moving by the (elastic) forces exerted on it by adjacent elements. These spring forces, tending to restore the element to its position of rest, ordinarily are roughly proportional to the displacement and so are represented by $-Ks$. While it is moving, the element is also acted on by damping forces that ordinarily are roughly proportional to the velocity and thus are represented by $-D \, ds/dt$. These are due to friction at the points of support, at joints, and in the beam material itself. Therefore, the equation of motion (Eq. 12-1) takes the general form

$$\underset{\substack{\text{Inertia} \\ \text{force}}}{\frac{M \, d^2s}{dt^2}} = \underset{\substack{\text{Applied} \\ \text{force}}}{F(t)} - \underset{\substack{\text{Damping} \\ \text{force}}}{\frac{D \, ds}{dt}} - \underset{\substack{\text{Spring} \\ \text{force}}}{Ks}$$

$$\text{or} \qquad \underset{\substack{\text{Inertia} \\ \text{force}}}{\frac{M \, d^2s}{dt^2}} + \underset{\substack{\text{Damping} \\ \text{force}}}{\frac{D \, ds}{dt}} + \underset{\substack{\text{Spring} \\ \text{force}}}{Ks} = \underset{\substack{\text{Applied} \\ \text{force}}}{F(t)} \tag{12-2}$$

The applied force $F(t)$ may be periodic or a single impulse, or it may vary in any prescribed manner, so that $F(t)$ in the general case is an arbitrary function of time. The coefficients (parameters) M, D, and K are assumed to be fixed, independent of changes in s and t, throughout this chapter.

Equation 12-2 contains both a first-order derivative, $ds/dt = s'$, and a second-order derivative, $d^2s/dt^2 = s''$, besides terms in s and t. It is, therefore, called a *differential equation*. The order of a differential equation is the order of the highest derivative it contains, in this case 2. A differential equation of the nth order is represented by

$$F(x,y,y',y'', \ldots ,y^n) = \phi(x) \tag{12-3}$$

If we are dealing with electric circuits (Sec. 14-5) instead of structures, the inertia, damping, and spring forces are proportional to the inductance L, resistance R, and the reciprocal of the capacitance of the circuit, $1/C$. In dealing with fluid flow, heat, and other problems, the same type of differential equation occurs frequently, the only difference being in the physical interpretation of the terms.

Therefore, an engineer must be familiar with differential equations, and be able to solve at least the simpler types, in order to deal adequately with quite ordinary problems.

To solve a differential equation, we must find a function $y = f(x)$, given explicitly, or defined implicitly by the relation $F(x,y) = 0$, such that the differential equation remains true for all the values of the independent variable x when $f(x)$, $f'(x)$, $f''(x)$, . . . are substituted for y, y', y'', . . . in Eq. 12-3.

The method of solution depends in large degree on the ingenuity of the solver. There are well-established procedures for solving the simplest types, as described in Secs. 12-2 to 12-9. The less familiar types may be solved by approximate methods, as described in Sec. 12-10 or by reference to treatises on this subject.

12-2 Differential Equations of Simple Curves. A curve showing the relation between two variables, x and y, can be represented by an ordinary equation $y = f(x)$ or by a corresponding differential equation $dy/dx = f'(x)$ (together with a suitable boundary condition). The ordinary equation for the parabola (Fig. 4-1) is

$$y = \sqrt{x} \tag{12-4}$$

Differentiating this gives the differential equation of the parabola:

$$dy = d\,(\sqrt{x}) = \frac{dx}{2\sqrt{x}}$$

or $$\frac{dy}{dx} = \frac{1}{2\sqrt{x}} = \frac{1}{2y} \tag{12-5}$$

By integrating this, we find the solution to be

$$y = \int_a^x \frac{dx}{2\sqrt{x}} = \sqrt{x} - \sqrt{a} = \sqrt{x} + C \tag{12-6}$$

The original equation of the curve is recovered, with the addition of a constant of integration C. Thus, the differential equation (Eq. 12-5) represents a whole family of curves, differing from each other only in the value of C, while the ordinary equation (Eq. 12-4) represents a single curve, with a particular value of C. If a differential equation includes only the first derivative, dy/dx, there is only one integration constant. If the equation includes derivatives up to the nth order, $d^n y/dx^n$, there are n integration constants, corresponding to the n integrations required to derive the ordinary equation from the differential equation.

With a little experience, the form of curve corresponding to a particular differential equation may be recognized as easily as that representing an ordinary equation. For example, the differential equation of a straight line, obtained by differentiating Eq. 4-4, is

$$a\,dx + b\,dy = 0 \qquad \text{or} \qquad \frac{dy}{dx} = -\frac{a}{b} = \text{a constant} \qquad (12\text{-}7)$$

The differential equation of a conic section, from Eq. 4-5, is

$$\frac{dy}{dx} = -\frac{2xa + yf + b}{2yd + xf + e} \qquad (12\text{-}8)$$

For the ellipse (Fig. 4-4), $f = 0$ and

$$\frac{dy}{dx} = -\frac{2xa + b}{2yd + e} \qquad (12\text{-}9)$$

For a circle, $a = d$ and $f = 0$

$$\frac{dy}{dx} = -\frac{x + b/2a}{y + c/2a} \qquad (12\text{-}10)$$

For the equilateral hyperbola (Fig. 4-5), $a = b = d = e = 0$ and

$$\frac{dy}{dx} = -\frac{y}{x} \qquad \text{or} \qquad x\,dy = y\,dx \qquad (12\text{-}11)$$

And, for the parabola of Fig. 4-1, $a = c = e = f = 0$ and $b = -1$:

$$\frac{dy}{dx} = \frac{1}{2y} \qquad (12\text{-}12)$$

Such differential equations specify interesting properties of curves. For example, Eq. 12-12 states that at every point on the parabola $y\,dy/dx = \frac{1}{2}$. Referring to Fig. 4-1, $y\,dy/dx$ is equal to the projection on the x axis of the normal to the curve, which is called the subnormal. Therefore, the family of parabolas, obtained by integrating Eq. 12-12, has the property that the length of the subnormal is a constant.

Similarly, Eq. 12-11 states the property of the equilateral hyperbola that the projection of the tangent on the x axis, or subtangent, is equal to x. And Eq. 12-10 states that the tangent to a circle is always perpendicular to its radius, so that the radius has a constant length.

12-3   The Falling Stone and Pendulum Equations.   Newton's second law of motion states that:

Change of momentum is proportional to the force and to the time during which it acts.

Since momentum is equal to mass times velocity, this gives the equation

$$\Delta(MV) = F\,\Delta t \qquad (12\text{-}13)$$

where, in the meter-kilogram-second system of units (see Sec. 3-10),
M = mass in kilograms (1 kilogram = 2.2046 pounds)
V = velocity, in meters per second (1 meter = 39.37 inches
   = 3.281 feet)
F = force in newtons (1 newton[1] = 10^5 dynes)
t = time in seconds

At the limit, for a very small interval of time, Δ may be replaced by d, and Eq. 12-13 becomes:

$$\frac{M\,dV}{dt} = F \qquad \text{or} \qquad dV = \frac{F\,dt}{M} \qquad (12\text{-}14)$$

which is the differential equation of motion of a mass M acted on by a force F, such as a freely falling stone. Air resistance is neglected. The velocity V is the rate of change of distance s, so that $V = ds/dt$. Hence, Eq. 12-14 may be written

$$\frac{dV}{dt} = \frac{d^2s}{dt^2} = \frac{F}{M} \qquad \text{meters per second per second} \qquad (12\text{-}15)$$

Integrating this between the initial time t_0 and the time t we have

$$\int_{t_0}^{t} \frac{d^2s}{dt^2}\,dt = \int_{t_0}^{t} \frac{F\,dt}{M}$$

or
$$\frac{ds}{dt} - V_0 = \frac{F(t - t_0)}{M} \qquad \text{meters per second} \qquad (12\text{-}16)$$

where V_0 is the initial velocity at time t_0.

[1] The newton is the force which will impart an acceleration of 1 meter per second per second to a mass of 1 kilogram.

Integrating a second time gives

$$\int_{t_0}^{t} ds = \frac{1}{M} \int_{t_0}^{t} F(t - t_0)\, dt + \int_{t_0}^{t} V_0\, dt$$

or $\qquad s - s_0 = \dfrac{F}{2M}\,(t - t_0)^2 + V_0(t - t_0) \qquad$ meters $\qquad$ (12-17)

The ratio, F/M, of gravitational force to mass is 9.80 newtons per kilogram (at the surface of the earth). Substituting this in the above three equations, we find

The velocity of a freely-falling stone increases at the rate of 9.80 meters per second (or 32.2 feet per second) during each second of fall if air resistance is neglected. The additional velocity the stone has acquired after t seconds is $9.80t$ meters per second. The distance fallen in t seconds after starting from rest is $4.90t^2$ meters.

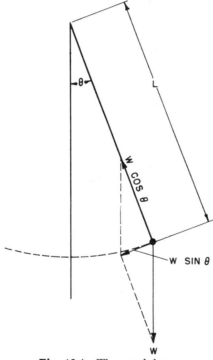

Thus, by writing down the differential equation of motion, as determined by physical laws, integrating the equation, and finding the integration constants from the known initial conditions, we solve the problem; i.e., we have derived formulas for the position and the velocity of the stone at each instant of its fall. This is a simple, but typical, example of the way that engineers use differential equations.

In this case, the equations were linear (only the first power of y and its derivatives appeared) and the variables were separated (dV or ds, with functions of V or s, appeared on one side of the equation, and dt with functions of t on the other side). The solution, therefore, took the simplest possible form.

Fig. 12-1 The pendulum.

The equation of the pendulum provides a slightly more difficult example. In Fig. 12-1, the forces acting on the bob of a pendulum are shown, when it makes an angle θ with the vertical. All the weight is assumed to be in the bob. The two forces are the weight, W kilograms, acting vertically downward, and the tension in the rod $W \cos \theta$, acting upward along the radius. The resultant of these is $W \sin \theta$, acting downward at right angles to the radius. In the absence of restraint, this unopposed resultant impels the bob downward along the arc of a circle. When it reaches the lowest point, the acquired velocity carries the bob up on the other side to the same angle that it started from, if there is no friction or air resistance, in accordance with Eq. 12-14. In this case

$L =$ length of pendulum rod, meters
$s = L\theta =$ distance moved along the arc, meters
$V = L \, d\theta/dt =$ velocity along the arc, meters per second
$F/M = 9.80 \sin \theta =$ force-to-mass ratio, newtons per kilogram
Substituting in Eq. 12-14 gives

$$\frac{dV}{dt} = \frac{L \, d^2\theta}{dt^2} = -9.80 \sin \theta \qquad \text{meters per second per second} \quad (12\text{-}18)$$

We cannot integrate this equation directly. However, we note that, usually, θ is quite small, so that θ may be substituted for $\sin \theta$ (Eq. 3-25) without serious error. (It turns out that this gives a solution in terms of trigonometric functions, whereas the exact solution is in terms of elliptic functions.) Recognizing that the second derivatives of the sine and cosine functions are also sines and cosines, we may try the experiment of assuming that θ has the form

$$\theta = \alpha \sin \omega t + \beta \cos \omega t \qquad \text{radians} \qquad (12\text{-}19)$$

Then, from Eqs. 8-11 and 8-13,

$$\frac{d^2\theta}{dt^2} = -\omega^2(\alpha \sin \omega t + \beta \cos \omega t) = -\omega^2\theta \qquad \text{radians per second}^2$$

$$(12\text{-}20)$$

Substituting this in Eq. 12-18 and putting $\sin \theta = \theta$, approximately, gives

$$\frac{d^2\theta}{dt^2} = -\omega^2\theta = -\frac{9.80\theta}{L}$$

or

$$\omega = \sqrt{\frac{9.80}{L}} \qquad \text{radians per second} \qquad (12\text{-}21)$$

Assuming $t = 0$ when θ has its maximum value of θ_0, Eq. 12-19 gives $\theta_0 = \beta$. When $t = 0$ and $\theta = \theta_0$, the velocity is zero, so that

$$\left.\frac{d\theta}{dt}\right]_{t=0} = \left[\omega\alpha \cos \omega t - \omega\beta \sin \omega t\right]_{t=0} = \omega\alpha = 0$$

giving $\alpha = 0$. Hence, finally, the solution of Eq. 12-18 is

$$\theta = \theta_0 \cos\left(t\sqrt{\frac{9.80}{L}}\right) \qquad \text{radians (approximately)} \quad \text{(12-22)}$$

This assumes that θ is a small angle, so that $\sin \theta$ can be assumed equal to θ, and neglects friction, air resistance, and the weight of the pendulum rod. All these omitted factors can be taken account of by adding second-order terms, in the manner indicated in Sec. 8-7.

To solve any differential equation, it is first necessary to put it in such a form that it can be integrated. This is feasible when the variables are separated so that only functions of y and its derivatives occur on one side of the equation and functions of t and its derivatives on the other. Then, the resulting expressions must be integrated by the methods indicated in Chap. 9, by reference to tables, or in some other way.

12-4   The Differential Operator, $p = d/dt$.   A great many of the differential equations that are important in physics and engineering are linear, with constant coefficients. That is, they have the form

$$A_n \frac{d^n y}{dt^n} + A_{n-1} \frac{d^{n-1} y}{dt^{n-1}} + \cdots + \frac{A_1 \, dy}{dt} + A_0 y = f(t) \quad \text{(12-23)}$$

Here t is used in place of x for the independent variable, because many equations of this type deal with time-varying functions; i.e., they define the way a quantity varies with time, for which t is the usual symbol. The equations for the currents and voltages in electrical circuits take this form, and the values of A then represent the resistance, inductance, etc., of the various circuit branches.

Such equations can be solved by the operational methods used by Oliver Heaviside, which depend on the similarity of the rules governing the differential operator d/dt and those governing the algebra of ordinary symbols of quantity.

The distinction between an operator and a symbol of quantity is that an operator must have its meaning completed by an associated quantity, just as a transitive verb requires an object; while a symbol of quantity, like a noun, can stand alone. Thus, $+$, $-$, $\int \cdots dx$, cos, and d/dt are operators that have substantial meaning only when symbols of quantity are attached to them, as $+6$, $-z$, $\int x^2 \, dx$, cos α, or dy/dt, whereas x, 8, and α represent definite quantities by themselves.

In keeping with Heaviside's notation, we shall use p for d/dt when its operational character is important. Therefore

$$\frac{d}{dt} = p \tag{12-24}$$

and

$$\frac{d^2}{dt^2} = p^2, \ldots, \frac{d^n}{dt^n} = p^n \tag{12-25}$$

The inverse differential operator is p^{-1}, which is defined as the operator that annuls the effect of p, so that

$$p^{-1}pf(t) = f(t) \tag{12-26}$$

The operation p^{-1} is an integration.

Carrying this notation a step further, we may write Eq. 12-23 as

$$F\left(\frac{d}{dt}\right)y = F(p)y = (p - p_1)(p - p_2)(p - p_3) \cdots (p - p_n)y$$
$$= f(t) \tag{12-27}$$

where $p_1, p_2, p_3, \ldots, p_n$ are the roots of $F(p)$ considered as an algebraic equation of the nth degree in p (see Eqs. 4-11 and 4-12).

With this notation, the equation

$$\frac{a\, d^2y}{dt^2} + \frac{b\, dy}{dt} + cy = f(t) \tag{12-28}$$

becomes

$$F(p)y = ap^2y + bpy + cy = f(t) \tag{12-29}$$

where

$$F(p) = ap^2 + bp + c \tag{12-30}$$

The reason for this choice of notation is that, when dealing with linear differential equations with constant coefficients, the operator p obeys the ordinary algebraic laws of addition, subtraction, multiplication, and division. For example, it is evident that

$$\frac{m\, dy}{dt} + \frac{n\, dy}{dt} = (m + n)\frac{dy}{dt}$$

or

$$(mp + np)y = (m + n)py \tag{12-31}$$

and this associative rule of addition holds for p^n as well as for p. Also, if we take the derivative of

$$z = \frac{m\, dy}{dt} + ny \tag{12-32a}$$

we obtain

$$\frac{dz}{dt} = \frac{m\, d^2y}{dt^2} + \frac{n\, dy}{dt} \tag{12-33a}$$

whence

$$\frac{q\, dz}{dt} + z = \frac{mq\, d^2y}{dt^2} + (nq + m)\frac{dy}{dt} + ny \tag{12-34a}$$

The same procedure in operational form is

$$z = (mp + n)y \qquad\qquad (12\text{-}32b)$$
$$pz = (mp^2 + np)y \qquad\qquad (12\text{-}33b)$$
$$(qp + 1)z = [mqp^2 + (nq + m)p + n]y \qquad (12\text{-}34b)$$

By substituting Eq. 12-32b in the left-hand member of Eq. 12-34b, we find

$$(qp + 1)(mp + n)y = [mqp^2 + (nq + m)p + n]y \quad (12\text{-}34c)$$

Multiplying through the left-hand factors algebraically gives the right-hand member. Thus, in multiplying as well as in addition, p behaves like an ordinary quantity. This applies to any degree, p^n, as well as to p.

The importance of this result is that the process can be reversed, enabling an nth-order expression in p to be factored into n first-order terms, just as we factored algebraic functions in Sec. 8-6.

We know from Eqs. 8-11 and 8-13 that $p \, (\sin \omega t) = \omega \cos \omega t$ and $p^2 \, (\sin \omega t) = -\omega^2 \sin \omega t$, so that, in general, if y is a sinusoidal function of ωt, $py = j\omega y$ and $p^2 y = -\omega^2 y$, where j has its usual meaning of a 90° counterclockwise rotation in the representation of phasor quantities (Sec. 3-12). Therefore, the steady-state solutions of differential equations that describe sinusoidally varying quantities can be solved by merely substituting $j\omega$ for p and solving the equations by complex algebra, as will be shown in Sec. 14-5.

To solve Eq. 12-27, we divide through by $F(p)$ and separate the right-hand side into partial fractions, by Eq. 8-53 or Eq. 8-54, giving

$$
\begin{aligned}
y &= \frac{f(t)}{F'(p_1)(p - p_1)} + \frac{f(t)}{F'(p_2)(p - p_2)} + \cdots + \frac{f(t)}{F'(p_n)(p - p_n)} \\
&= \quad y_1 \quad + \quad y_2 \quad + \cdots + \quad y_n
\end{aligned}
$$
$$(12\text{-}35)$$

Here, $F'(p_n)$ is the value of $F'(p)$ obtained by substituting the nth root, p_n, for p in $dF(p)/dp$. It should be clearly understood that p_1, p_2, $\ldots$, p_n are algebraic quantities, like the roots of any algebraic equation. Only p without a subscript is an operator.

Since Eq. 12-27 is linear, each term, y_n, on the right side of Eq. 12-35 may be considered separately as the solution of a corresponding first-order equation, and the general solution y may be obtained by adding y_1, y_2, $\ldots$, y_n.

In this way, the process of solving such an nth-order equation as Eq. 12-27 is reduced to that of solving n first-order equations. The solution of each of these first-order equations will include an arbitrary constant of integration, and the sum of the n solutions, which constitutes the general solution of the original nth-order equation, will include n constants of integration. Physically, this means that the behavior of an entire system, with n degrees of freedom, can be determined by solving separate equations that describe the motion in each of the n separate modes, subject to the determination of the corresponding n integration constants on a consistent basis.

For example, to solve the equation

$$F(p)y = (p^2 + 2ap + b)y = f(t) \qquad (12\text{-}36)$$

we divide through by $F(p) = (p - p_1)(p - p_2)$ and obtain

$$y = \frac{f(t)}{2(p_1 + a)(p - p_1)} + \frac{f(t)}{2(p_2 + a)(p - p_2)} \qquad (12\text{-}37)$$

since $F'(p) = 2(p + a)$. Here, $p_1 = -a - j\sqrt{b - a^2}$ and

$$p_2 = -a + j\sqrt{b - a^2}$$

The problem of solving Eq. 12-27, therefore, is reduced to that of solving n equations of the general type:

$$(p + b)y = f(t) \qquad \text{or} \qquad \frac{dy}{dt} = -by + f(t) \qquad (12\text{-}38)$$

where $p_1 = -b$ is the root of the equation $p + b = 0$. Here, $-b$ is chosen rather than b because p_1 is usually negative in practical problems.

Comparing the first-order equation (12-38) with Eq. 12-2, we see that py corresponds to an inertia force, $M\,d^2s/dt^2$, and by to a damping force, $D\,ds/dt$. Therefore, Eq. 12-38 has inertia and damping forces only; y represents a velocity in a mechanical system, or a current in an electrical system; and b represents the ratio of the damping to the inertia constants, D/M in a mechanical or R/L in an electrical system. The applied force $f(t)$ represents the actual force divided by the inertia constant or the voltage divided by the inductance.

12-5   The Complementary Function. Let y_p be a particular value of y which satisfies the equation

$$F(p)y = (p - p_1)(p - p_2) \cdots (p - p_n)y = f(t) \quad (12\text{-}27)$$

and let $y = y_p + y_c$. Then, substituting this value for y in the above, we have, since the equation is linear,

$$F(p)y_p + F(p)y_c = f(t)$$

By definition, y_p is a solution of Eq. 12-27. We therefore must have

$$F(p)y_c = (p - p_1)(p - p_2) \cdots (p - p_n)y_c = 0 \quad (12\text{-}39)$$

Thus, to find the complete solution of the original equation (12-27), we generally need also to solve Eq. 12-39, which is the same as the original equation except that the right-hand side is now zero instead of $f(t)$.

Equation 12-39 is called the *homogeneous equation* of Eq. 12-27.

The solution y_p is called the *particular integral* of Eq. 12-27. It does not include any arbitrary constants of integration.

The solution y_c is called the *complementary function*. It is the general solution of the homogeneous equation (12-39), and it includes n arbitrary constants of integration if p^n is the highest-order derivative in $F(p)$.

It is customary to divide the process of solving a differential equation, such as Eq. 12-27, into these two distinct steps, finding y_p and y_c independently, and adding them to obtain the complete solution, y.

The solution of the homogeneous equation (12-39) requires the solution of n separate first-order equations, each similar to the homogeneous equation of Eq. 12-38, which is

$$(p + b)y = 0 \quad \text{or} \quad \frac{dy}{dt} = -by \quad \text{or} \quad \frac{dy}{y} = -b \, dt \quad t > 0 \quad (12\text{-}40)$$

This can be integrated directly. If we assume that initially, at time $t = 0$, the value of y is y_0, the integration gives

$$\ln y \Big]_{y_0}^{y} = -bt \Big]_{0}^{t} \quad \text{or} \quad \ln \frac{y}{y_0} = -bt \quad t > 0 \quad (12\text{-}41)$$

which gives

$$y = y_0 e^{-bt} \quad (12\text{-}42)$$

This is the complementary function for Eq. 12-38. It should be noted that it satisfies Eq. 12-40 and is therefore not a complete solution of Eq. 12-38. As a check, by substituting Eq. 12-42 in Eq. 12-38, we find

$$\frac{dy}{dt} + by = -y_0 b e^{-bt} + b y_0 e^{-bt} = 0$$

Equation 12-42 shows that if $f(t) = 0$ when $t > 0$, y decays exponentially from its initial value of y_0 toward a final value of zero (Fig. 12-2). If the force applied was unity when $t < 0$, the value of $y_0 = 1/b$.

There are many ways of finding the particular solution. One of these is that the particular solution of Eq. 12-38 is found by the rule,

To find the particular solution of a differential equation of the form $[p + G(t)]y = f(t)$, multiply both sides by the "integrating factor" $\exp\left[\int^t G(t)\, dt\right]$, and then integrate the equation directly, without regard to any lower limit of integration.

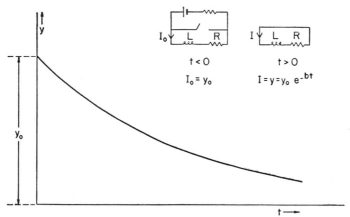

$$t < 0$$
$$I_0 = y_0$$

$$t > 0$$
$$I = y = y_0\, e^{-bt}$$

Fig. 12-2 Decay of current in a circuit when the voltage is suddenly removed at the time $t = 0$.

In Eq. 12-38, $G(t) = b$, so that $\exp\left[\int^t G(t)\, dt\right] = e^{bt}$. Multiplying by this and by dt, we obtain

$$e^{bt}\, dy + bye^{bt}\, dt = e^{bt}f(t)\, dt$$

which gives

$$e^{bt}y = \int^t e^{bt}f(t)\, dt$$

or

$$y = e^{-bt} \int^t e^{bt}f(t)\, dt \tag{12-43}$$

This is the particular integral of Eq. 12-38.

Therefore, the general solution of Eq. 12-38 is the sum of Eqs. 12-42 and 12-43, or

$$y = e^{-bt} \left[y_0 + \int^t e^{bt}f(t)\, dt\right] = e^{-bt}\,[y_0 + F(t)] \tag{12-44}$$

The integration constant y_0 is determined by the initial conditions. For example, if $f(t) = 0$ when $t < 0$, so that $y = 0$ when $t < 0$, and $f(t) = 1$ when $t > 0$, Eq. 12-44 becomes

$$y = y_0 e^{-bt} + \frac{1}{b} \qquad t > 0$$

To find y_0, we know from energy considerations that y cannot change abruptly, so that y must still be equal to zero at the first instant after $t = 0$. Therefore, when $t = 0$,

$$y = 0 = y_0 + \frac{1}{b}$$

so that $y_0 = -1/b$, and Eq. 12-44 becomes

$$
\begin{aligned}
y &= 0 & t &< 0 \\
y &= \frac{1}{b}(1 - e^{-bt}) & t &> 0
\end{aligned}
\tag{12-45}
$$

This gives the response of a system that is initially at rest to a suddenly applied unit force that remains constant thereafter.

A system in the steady state, with no applied force, $f(t) = 0$, will be completely at rest, with no motion; $y = 0$ when $f(t) = 0$, since perpetual motion without energy supply is contrary to natural laws. The only motion a system can have when $f(t) = 0$ is the dying away of motion due to previously applied forces. Hence, behavior of the system when $t > 0$ depends on what happened before $t = 0$. The behavior described by the homogeneous equation occurs after an initial instant, $t = 0$, and gives the result due to a force that was acting on the system prior to $t = 0$. That is, $f(-t) \neq 0$, and the equations that hold when $t > 0$ do not apply when $t < 0$. Therefore, the limitation $t > 0$ should be placed after every homogeneous equation and its solutions, as for Eq. 12-40 above.

When the n first-order homogeneous equations similar to Eq. 12-40 have been solved, their solutions y_1, y_2, . . . , y_n are added to give an expression for y_c that includes n constants of integration. To determine these n constants, it is then necessary to calculate y, y', y'', . . . , y^n, from the expression so obtained, at the time $t = 0$, and to equate these to the known values of y, y', y'', . . . , y^n that preexisted at time $t = 0$, as given by the initial conditions of the particular problem. The integration constants are finally determined by solving these n equations simultaneously.

This procedure may be difficult, especially for second- and higher-order equations. A more satisfactory procedure was developed by Heaviside, employing the unit function and the superposition theorem, as described in the next two sections. Another, more sophisticated, procedure is to make use of the Laplace transform (Sec. 12-9).

12-6   Use of the Unit Function.   Heaviside avoided the difficulties in finding the integration constants, by assuming that the system is initially at rest. Thus there are no effects of previously applied forces to be considered. Then, he assumed that a unit force 1 or H

(Eq. 9-69) is suddenly applied at the time $t = 0$. This unit force remains constant and equal to 1 continuously after time $t = 0$. Hence, the steady-state response of the system to a constant force is found by making $p = 0$.

For example, putting H for $f(t)$ in Eq. 12-38 gives

$$(p + b)yH = H \qquad \text{or} \qquad yH = \frac{H}{p + b} \qquad (12\text{-}46)$$

H appears on both sides of the equation to show that $yH = 0$ when $t < 0$. With H present as a factor, the equation is valid when $t < 0$ as well as when $t > 0$, and there is no longer any need for the limitation of $t > 0$ placed on Eq. 12-40.

Putting $p = 0$ in Eq. 12-46, we find its solution to be

$$Hy = \frac{H}{b} \qquad (12\text{-}47)$$

which means that

$$
\begin{aligned}
y &= 0 & t &< 0 \\
y &= \frac{1}{b} & t &\gg 0
\end{aligned}
\qquad (12\text{-}48)
$$

The term when $t \gg 0$ is the steady-state response of the system to a steady applied force equal to 1, after the transient has died away.

However, the use of the unit function enables the complete solution of the equation to be found when $f(t)$ is replaced by H, including both the transient and the steady-state response. The sum of these two responses, or total response, to a suddenly applied unit force is called the *indicial response*, and is designated by the symbol $I(t)$.

To find the indicial response of Eq. 12-38, we have to evaluate Eq. 12-46. For this purpose, we may first put $b = 0$ and determine the meaning of

$$Hy = \frac{H}{p} = p^{-1}H \qquad (12\text{-}49)$$

Since p^{-1} is an integration, this is, by Eq. 9-73,

$$p^{-1}H = \int_0^t H \, dt = tH \qquad (12\text{-}50)$$

More generally, by Eq. 9-74,

$$p^{-2}H = H \int t \, dt = \frac{Ht^2}{2}$$

$$p^{-3}H = H \int \frac{t^2}{2} \, dt = \frac{Ht^3}{6}$$

and

$$p^{-m}H = \frac{Ht^m}{m!} \qquad (12\text{-}51)$$

We may now expand Eq. 12-46 by Eq. 5-4 or by the binomial theorem (Eq. 5-22):

$$Hy = (p + b)^{-1}H = (p^{-1} - p^{-2}b + p^{-3}b^2 - \cdots)H \quad (12\text{-}52)$$

and we can make use of Eq. 12-51 to evaluate this:

$$Hy = H\left(t - \frac{bt^2}{2} + \frac{b^2t^3}{6} - \frac{b^3t^4}{24} + \cdots\right) \quad (12\text{-}53)$$

which is recognized from Eq. 8-24 to be

$$Hy = \frac{1}{p + b} H = \frac{H}{b}(1 - e^{-bt}) = I(t) \quad (12\text{-}54)$$

which means that

$$
\begin{aligned}
y &= 0 & t &< 0 \\
y &= \frac{1}{b}(1 - e^{-bt}) & t &> 0
\end{aligned}
\quad (12\text{-}45)
$$

Equation 12-54 is the solution of Eq. 12-46. It checks with the solution (Eq. 12-45) found previously by the conventional method. It is an operational formula that is useful in solving linear differential equations in the same way that the integral formulas of Appendix D are useful in performing integration. The operational formula consists of two terms, the term with a decrement factor, or transient response, and the term without a decrement factor, or steady-state response. The steady-state response is the same as found by making $p = 0$ originally (Eq. 12-48). Note that the equation was solved without finding any integration constants as such.

Placing $t = 0$ in Eq. 12-54, we find $y = 0$. That is to say, if $y = 0$ initially (instead of y_0 as in Eq. 12-42) and if a unit force, $f(t) = H$, is suddenly applied at time $t = 0$, y remains 0 at the first instant, but approaches exponentially a new value $1/b$. If $y = y_0$ initially and a negative force $-Hby_0$ is suddenly applied, at time $t = 0$, the response due to the force will be added to the initial value and the equation for y becomes

$$
\begin{aligned}
y &= y_0 & t &< 0 \\
y &= y_0 - \frac{by_0}{b}(1 - e^{-bt}) = y_0 e^{-bt} & t &> 0
\end{aligned}
\quad (12\text{-}55)
$$

This is the same as Eq. 12-42 found by the conventional method of solving the homogeneous equation. In using the conventional method, we found the integration constant, $\ln y_0$ in Eq. 12-41, from the assumption that y was equal to y_0 when $t = 0$. Using the unit function, we found the response of a system at rest to a suddenly applied unit force (in this case a negative force) without needing any constant of integration. The general method of solving a linear differential equation (12-46) using the operational method is to derive an operational formula (Eq. 12-54), then add to the steady state of the system at $t = 0$ the indicial response, which is found by multiplying the suddenly applied force by H in the operational formula (Eq. 12-55). From then on the solution becomes a matter of algebra only.

To solve Eq. 12-36 for a suddenly applied constant force, we substitute H for $f(t)$, $-a - jm$ for p_1, and $-a + jm$ for p_2 in Eq. 12-37, where $m = \sqrt{b - a^2}$, obtaining

$$I(t) = Hy = \frac{-H}{2jm(p + a + jm)} + \frac{H}{2jm(p + a - jm)}$$

From Eq. 12-54, this becomes

$$Hy = \frac{jH[1 - e^{-(a+jm)t}]}{2m(a + jm)} - \frac{jH(1 - e^{-(a-jm)t})}{2m(a - jm)}$$

$$= \frac{-Hae^{-at} \sin mt}{bm} + \frac{H}{b}(1 - e^{-at} \cos mt)$$

$$= \frac{H}{b}\left[1 - e^{-at}\left(\cos mt + \frac{a}{m} \sin mt\right)\right] \qquad (12\text{-}56)$$

or by Eq. 2-47, the indicial response of Eq. 12-36 is

$$I(t) = Hy = \frac{H}{p^2 + 2ap + b} = H\left[\frac{1}{b} - \frac{e^{-at} \sin(mt + \theta)}{m\sqrt{b}}\right] \qquad (12\text{-}57)$$

where $\theta = \cos^{-1}(a/\sqrt{b})$

$$m = \sqrt{b - a^2}$$

If $a = 0$, the system has no damping, and the original Eq. 12-36 becomes

$$(p^2 + b)y = H \qquad (12\text{-}58)$$

and its solution, from Eq. 12-57, is

$$I(t) = Hy = \frac{H}{p^2 + b} = \frac{H}{b}(1 - \cos t\sqrt{b}) \qquad (a = 0) \quad (12\text{-}59)$$

If $b = a^2$, the system is critically damped, and $p_1 = p_2 = -a$. In this case, Eq. 12-36 becomes, putting H for $f(t)$ and a^2 for b,

$$H(p^2 + 2ap + a^2)y = H(p + a)^2y = H$$

or

$$Hy = \frac{H}{(p + a)^2} \qquad (12\text{-}60)$$

To solve this, we note, from Eq. 12-54, that

$$\frac{H}{(p + a)^2} = \frac{d}{da}\left(-\frac{H}{p + a}\right) = \frac{-d}{da}\left[\frac{H}{a}(1 - e^{-at})\right] \quad (12\text{-}61)$$

Carrying through the indicated differentiation with respect to a gives

$$\frac{H}{(p + a)^2} = \frac{H}{a^2}(1 - e^{-at}) - \frac{Ht}{a}e^{-at}$$

or $\quad Hy = \dfrac{H}{(p + a)^2} = \dfrac{H}{a^2}[1 - e^{-at}(1 + at)] \quad (b = a^2) \quad (12\text{-}62)$

which is the solution of Eq. 12-60.

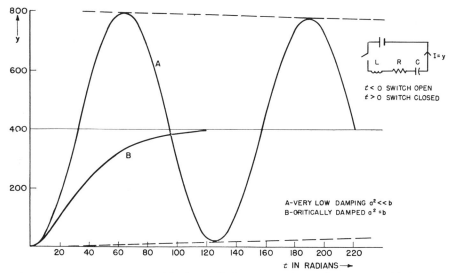

Fig. 12-3 Response to a suddenly applied constant force of a system with inertia, damping, and elasticity.

If $b = 0$, the system has inertia and friction (damping) only, and $p_1 = 0$, $p_2 = -2a$, so that the indicial response of Eq. 12-36 becomes

$$I(t) = Hy = \frac{H}{p^2 + 2ap} = \frac{H}{2ap} - \frac{H}{2a(p + 2a)} \quad (12\text{-}63)$$

whose solution is, from Eqs. 12-50 and 12-54,

$$Hy = \frac{H}{2a}\left[t - \frac{1}{2a}(1 - e^{-2at})\right] \quad (b = 0) \quad (12\text{-}64)$$

Equations 12-57, 12-59, 12-62, and 12-64 are different forms of the solution of Eq. 12-36 when $f(t) = H$. They give the indicial response of the system in the general case, and the cases of no damping ($a = 0$), critical damping ($b = a^2$), and no restoring force ($b = 0$), respectively. Two of these solutions are illustrated in Fig. 12-3. The inductance L, resistance R, and the reciprocal of the capacitance, $1/C$, of an electrical system correspond to the inertia, damping, and spring constants of a mechanical system (see Sec. 12-1).

Equations 12-54, 12-57, 12-59, 12-62, and 12-64 are examples of operational formulas that are highly useful in solving linear differential equations, just as Eq. 12-54 gives the solution of Eq. 12-46. In general, the procedure in deriving the operational formula for any expression $y = H/F(p)$ is to expand y in an infinite (convergent) series of negative powers of p and to perform the indicated integrations, obtaining a new (convergent) infinite series in positive powers of t. By comparing this with known series expressions, such as those in Appendix E, and with already known operational formulas, the desired expression for y in terms of t is found, as in deriving Eqs. 12-54, etc.

12-7   The Superposition Theorem.

The procedures considered in Sec. 12-6 give the indicial response $I(t)$ of a system, $I(t)$ being defined as the sum of the transient and steady-state responses of the system [defined by Eq. 12-27, $F(p)y = f(t)$] to a suddenly applied unit force H. When the applied force is $f(t)$, instead of H, the resulting motion, y, can be found by using the superposition theorem. This theorem states that the value of y at time t is the sum of all the increments in y that would be produced by successive increments of force, each suddenly applied in turn, over the period between $t = 0$ and $t = t$.

That is, the force $f(0)$ applied at time $t = 0$ produces a subsequent value of y at the time $t = t$ equal to $f(0)I(t)$. Also, a force $\Delta f(x)$, applied at a time $t = x$, produces a motion $\Delta y = \Delta f(x)I(t - x)$ at the time $t = t$. Thus the successive increments in the applied force, $\Delta f(x)$, determined by the function $f(t)$, produce corresponding increments in the motion, Δy, that are each given by the indicial response at time $t = t$ to a force $\Delta f(x)$, suddenly applied at the time $t = x$.

If the increments in t are very small, we can replace Δ by d, and the increment in force becomes $df(x) = f'(x)\, dx$. Hence the total value of y, at time t, due to $f(t)$ is

$$y = f(0)I(t) + \int_0^t I(t - x)f'(x)\, dx \qquad (12\text{-}65)$$

as indicated in Fig. 12-4.

Equation 12-65 is called the *superposition theorem.* It can be rearranged in many different forms. For our purposes, the most useful form is that obtained by integrating the last term of Eq. 12-65 by parts, giving

$$y = f(0)I(t) + f(x)I(t - x) \Big]_0^t + \int_0^t I'(t - x)f(x) \, dx$$
$$= f(t)I(0) + \int_0^t I'(t - x)f(x) \, dx \qquad (12\text{-}66)$$

The equation can be visualized as the statement that the motion is the sum of the separate motions caused by applying successive increments of force, $df(x)$, each over a time interval of dx, during the entire time from $x = 0$ to $x = t$ (Fig. 12-4). Here x is a parameter of integration, which disappears when the integration is performed.

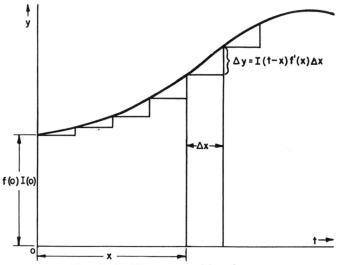

Fig. 12-4   The superposition theorem.

For example, to solve Eq. 12-38,

$$(p + b)y = f(t) \qquad \text{or} \qquad y = \frac{f(t)}{p + b} \qquad (12\text{-}38)$$

we know $I(t)$ from Eq. 12-54. Differentiating this gives $I'(t)$:

$$I(t) = \frac{H}{b}(1 - e^{-bt}) \qquad (12\text{-}54)$$

whence $I(0) = 0$, and

$$I'(t) = He^{-bt}$$

Substituting these in Eq. 12-66 gives

$$Hy = H \int_0^t e^{-b(t-x)}f(x) \, dx$$

or $$Hy = He^{-bt} \int_0^t e^{bx}f(x) \, dx \qquad (12\text{-}67)$$

This is the general solution of Eq. 12-38. The integration may be carried out formally when $f(x)$ is an elementary function; otherwise, it may be performed after first expanding $e^{bx}f(x)$ in infinite series.

For example, if we substitute H for $f(t)$ in Eq. 12-38, obtaining Eq. 12-46, we can integrate directly, finding

$$Hy = \frac{H}{b}(1 - e^{-bt}) \tag{12-54}$$

which is the same as Eq. 12-54 found previously.

If the suddenly applied force is sinusoidal, $f(t) = HF \sin(\omega t - \phi)$ (Eq. 12-38), representing a system with inertia and damping forces only, becomes

$$Hy = \frac{HF \sin(\omega t - \phi)}{p + b} \tag{12-68}$$

and its complete solution is found by substituting $HF \sin(wx - \phi)$ for $f(x)$ in Eq. 12-67:

$$Hy = HFe^{-bt} \int_0^t e^{bx} \sin(\omega x - \phi)\, dx$$

$$= \frac{HFe^{-bt}}{b^2 + \omega^2}[e^{bx}[b \sin(\omega x - \phi) - \omega \cos(\omega x - \phi)]]_0^t$$

$$= \frac{HF}{(b^2 + \omega^2)}[b \sin(\omega t - \phi) - \omega \cos(\omega t - \phi)$$

$$+ e^{-bt}(b \sin \phi + \omega \cos \phi)]$$

or

$$Hy = \frac{HF}{\sqrt{b^2 + \omega^2}}[\sin(\omega t - \phi - \theta) + e^{-bt} \sin(\phi + \theta)] \tag{12-69}$$

where $\cos \theta = b/\sqrt{b^2 + \omega^2}$

In Eq. 12-69, as in Eq. 12-54, there is a steady-state component of y equal to the applied force divided by the impedance of the system and a transient component that is initially equal and opposite to the steady-state component at time $t = 0$ and thereafter dies away exponentially.

12-8 Solution of Second-order Linear Differential Equations.

Having obtained the indicial response $I(t)$ of the system due to a suddenly applied unit force, this may be introduced in Eq. 12-66 to find the complete solution of a second- or higher-order equation, just as we found the solution (Eq. 12-69) of the first-order equation (12-68).

For example, to find the general solution of Eq. 12-36 when the suddenly applied force is sinusoidal, $f(t) = HF \sin(\omega t - \phi)$, we have

$$F(p)y = (p^2 + 2ap + b)y = HF \sin(\omega t - \phi) \qquad (12\text{-}70)$$

We have already found the indicial response of this equation to be Eq. 12-57. Differentiating Eq. 12-57 with respect to t, we find $I'(t)$ to be

$$I'(t) = \frac{He^{-at} \sin mt}{m}$$

Also, substituting $t = 0$ in Eq. 12-57, we find $I(0) = 0$. Putting these results in Eq. 12-66 gives

$$Hy = \frac{HF}{m} \int_0^t e^{-a(t-x)} \sin[m(t-x)] \sin(\omega x - \phi)\, dx \qquad (12\text{-}71)$$

From Eq. 2-35, this is

$$Hy = \frac{HFe^{-at}}{2m} \int_0^t e^{ax} \{\cos[mt - (\omega + m)x + \phi] \\ - \cos[mt + (\omega - m)x - \phi]\}\, dx$$

$$= \frac{HFe^{-at}}{2m} \left[e^{ax} \left\{ \frac{a\cos[mt - (\omega+m)x + \phi] - (\omega+m)\sin[mt - (\omega+m)x + \phi]}{a^2 + (\omega+m)^2} \right\} \right.$$

$$\left. - e^{ax} \left\{ \frac{a\cos[mt + (\omega-m)x - \phi] + (\omega-m)\sin[mt + (\omega-m)x - \phi]}{a^2 + (\omega-m)^2} \right\} \right]_0^t \qquad (12\text{-}72)$$

$$Hy = \frac{HFe^{-at}}{2m} \left\{ \frac{e^{at}[a\cos(\omega t - \phi) + (\omega+m)\sin(\omega t - \phi)] - a\cos(mt + \phi) + (\omega+m)\sin(mt + \phi)}{a^2 + (\omega+m)^2} \right.$$

$$\left. - \frac{e^{at}[a\cos(\omega t - \phi) + (\omega-m)\sin(\omega t - \phi)] - a\cos(mt - \phi) - (\omega-m)\sin(mt - \phi)}{a^2 + (\omega-m)^2} \right\} \qquad (12\text{-}73)$$

whence, by Eq. 2-47,

$$Hy = \frac{HF}{2m} \left[\frac{\sin(\omega t - \phi + \theta_1) + e^{-at}\sin(mt + \phi - \theta_1)}{\sqrt{a^2 + (\omega+m)^2}} \right.$$

$$\left. - \frac{\sin(\omega t - \phi + \theta_2) - e^{-at}\sin(mt - \phi + \theta_2)}{\sqrt{a^2 + (\omega-m)^2}} \right] \qquad (12\text{-}74)$$

where $\tan\theta_1 = a/(\omega + m)$
$\tan\theta_2 = a/(\omega - m)$

The response consists of two out-of-phase sine terms with the frequency of the applied force, which make up the steady-state response;

and two other sine terms with the resonant frequency of the system, multiplied by a decrement factor, which make up the transient response. Each pair of terms is the result of modulation of the impressed frequency by the resonant frequency, giving rise to the terms with angular velocities of $(\omega + m)$ and $(\omega - m)$ that appear in Eq. 12-72 before integration.

A more usual form of the solution is found by combining the two pairs of terms into two single terms. By grouping the terms in Eq. 12-73 with like numerators, instead of those with like denominators as in Eq. 12-74, we obtain

$$Hy = \frac{HF}{M^2}[-2a\omega \cos(\omega t - \phi) - (\omega^2 - b)\sin(\omega t - \phi)]$$

$$-\frac{HFe^{-at}}{2mM^2}[a(\omega^2 - 2\omega m + b)\cos(mt + \phi)$$
$$-a(\omega^2 + 2\omega m + b)\cos(mt - \phi)$$
$$-(\omega + m)(\omega^2 - 2\omega m + b)\sin(mt + \phi)$$
$$-(\omega - m)(\omega^2 + 2\omega m + b)\sin(mt - \phi)] \quad (12\text{-}75)$$

where $M^2 = [a^2 + (\omega + m)^2][a^2 + (\omega - m)^2] = 4a^2\omega^2 + (\omega^2 - b)^2$

$$m = \sqrt{b - a^2}$$

This gives, by Eq. 2-47,

$$Hy = -\frac{HF\sin(\omega t - \phi + \alpha)}{M}$$

$$+\frac{HFe^{-at}}{M^2}[2a\omega \cos\phi - (\omega^2 - b)\sin\phi]\cos mt$$

$$+\frac{HFe^{-at}}{mM^2}[a(\omega^2 + b)\sin\phi + \omega(\omega^2 + 2a^2 - b)\cos\phi]\sin mt \quad (12\text{-}76)$$

or

$$Hy = -\frac{HF\sin(\omega t - \phi + \alpha)}{M} - \frac{HFe^{-at}\sin(\phi - \alpha)\cos mt}{M}$$

$$+\frac{HFe^{-at}(a^2 + \omega^2)^{1/2}\cos(\phi - \beta)\sin mt}{mM} \quad (12\text{-}77)$$

where $\tan\alpha = 2a\omega/(\omega^2 - b)$

$$\tan\beta = a(\omega^2 + b)/\omega(\omega^2 + 2a^2 - b)$$

Equation 12-77 is the complete solution of Eq. 12-70, which is identical with the previously found solution (Eq. 12-74) but is arranged in a more useful form.

If the system has no damping, $a = 0$, also $\alpha = \beta = 0$, and Eq. 12-77 becomes

$$Hy = -\frac{HF}{\omega^2 - b}\left[\sin(\omega t - \phi) + \sin\phi\cos t\sqrt{b}\right.$$
$$\left. -\frac{\omega}{\sqrt{b}}\cos\phi\sin t\sqrt{b}\right] \qquad (a=0) \quad (12\text{-}78)$$

The use of Heaviside's unit function, together with the superposition theorem, has enabled us to find the complete solution of the linear second-order differential equation (12-70) without determining any integration constants, other than those naturally resulting from the zero lower limit of integration in Eq. 12-66. However, this solution assumed that the system was initially at rest, with $y = 0$ when $t = 0$. If there is an initial displacement, $y = y_0$ when $t = 0$, the applied force should be taken to be $-HF_0 + f(t)$, instead of merely $f(t)$, the value of F_0 being chosen so that it corresponds to a steady-state displacement equal to y_0, as determined from the indicial response equation for the system. The complete solution of the equation will then include a term representing the dying away of y_0 to zero, in addition to the terms found for the system initially at rest. This assumes that the system response is linear throughout.

If the system is critically damped, $b = a^2$, $m = 0$, and Eq. 12-70 becomes

$$F(p)y = (p + a)^2 y = HF\sin(\omega t - \phi) \qquad (12\text{-}79)$$

To find the solution for this case, we need to go back to Eq. 12-62 to find $I(t)$ and to use this in place of Eq. 12-57 in applying the superposition theorem to avoid the difficulty caused by making $m = 0$ in the latter.

Then, making $t = 0$ in Eq. 12-62, we find $I(0) = 0$ and differentiating it, we find

$$I'(t) = Hte^{-at}$$

Substituting these in Eq. 12-66, with the applied force equal to $HF\sin(\omega t - \phi)$, gives

$$Hy = HF\int_0^t (t - x)e^{-a(t-x)}\sin(\omega x - \phi)\,dx$$

$$= -\frac{HF\sin(\omega t - \phi + \alpha)}{a^2 + \omega^2} - \frac{HFe^{-at}\sin(\phi - \alpha)}{a^2 + \omega^2}$$

$$+ \frac{HFte^{-at}\cos(\phi - \beta)}{(a^2 + \omega^2)^{1/2}} \qquad (b = a^2) \quad (12\text{-}80)$$

where $\tan\alpha = 2a\omega/(\omega^2 - a^2)$
$\tan\beta = a/\omega$

If there is no restoring force in the system, $b = 0$, and Eq. 12-70 becomes

$$Hy = \frac{HF \sin (\omega t - \phi)}{p^2 + 2ap}$$

$$= \frac{HF \sin (\omega t - \phi)}{2ap} - \frac{HF \sin (\omega t - \phi)}{2a(p + 2a)}$$

$$= \frac{HF}{2a\omega} [\cos \phi - \cos (\omega t - \phi)]$$

$$- \frac{HF}{2a \sqrt{4a^2 + \omega^2}} [\sin (\omega t - \phi - \theta) + e^{-2at} \sin (\phi + \theta)] \qquad (12\text{-}81)$$

where $\tan \theta = \omega/2a$.

12-9 The Laplace Transform Method. In Sec. 1-13, we found that, with the aid of a table of logarithms, we can obtain the product of two numbers, a and b, by the process of addition instead of by the more complicated process of multiplication. This is done by transforming a and b into their logarithms (looking them up in the table), then adding, $\log a + \log b = \log ab$, then using the table again to find the antilog, or inverse transform of $\log ab$, which gives the desired product ab.

The table of logarithms is a table of transform-pairs. By first transforming a number, then operating on it, then finding its inverse transform, we are able to use a simpler mathematical process to obtain a desired result than would be required if we did not use the table.

In a similar way, we can use the Laplace transform to change a differential equation into another form that enables most of the work of solution to be carried through by an algebraic instead of by an integration process. Then, by finding the inverse Laplace transform of the modified equation, from a table of Laplace transform pairs, Appendix I, the solution of the equation is found.

The Laplace transform of a function $y = f(t)$ is defined by the equation

$$F(s) = \mathcal{L}[f(t)] = \int_0^\infty e^{-st} f(t) \, dt \qquad (12\text{-}82)$$

and the inverse Laplace transform is

$$f(t) = \mathcal{L}^{-1}[F(s)] \qquad (12\text{-}83)$$

$F(s)$ is similar to the integral in Eq. 12-67, except that in Eq. 12-82 the upper limit of integration is ∞ instead of t. In these equations s is normally a complex quantity, *which must have a positive real term*, so that

e^{-st} will be zero when $t = \infty$. With this limitation on s, the value of the integral at the upper limit of integration, ∞, will always be zero, and that at the lower limit, 0, will have no decrement factor, since $e^{-st} = 1$ when $t = 0$. Thus the Laplace transform of $f(t)$ is normally a relatively simple algebraic function.

To find the Laplace transform of $f(t) = \sin at$, for example, we substitute $\sin at$ for $f(t)$ in Eq. 12-82, and integrate by parts:

$$F(s) = \mathcal{L}[\sin at] = \int_0^\infty e^{-st} \sin at \, dt$$

$$= \frac{-e^{-st}}{s} \sin at \Big]_0^\infty + \frac{a}{s} \int_0^\infty e^{-st} \cos at \, dt$$

$$= 0 - \frac{ae^{-st}}{s^2} \cos at \Big]_0^\infty - \frac{a^2}{s^2} \int_0^\infty e^{-at} \sin at \, dt$$

or $\qquad F(s) = \dfrac{a}{s^2} - \dfrac{a^2}{s^2} F(s) = \dfrac{a}{s^2 + a^2}$ \hfill (12-84)

A table of the Laplace transforms of elementary functions is given in Appendix I.

To use the Laplace transform in solving an equation, such as Eq. 12-38, $y' + by = f(t)$, for example, we first transform the entire equation (multiply each term by $e^{-st} dt$ and integrate between 0 and ∞):

$$\int_0^\infty e^{-st}y' \, dt + b \int_0^\infty e^{-st}y \, dt = \int_0^\infty e^{-st}f(t) \, dt \qquad (12\text{-}85)$$

Placing $F(s) = \mathcal{L}(y)$, we have, from entry 10 in Appendix I:

$$\int_0^\infty e^{-st}y' \, dt = \mathcal{L}(y') = sF(s) - y(0) \qquad (12\text{-}86)$$

so that Eq. 12-85 becomes:

$$(s + b)F(s) = y(0) + \mathcal{L}[f(t)] \qquad (12\text{-}87)$$

We shall first assume that y when $t = 0$ is $y(0) = 1/b$, and that $f(t) = 0$. Then, Eq. 12-87 becomes

$$F(s) = \frac{1}{b(s + b)} \qquad (12\text{-}88)$$

and from entry 2 in Appendix I, this gives

$$y = \mathcal{L}^{-1}\left[\frac{1}{b(s + b)}\right] = \frac{e^{-bt}}{b} \qquad (12\text{-}89)$$

which agrees with the solution previously found, Eq. 12-42.

If we assume that $y(0) = 0$, and that $f(t) = H$, Eq. 12-87 becomes, from entry 1 of Appendix I,

$$(s + b)F(s) = 0 + F(H) = \frac{H}{s} \qquad (12\text{-}90)$$

or

$$F(s) = \frac{H}{s(s + b)} \qquad (12\text{-}91)$$

From entry 34 in Appendix I, this gives for y

$$y = \mathcal{L}^{-1}\left[\frac{H}{s(s + b)}\right] = \frac{H}{b}(1 - e^{-bt}) \qquad (12\text{-}92)$$

which agrees with the solution (Eq. 12-54) found previously for this case.

To solve Eq. 12-36

$$y'' + 2ay' + by = f(t) \qquad (12\text{-}36)$$

we have

$$\mathcal{L}(y'') + 2a\,\mathcal{L}(y') + bF(s) = \mathcal{L}[f(t)] \qquad (12\text{-}93)$$

or from entries 10 and 11 in Appendix I

$$(s^2 + 2as + b)F(s) = (s + 2a)y(0) + y'(0) + \mathcal{L}[f(t)] \qquad (12\text{-}94)$$

If we assume that $y = y' = 0$ when $t = 0$ and that $f(t) = H$, this gives

$$F(s) = \frac{\mathcal{L}(H)}{s^2 + 2as + b} = \frac{H}{s(s^2 + 2as + b)} \qquad (12\text{-}95)$$

Usually the right-hand side of this equation must be expanded in partial fractions, by Eq. 8-53 or Eq. 8-54, and the separate terms can then be found in the table of Appendix I. In this case, however, we see that by putting $s^2 + 2as + b = (s - p_1)(s - p_2)$, $F(s)$ matches item 32 in Appendix I. This gives

$$y = \mathcal{L}^{-1}\left[\frac{H}{s(s - p_1)(s - p_2)}\right] = \frac{H}{p_1 p_2}\left[1 + \frac{p_1 \exp\,(p_2 t) - p_2 \exp\,(p_1 t)}{p_2 - p_1}\right] \qquad (12\text{-}96)$$

Since $p_1 = -a - jm$ and $p_2 = -a + jm$, where $m = \sqrt{b - a^2}$, this reduces to

$$y = \frac{H}{b}\left[1 - e^{-at}\left(\cos mt + \frac{a}{m}\sin mt\right)\right] \qquad (12\text{-}56)$$

which agrees with Eq. 12-56 previously found for this case.

In this manner, the Laplace transform method enables the solution of linear differential equations with constant coefficients to be found by reference to tables, with a minimum of mathematical labor.

If we assume that $f(t) = H \sin(\omega t - \phi)$, with $y = 0$ and $y' = 0$, when $t = 0$, Eq. 12-94 becomes

$$F(s) = \frac{\mathcal{L}[H \sin(\omega t - \phi)]}{s(s^2 + 2as + b)} = \frac{\mathcal{L}(H \cos \phi \sin \omega t) - \mathcal{L}(H \sin \phi \cos \omega t)}{s(s^2 + 2as + b)}$$
(12-97)

From items 3 and 4 of Appendix I, this is

$$\mathcal{L}(y) = F(s) = \frac{H\omega \cos \phi}{s(s^2 + \omega^2)(s^2 + 2as + b)} - \frac{H \sin \phi}{(s^2 + \omega^2)(s^2 + 2as + b)}$$
(12-98)

These transforms can be found in available tables, or they can be expanded in partial fractions, when the separate terms can be found in the limited table in Appendix I. To work through this expansion without the use of tables is quite laborious, so that the straightforward method used in Sec. 12-8 to find the solution (Eq. 12-77) may be preferable in such cases.

It should be noted that the Laplace transform of any function, $f(t)$, can always be found from the operational formula for $Hf(t)$, by dividing the latter by pH and substituting s for p. For example, the Laplace transform for $\sin at$ is $a/(s^2 + a^2)$, while the operational formula for $H \sin at$ is $apH/(p^2 + a^2)$.

12-10 Method of Undetermined Coefficients. When it is hard to separate the variables in a differential equation, or it is hard to integrate the expression for y', the solution may sometimes be found by the method of undetermined coefficients. Suppose the equation is of the first order and has the form

$$y' = \frac{dy}{dx} = F(x,y)$$
(12-99)

Since there is one arbitrary integration constant in the solution, we shall take this to be the value y_0 of y when $x = x_0$. We then represent the solution y by the power series

$$y = y_0 + a_1(x - x_0) + a_2(x - x_0)^2 + a_3(x - x_0)^3 + \cdots$$
(12-100)

and take the derivative

$$y' = a_1 + 2a_2(x - x_0) + 3a_3(x - x_0)^2 + \cdots$$
(12-101)

By substituting Eq. 12-100 in Eq. 12-99, and developing all the terms in a power series, we obtain a second expression for y':

$$y' = A_0 + A_1(x - x_0) + A_2(x - x_0)^2 + A_3(x - x_0)^3 + \cdots \quad (12\text{-}102)$$

Since the two values of y' must be equal for all values of x, the coefficients of like powers of $(x - x_0)$ must be equal. The resulting set of equations

$$A_0 = a_1, \, A_2 = 2a_2, \, A_3 = 3a_3, \, \cdots \quad (12\text{-}103)$$

when solved successively, give the values of the coefficients a_1, a_2, a_3, $\ldots$, and thus determine the value of y by Eq. 12-100.

For example, to solve the equation:

$$y' = \frac{dy}{dx} = \sqrt{x + y} \quad (12\text{-}104)$$

we choose a point, say $x_0 = 3$, $y_0 = 1$, that we desire the solution to pass through, and equate y to

$$y = 1 + a_1 t + a_2 t^2 + a_3 t^3 + a_4 t^4 + \cdots \quad (12\text{-}105)$$

where $t = x - 3$ is used for simplicity in writing the equations. Then $y = y_0 = 1$ when $x = 3$, and

$$y' = a_1 + 2a_2 t + 3a_3 t^2 + 4a_4 t^3 + \cdots \quad (12\text{-}106)$$

and also, from Eqs. 12-104 and 12-105:

$$y' = \sqrt{t + 3 + 1 + a_1 t + a_2 t^2 + a_3 t^3 + \cdots} = 2\sqrt{1 + h} \quad (12\text{-}107)$$

where

$$h = \frac{(1 + a_1)t}{4} + \frac{a_2 t^2}{4} + \frac{a_3 t^3}{4} + \frac{a_4 t^4}{4} + \cdots \quad (12\text{-}108)$$

Expanding Eq. 12-107 in powers of h, by Eq. 5-22, and substituting from Eq. 12-108 gives

$$\begin{aligned}
y' &= 2\left(1 + \frac{h}{2} - \frac{h^2}{8} + \frac{h^3}{16} - \frac{5h^4}{128} + \cdots\right) \\
&= 2\left\{1 + \frac{(1 + a_1)}{8} t + \left[\frac{a_2}{8} - \frac{(1 + a_1)^2}{128}\right] t^2 \right. \\
&\qquad \left. + \left[\frac{a_3}{8} - \frac{a_2(1 + a_1)}{64} + \frac{(1 + a_1)^3}{1{,}024}\right] t^3 + \cdots\right\} \quad (12\text{-}109)
\end{aligned}$$

Equating the coefficients of like terms in Eqs. 12-106 and 12-109, we have

$$a_1 = 2, \ a_2 = \frac{1}{2}\left(\frac{3}{4}\right) = \frac{3}{8}, \ a_3 = \frac{1}{3}\left(\frac{3}{32} - \frac{9}{64}\right) = -\frac{1}{64},$$

$$a_4 = \frac{2}{4}\left(-\frac{1}{512} - \frac{9}{512} - \frac{27}{1,024}\right) = \frac{7}{2,048}, \ \cdots$$

Substituting these values in Eq. 12-103, we find the desired solution of Eq. 12-104 to be

$$y = 1 + 2(x - 3) + \frac{3}{8}(x - 3)^2 - \frac{1}{64}(x - 3)^3 + \frac{7}{2,048}(x - 3)^4$$
$$+ \cdots \quad (12\text{-}110)$$

If an equation is symmetrical with respect to x, so that a change from x to $-x$ does not alter the value of y, the series expansion for y will contain only even powers of x, and $a_1, a_3, a_5, \ldots$ in Eq. 12-100 will be zero. Or, if a change from x to $-x$ changes y to $-y$ without changing its numerical value, the equation is symmetrical with respect to the origin and only odd powers of x will appear, since $a_0, a_2, a_4, \ldots$ will be zero.

This method of undetermined coefficients can be used to solve higher-order equations also. For an nth-order differential equation there will be n arbitrary integration constants that are represented by the values of $y, y', y'', \ldots, y^{n-},^1$ when x has some arbitrarily chosen value, x_0. For example, in the case of a second-order differential equation

$$y'' = \phi(x,y,y') \quad (12\text{-}111)$$

we assume

$$y = y_0 + y_0'(x - x_0) + a_2(x - x_0)^2 + a_3(x - x_0)^3 + \cdots \quad (12\text{-}112)$$

whence

$$y' = y_0' + 2a_2(x - x_0) + 3a_3(x - x_0)^2 + \cdots \quad (12\text{-}113)$$

and

$$y'' = 2a_2 + 6a_3(x - x_0) + 12a_4(x - x_0)^3 + \cdots \quad (12\text{-}114)$$

By substituting the expressions for y and y' in Eq. 12-111 and expanding all the terms in power series, a second expression for y'' is obtained:

$$y'' = A_0 + A_1(x - x_0) + A_2(x - x_0)^2 + A_3(x - x_0)^3 + \cdots$$
$$(12\text{-}115)$$

Equating the coefficients of like powers of $(x - x_0)$ in Eqs. 12-114 and 12-115, term by term, gives equations that determine the values of $a_2, a_3, a_4, \ldots$, and therefore give the solution y, by Eq. 12-112.

PROBLEMS

1. Solve the following differential equations:

    a. $(y^2 - 2y) \, dy + (x^2 - 3x) \, dx = 0$

    b. $EI \dfrac{d^2y}{dx^2} = \omega(l - x)$

    c. $\sin \theta \cos \phi \, d\theta - \cos \theta \sin \phi \, d\phi = 0$

    d. $\dfrac{dy}{dx} = 2x^2 - 5e^{-2ax} + \dfrac{5}{(2x + 3)^2}$

    e. $x \, dy = (y + x^2 + y^2) \, dx$ (HINT: Substitute $y = zx$.)

2. Find the operational solutions of the following differential equations:

    a. $p^2y + 4py + 5y = H$ **c.** $(p^2 = 8p + 16)y = p^2H$
    b. $(p^2 + p + 1)y = pH$
    d. $9p^2y + 24pby + 41y = apH$

    e. $p^2y + 7py + 12y = p^2H$ **h.** $\dfrac{p^2y + 10py + 24y}{p} = H$

    f. $p^2y + 16y - p^2 - 8 = 0$ **i.** $p^2y + 50py + 625y = H$

    g. $\dfrac{p^2y - 225y}{p^2} = H$

    j. $p^3y + 9p^2y + 27py + 27y = pH$

    k. $(p^2 + 49)y = 59H$ **l.** $\dfrac{(p^2 + 36)y}{6p} = H$

3. The differential equation for the deflection y of a uniformly loaded beam of length L that is freely supported at both ends is

$$EI \frac{d^2y}{dx^2} = \frac{\omega}{2} (Lx - x^2)$$

where E is the modulus of elasticity of the beam material, I is the moment of inertia, ω the load per foot, and x the distance from one end. Find the formula for the deflection and its maximum value. (The slope of the beam, dy/dx, equals zero when $x = L/2$.)

4. Using an operational formula, find the equation for the current when a capacitance C charged to a voltage E is suddenly short-circuited through a noninductive resistance R. The differential equation is

$$Ri + \frac{1}{C} \int i\, dt = f(t) = -HE$$

5. If a mass M is dropped from a height h on a frictionless and weightless spring, find the subsequent motion of the mass, using the Laplace transform method. The differential equation is

$$(Mp^2 + k)x = Mg \qquad t > 0$$

where x is the distance the spring is compressed, kx is the force exerted by the spring, and g is the acceleration of gravity. At the initial instant, when the mass strikes the spring, $x = 0$, and the velocity of the mass is $px = \sqrt{2gh}$.

6. A steady force, P, is suddenly applied to a control valve. Find the subsequent motion of the valve. The differential equation of motion is

$$(Mp^2 + Dp + k)x = f(t) = HP$$

where x is the displacement, M is the mass of the valve, D is the damping constant, and k is the spring stiffness constant.

Bibliography

1. Bennett, A. A., W. E. Milne, and H. Bateman: "Numerical Integration of Differential Equations," Dover Press, New York, 1956.
2. Berg, E. J.: "Heaviside's Operational Calculus," 2d ed., McGraw-Hill Book Company, New York, 1936.
3. Bronwell, A.: "Advanced Mathematics in Physics and Engineering," McGraw-Hill Book Company, New York, 1953.
4. Bush, V.: "Operational Circuit Analysis," John Wiley & Sons, Inc., New York, 1929.
5. Churchill, R. V.: "Operational Mathematics," 2d ed., McGraw-Hill Book Company, New York, 1958.
6. Franklin, Philip: "Differential Equations for Engineers," John Wiley & Sons, Inc., New York, 1933.
7. Fry, T. C.: "Elementary Differential Equations," D. Van Nostrand Company, Inc., Princeton, N.J., 1929.
8. Gardner, M. F., and J. L. Barnes: "Transients in Linear Systems," John Wiley & Sons, Inc., New York, 1942.
9. Jeffreys, H.: "Operational Methods in Mathematical Physics," Cambridge University Press, New York, 1927.
10. Kaplan, Wilfred: "Ordinary Differential Equations," Addison-Wesley Publishing Company, Reading, Mass., 1958.
11. Kells, L. M.: "Elementary Differential Equations," McGraw-Hill Book Company, New York, 1954.
12. McLachlan, N. W.: "Ordinary Non-linear Differential Equations in Engineering and Physical Sciences," Oxford University Press, New York, 1954.

13. Milne, W. E.: "Numerical Solution of Differential Equations," John Wiley & Sons, Inc., New York.
14. Sokolinikoff, I. S., and E. S. Sokolinikoff: "Higher Mathematics for Engineers and Physicists," McGraw-Hill Book Company, New York, 1941.
15. Thomson, W. T.: "Laplace Transformation," Prentice-Hall, Inc., Englewood Cliffs, N.J., 1950.
16. Weber, Ernst: "Linear Transient Analysis," John Wiley & Sons, Inc., New York, 1954.
17. Widder, D. V.: "The Laplace Transform," Princeton University Press, Princeton, N.J., 1941.
18. Wilson, E. B.: "Advanced Calculus," Ginn and Company, Boston, 1912.
19. Wylie, C. R., Jr.: "Advanced Engineering Mathematics," McGraw-Hill Book Company, New York, 1951.

Chapter 13 PROBABILITY

13-1 The Unlikeness of Similar Objects. No two people, nor two apples, nor even two coins, are exactly alike. However much care is taken, two castings from the same mold will differ, at least in microscopic detail. No two measurements of the same distance, or the same weight, or of anything else, will give *exactly* the same value when carried to the limits of possible precision.

Therefore, in describing an object, or in making calculations, we must deal with "average," or approximate, values, which we choose to represent the normal condition, and we must provide for the real thing's being always a little different from what is assumed.

In engineering, it is especially important to allow for these uncertainties. Our theory may be incomplete or not exact. Our materials and dimensions are not uniform. The requirements may not be clear, and they may vary after the equipment is in service. And so on. In the early days, large "ignorance factors" were used in design calculations to allow for such things. Later, after sufficient trials, these became "experience factors." Many engineering calculations are now so exact that we speak only of "factors of safety," or "margins of performance," which are simply calculated allowances for the expected variations that normally occur in manufacture and in service. These margins are coming more and more to be set at values that will give a definite risk of failure, chosen in accordance with the economic and human factors. That is, the engineer, as well as the insurance expert, estimates the costs and the risks of alternate ways of getting desired results and makes decisions in the way that promises to give the least cost, everything considered.

Statistical theory, the branch of mathematics which deals with the chance variations that occur in materials, processes, and life generally, is, therefore, a valuable aid to the engineer. Its earliest engineering uses were to reconcile conflicting measurements in the fields of surveying and astronomy, by the method of least squares. It is now widely applied to reduce manufacturing losses under the term *statistical*

[296]

quality control. It is coming into widespread use for the planning and conduct of research and development, with a view to obtaining the greatest possible amount of useful information from a limited series of experiments. And, of course, it is the basis of all insurance and actuarial theory.

13-2 The Method of Least Squares. The uncertainties of life being what they are, it is customary to make more than one measurement of any quantity of importance. Often, as in astronomy, a great many measurements are made to obtain the most nearly right value that we can. The way to decide what is the most nearly correct value from conflicting data, and how reliable the result is, is often called the *method of least squares.*

We assume that, in successive measurements, plus and minus errors are equally likely to occur and that the average of all the (similar) measurements is the best possible estimate of the true value. These assumptions, formally stated, are that

(*a*) If we measure a given quantity n times, obtaining values M_1, M_2, M_3, . . . , M_n, whose arithmetic average value is M_0, then

(*b*) M_0 is the best estimate we can make of the true value, M. Therefore

(*c*) The equation that defines the maximum probability is that the sum of all the n differences, $x_1 = M_1 - M_0$, $x_2 = M_2 - M_0$, $x_3 = M_3 - M_0$, . . . , $x_n = M_n - M_0$, between the measured values and their average, is zero, or

$$x_1 + x_2 + x_3 + \cdots + x_n = 0 \qquad (13\text{-}1)$$

As shown in Sec. 11-1, the condition for a function to be a maximum or a minimum is that its derivative shall be zero. In this case, the function $F(x)$ that we are concerned with is that function of the errors that determines the value of M_0 with the smallest probable error from the true value M. Therefore Eq. 13-1 must represent the derivative of $F(x)$, or $F'(x)$, whence

$$F'(x) = \frac{dF(x)}{dx} = x_1 + x_2 + x_3 + \cdots + x_n$$

or $$F(x) = \int (x_1 + x_2 + x_3 + \cdots + x_n) \, dx$$

In this equation, dx is the change in each error x_n, due to a displacement dx of the most probable value of M from the assumed value M_0. Since this relation must be true whatever the number of observations, it must be true for each measurement separately, and we have

$$F(x) = \int_0^{x_1} x_1 \, dx + \int_0^{x_2} x_2 \, dx + \int_0^{x_3} x_3 \, dx + \cdots + \int_0^{x_n} x_n \, dx$$
$$= k(x_1^2 + x_2^2 + x_3^2 + \cdots + x_n^2) \qquad (13\text{-}2)$$

Since the derivative of Eq. 13-2 is Eq. 13-1, and thus is equal to zero when the arithmetic average M_0 is taken to be the most probable value, we conclude that

The most probable estimate of the true value of a measured quantity is that value M_0 which gives a minimum for the sum of the squares of the successive differences between M_0 and the measured values.

From this principle, the name *method of least squares* is derived.

This principle is merely an alternative way of stating the original assumption made above, that the arithmetic average of the measurements is the most probable true value of a quantity.

Many sets of measurements evidently do not obey this rule, because they are skewed, or unsymmetrical in one way or another. However, the range of valid application of the least-squares principle can be extended by proper choice of the variable used in the calculations.

For example, we may take the logarithms of the n measurements and then use the logarithms instead of the numbers themselves in the averaging process. The mean value M_0 corresponding to the average of the logarithms is the geometric mean of the measurements, as pointed out in Sec. 1-15. Thus, when the conditions of the problem indicate that the arithmetic mean of the direct measurements is not the most probable true value, it is often possible to transform the measured values into a more symmetrical set of values to which the least-square principle will more nearly apply. For widely scattered measurements especially, it is appropriate to average the logarithms of the measurements instead of the measurements themselves.

13-3 Example. For example, suppose an angle is measured ten times with a transit, giving the values shown in Table 13-1.

The average difference from the mean, called a.d., is 0.0108, and the square root of the mean-square difference, called the *standard deviation*, or simply *s*, or the Greek letter sigma, σ, is 0.0135.

The average of the ten readings, 4.134, is probably closer to the true value than any one reading. Thus, the skilled experimenter makes up for shortcomings of his equipment by taking many readings and analyzing his results to find and remove the sources of his errors. The sum of the squares of the differences, 18.4, is smaller when M_0 is taken as 4.134 than for any other value. If the answer were taken to be 4.135, the sum of the $(100x)^2$ values would become 18.5 and for 4.136 it would be 18.8.

Table 13-1 Determining the Best Measurement of an Angle by the Method of Least Squares

Measurement	Reading M degrees	100 × difference $100x$		$(100x)^2$
		−	+	
1	4.13	0.4		0.16
2	4.14		0.6	0.36
3	4.15		1.6	2.56
4	4.13	0.4		0.16
5	4.11	2.4		5.76
6	4.13	0.4		0.16
7	4.13	0.4		0.16
8	4.12	1.4		1.96
9	4.14		0.6	0.36
10	4.16		2.6	6.76
Sum:	41.34	−5.4	+5.4	18.40

Average
$M_0 = 4.134$ a.d. $= 0.0108$ $(100s)^2 = 1.84$ $s = 0.0135$

13-4 The Normal Law of Probability. The probability, or chance, of an event happening is defined as the ratio of the number of ways in which that particular event can occur to the total number of equally likely alternatives that could occur, in a single trial. For example, there are only two equally likely events, heads or tails, that can occur when a coin is thrown. So we say that the chance of a head coming up is 0.5. The chance of drawing an ace from a full pack of 52 cards is $\frac{4}{52}$, or 0.077.

If we denote by y the chance of a particular measurement having a difference from the mean exactly equal to x, then the law of probability is defined by the equation

$$y = f(x) \tag{13-3}$$

This is a maximum when $x = 0$, in accordance with Eq. 13-1. y measures the degree of confidence that we have in the happening of a particular event, and is always expressed by a positive fraction. An event that is certain to happen has a probability of unity, or $y = 1$.

If the chance of a particular event happening is y_1 and that of another event is y_2, the chance that both events will happen in any two trials is the product $y_1 y_2$. Thus, the chance of two heads in succession in tossing a coin is

$$\tfrac{1}{2} \times \tfrac{1}{2} \text{ or } \tfrac{1}{4}$$

For, there are only four possibilities, each equally likely:

> 2 heads
> 1 head and 1 tail
> 1 tail and 1 head
> 2 tails

and 2 heads will, therefore, occur, on the average, once in each four trials of the double throw.

Therefore, the chance that n successive measurements M_1, M_2, . . . , M_n will have the particular differences from the mean x_1, x_2, x_3, . . . , x_n is expressed by the product of their separate probabilities:

$$P = y_1 y_2 y_3 \cdot \cdot \cdot y_n \tag{13-4}$$

We assume that the actual measurements represent the most likely occurrence. Thus the form of the function $y = f(x)$ must be that which makes P in Eq. 13-4 a maximum. To find this (Sec. 11–2), we may take the logarithm of Eq. 13-4 to separate the terms, then take its derivative and equate to zero, obtaining

$$\ln P = \ln y_1 + \ln y_2 + \ln y_3 + \cdot \cdot \cdot + \ln y_n \tag{13-5}$$

and
$$\frac{d(\ln P)}{dx} = \frac{dy_1}{y_1 \, dx} + \frac{dy_2}{y_2 \, dx} + \frac{dy_3}{y_3 \, dx} + \cdot \cdot \cdot + \frac{dy_n}{y_n \, dx} = 0 \tag{13-6}$$

Comparing Eq. 13-6 with Eq. 13-1, we see that the two equations become the same if dy/dx has the form

$$\frac{dy}{dx} = -kxy = -kxf(x) \tag{13-7}$$

for, in this case, the nth term of Eq. 13-6, $dy_n/y_n \, dx$ is equal to $-kx_n$ and the sum of all the terms is zero, by Eq. 13-1. The coefficient of xy is negative, because the bigger an error, the smaller the chance of its happening.

Integrating Eq. 13-7 gives

$$\frac{dy}{y} = -kx \, dx$$

$$\ln y = -\frac{kx^2}{2} + C \qquad (13\text{-}8)$$

Thus, y comes out to be a positive fraction, less than 1, as expected. C is an arbitrary constant of integration.

In these equations k is an inverse measure of the accuracy of the measurements. For a given probability y, the larger k is, the smaller the average difference from the mean. The exponent of any quantity must be merely a number; that is, it cannot be expressed as so many horses, or apples, or inches (Sec. 3-9). Hence, k must be measured in the same units as $1/x^2$. It is, therefore, convenient to express k as $1/s^2$, in terms of the standard deviation, or root-mean-square (rms) value of the differences, which we shall call s (it is often designated by the Greek letter sigma, σ). The definition of s is

$$s = \sqrt{\frac{x_1^2 + x_2^2 + x_3^2 + \cdots + x_n^2}{n}} = \sqrt{\frac{\Sigma x^2}{n}} \qquad (13\text{-}9)$$

If $1/s^2$ is substituted for k, Eq. 13-8 becomes

$$\ln y = -\frac{x^2}{2s^2} + C$$

or

$$y = \frac{1}{s\sqrt{2\pi}} \exp\left(\frac{-x^2}{2s^2}\right) = \frac{0.399}{s} \exp\left(-\frac{x^2}{2s^2}\right) \qquad (13\text{-}10)$$

This is the equation of the normal law of probability, shown in Fig. 13-1. The area under the probability curve between $x = -\infty$ and $x = \infty$ represents the sum of all the probabilities of all the events that can occur, which is unity. The factor $1/s\sqrt{2\pi}$ in Eq. 13-10 (which represents the integration constant C) is chosen to make this relation true.

In Eq. 13-10 y is the fraction of all the measurements M_1, M_2, $\ldots$, M_n (whose mean value is M_0) that will normally fall within a band of width Δx, centered on a value $M_0 + x$.

To remove the dimensional character of y, it is customary to employ the value

$$Y = 0.399 \exp\left(-\frac{x^2}{2s^2}\right) \qquad (13\text{-}11)$$

in tables and calculations, obtained by choosing $\Delta x = s$ in Eq. 13-10. Values of Y are given in Appendix G.

The value of s given by Eq. 13-9 is not the same as the standard deviation from the true value, since the true value of the measured quantity is not exactly equal to the average value, M_0, of the n actual measurements. To find a more precise value, S, of the standard deviation, we may assume that the deviations of the n measurements from the true value are $v_1, v_2, v_3, \ldots, v_n$, so that the root-mean-square

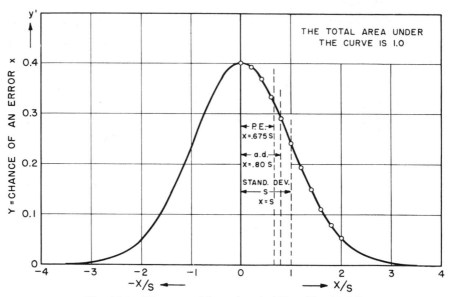

Fig. 13-1 The normal law of probability (Eq. 13-11).

value of these, S, is given by the equation $\Sigma v^2 = nS^2$. Also, we may assume that Σv^2 is greater than the sum of the squares, Σx^2, of the deviations from M_0 by a small amount k^2. Then, from Eq. 13-9,

$$\Sigma v^2 = nS^2 = \Sigma x^2 + k^2 = ns^2 + k^2 \qquad (13\text{-}12)$$

On this basis, the probability P_n of the occurrence of the actual set of observations, with errors $v_1, v_2, v_3, \ldots, v_n$ from the true value of the measured quantity, is proportional to the product of their separate probabilities, or from Eq. 13-10,

$$P_n = C \exp\left(-\frac{\Sigma v^2}{2s^2}\right) = Ce^{-n/2} \exp\left(-\frac{k^2}{2s^2}\right) \qquad (13\text{-}13)$$

If k is to have a value between $k - \Delta x/2$ and $k + \Delta x/2$, the coefficient of Eq. 13-13 will be similar to that of Eq. 13-10, or

$$Ce^{-n/2} = \frac{0.399}{s}$$

The most probable value of k will then correspond to the value of S which makes P_n a maximum. This occurs when $dP_n/dS = 0$. In performing this differentiation, S is used in Eq. 13-13 in place of s because s is the fixed value given by Eq. 13-9, while S varies depending on the unknown true value of the quantity being measured.

Hence, we have

$$\frac{dP_n}{dS} = \frac{d}{dS}\left[\frac{0.399}{S}\exp\left(-\frac{k^2}{2S^2}\right)\right]$$

$$= 0.399 \exp\left(-\frac{k^2}{2S}\right)\left(-\frac{1}{S^2}+\frac{k^2}{S^4}\right) = 0$$

giving

$$k^2 = S^2 \qquad (13\text{-}14)$$

Substituting this in Eq. 13-12 gives

$$nS^2 = ns^2 + S^2$$

or

$$S = s\sqrt{\frac{n}{n-1}} = \sqrt{\frac{x_1^2 + x_2^2 + \cdots + x_n^2}{n-1}} \qquad (13\text{-}15)$$

Thus, the most probable value, S, of the standard deviation of n measurements is found by dividing the sum of the squares of the deviations from the mean of the observations by $n - 1$ instead of by n, as when s was found by Eq. 13-9. S and s can be used interchangeably in most cases when $n > 10$. S should be used when very few measurements are available. When only one measurement has been made, the standard deviation is, of course, indeterminate, and for this case Eq. 13-15 gives

$$S = \sqrt{\frac{\Sigma x^2}{n-1}} = \frac{0}{0} \qquad \text{if } n = 1 \qquad (13\text{-}16)$$

13-5 The Error Function. The chance P that the error of any particular measurement will fall between x_1 and x_2, called the *error function*, is found by integrating y (Eq. 13-10) between x_1 and x_2:

$$P = \frac{0.399}{s}\int_{x_1}^{x_2}\exp\left(-\frac{x^2}{2s^2}\right)dx \qquad (13\text{-}17)$$

This reduces to y (Eq. 13-10) if $x_2 - x_1 = \Delta x$ is small.

The fraction of all the measurements that will have errors (half plus and half minus) numerically greater than x is

$$P_1 = \frac{0.798}{s} \int_s^\infty \exp\left(-\frac{x^2}{2s^2}\right) dx \qquad (13\text{-}18)$$

A series of values of P_1 is given in Appendix G, and it is plotted in Fig. 13-2.

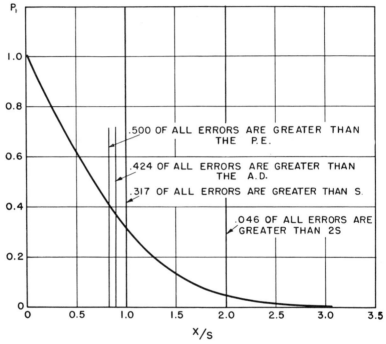

Fig. 13-2 The error function (Eq. 13-18).

The fraction x/s is the ratio of a particular error to the standard deviation, or rms difference from the mean. P_1 is the fraction of all the measurements for which the difference is expected to be greater than the particular value x.

The value $x = 0.675s$, for which $P_1 = 0.50$, is called the *probable error*, or P. E., since it is equally likely that any given error will be numerically larger or smaller than this; i.e., the ordinate $0.675s$ divides the (half) area of the probability curve into two equal parts. The average error is $x = 0.80s$. Any one of these three quantities may be used to describe the accuracy of the measurements, depending on the purpose in view:

s or S = standard deviation = square root of the mean-square difference (Eq. 13-9 or Eq. 13-15)
$0.80s$ = a.d. = average difference from the mean
$0.675s$ = P.E. = probable error

The normal law of probability (Eq. 13-11) applies to those accidental and irregular variations which remain after all known sources of error and mistakes have been excluded, in the absence of knowledge of any dissymmetry that would make the normal law inapplicable. It assumes that plus and minus variations of the same size are equally likely. Despite these limitations, it can be usefully applied in a great many ways. It is especially helpful in examining data from tests or inspection records to locate gross errors or mistakes.

For example, Fig. 13-2 shows that 38.3 per cent of all the measurements will vary by less than $0.50s$ from the mean if the distribution is normal and 57.6 per cent will vary by less than the average difference. The chance of a difference greater than $2s$ occurring is only 0.046 and greater than $3s$ is only 0.0027.

Thus, normally, fewer than five measurements in 100 will differ from the mean by more than $2s$, and fewer than three measurements in 1,000 will differ from the mean by more than $3s$. Conversely, whenever a single measurement does differ from the mean (of a large number of earlier values) by more than $3s$, it almost certainly indicates a gross error or mistake. Such an occurrence is a signal to the observer, or the foreman of a manufacturing process, to halt operations at once and look for the trouble before proceeding. An extensive statistical quality control procedure has been developed on the basis of this simple principle: Whenever a measurement falls well outside of the range set by the normal law (with a value of s set by previous experience), there almost certainly has been a significant change in the manufacturing process or some gross mistake in recording the data.

13-6 Examples. Another simple use for the normal law is to check for the presence of some abnormality in the data, as may occur when there are two or more independent sources of variation. One way to do this is to see how nearly the average deviation of a set of measurements equals 0.80 of the standard deviation. The data of Table 13-1, for example, give an a.d. of 0.0108 and s of 0.0135, with a ratio of just 0.80. Thus, the distribution is normal in this respect.

Suppose measurements of 20 samples of sheet steel give the results shown in Table 13-2 for the thickness of each sample, in mils.

Table 13-2   An Analysis of Data by the Normal Law of Probability

Reading M	(1) All $M_0 = 25.1$ 10 × difference		(10x)²	(2) 10 Smallest $M_0 = 24.6$ 10 × difference		(10x)²	(3) 10 Largest $M_0 = 25.6$ 10 × difference		(10x)²
	−	+		−	+		−	+	
24.2	9		81	4		16			
24.7	4		16		1	1			
25.7		6						1	1
24.4	7		49	2		4			
25.9		8						3	9
25.8		7						2	4
24.6	5		25		0	0			
25.0	1		1		4	16			
24.9	2		4		3	9			
25.4		3					2		4
26.0		9						4	16
25.5		4					1		1
24.3	8		64	3		9			
25.6		5					0		0
24.8	3		9		2	4			
25.3		2						3	9
24.6	5		25	0		0			
25.2		1					4		16
24.5	6		36	1		1			
25.6		5						0	0
Sum: 502.0	−50	+50	310	−10	+10	60	−10	+10	60

Av $M_0 = 25.1$	a.d. = 0.50 $s = 0.556$ Ratio a.d./s = 0.90	a.d. = 0.20 $s = 0.245$ Ratio a.d./s = 0.82	a.d. = 0.20 $s = 0.245$ Ratio a.d./s = 0.82

The average thickness of the entire group of 20 is 25.1 mils (column 1), the corresponding a.d. is 0.50 mil, and the standard deviation is 0.556 mil. The ratio a.d./s is, therefore, 0.90, which is materially higher than the normal ratio of 0.80. This leads us to suspect that the sample is not homogeneous, but, in fact, consists of a mixture of two lots. Dividing the readings into two sets of the ten largest and ten smallest confirms this, showing that there are two kinds of samples: one with an average thickness of 24.6 mils, and the other with an average thickness of 25.6. With respect to their own values of M_0, the a.d. of each group is 0.20, and its standard deviation is 0.245 mil, as shown in columns 2 and 3 of Table 13-2. For each of these groups of 10, the ratio of a.d. to s is 0.82, which is normal.

Thus, any departure of the error distribution curve from the normal shape is an indication that there is some systematic source of variation, entirely aside from the normal effects of chance. Such techniques as this are extremely useful in the study of manufacturing processes, to eliminate sources of variation or poor quality.

The value of s determined from a series of measurements gives a simple numerical measure of their accuracy. By repetition of a series of tests, or of manufacturing operations, first with one set of instruments or tools, then with another, then with two or more different operators, and finally with materials coming from different sources, distinct s values can be associated with each instrument or tool, each operator, and each kind of material or supplier. In this way, all the factors that contribute to variations in the product may be separately evaluated.

If there are two or more independent sources of variation in a given measurement, the standard deviation of the result will be equal to the square root of the sum of the squares of the standard deviations due to the independent causes. That is, the over-all standard deviation is

$$s = \sqrt{s_1^2 + s_2^2 + s_3^2 + \cdots} \tag{13-19}$$

That this is true may be seen easily from the consideration that, if x and y are two independent errors in a single measurement, the combined error is $x + y$ and the square of the combined error is

$$(x + y)^2 = (x^2 + y^2) + 2xy$$

The average of this is

$$\text{av } (x + y)^2 = \text{av } (x^2) + \text{av } (y^2) + [\text{av } (2xy) = 0]$$

As the errors are independent, the sum of all the x values is zero and also of the y values and there are equal numbers of plus and of minus values of both x and y. It follows that the sum of all the products xy must be zero. Hence, only the x^2 and y^2 terms need be considered in calculating the combined value of s.

For example, if the allowed tolerances in manufacture of three pieces of metal which are to be assembled in a stack are 10 mils, 20 mils, and 30 mils, respectively, the corresponding tolerance in the over-all measurement of the stack will be

$$s = \sqrt{(10)^2 + (20)^2 + (30)^2} = 37.5 \text{ mils} \tag{13-20}$$

In this case, therefore, if greater uniformity is required, all effort should be put on improving the accuracy of the piece with 30-mil tolerance and nothing will be gained by working on the one with 10-mil tolerance. This principle of the root-mean-square addition of independent errors is an invaluable aid in manufacturing assemblies such as small gear trains. Much greater latitude in each part is permissible than there would be if the over-all tolerance was equal to the sum of the individual tolerances. It is true that, by the laws of chance, a very few assemblies may include pieces that are all at the extreme limits of tolerance in one direction, but these cases will be exceedingly rare.

13-7   Accuracy of the Mean of n Measurements.   If the mean of n measurements differs from the true value of the quantity by X, the differences of the n separate measurements will be

$$x_1 + X, \, x_2 + X, \, x_3 + X, \, \ldots, \, x_n + X$$

and the sum of the squares of these will be equal to

$$(x_1{}^2 + x_2{}^2 + x_3{}^2 + \cdots + x_n{}^2) + nX^2$$

(The sum of the Xx_n terms is zero, by Eq. 13-1.)

Hence, the probability of an error X in the mean of n measurements, by Eq. 13-11, is the product of the separate probabilities, or

$$Y_n = (0.4)^n \exp\left[-\frac{(x_1{}^2 + x_2{}^2 + \cdots + x_n{}^2 + nX^2)}{2s^2} \right] \quad (13\text{-}21)$$

The ratio of the chance of an error of the mean, equal to X, to that of a zero error ($X = 0$) is therefore

$$\frac{Y_n\big]_{X=X}}{Y_n\big]_{X=0}} = \exp\left(-\frac{nX^2}{2s^2} \right) \quad (13\text{-}22)$$

From Eq. 13-11, the corresponding ratio of the chance of an error X to that of a zero error in a single measurement is $\exp(-X^2/2s^2)$. Comparing these two ratios, we see that if s is the standard deviation of any one measurement, the standard deviation of the mean of n measurements is $s/\sqrt{n}$. That is, under the normal law of probability, the standard deviation (also the probable error) of a measured quantity is reduced by a factor $1/\sqrt{n}$, when the number of readings is increased by a factor n. By taking 25 independent measurements, the probable error of the resulting mean value will be reduced to one-fifth the probable error of any single measurement, as far as the chance factors in the observations are concerned.

13-8 Probability Paper. It is convenient in analyzing repeated measurements to arrange the readings in the order of their numerical magnitudes and to group together all the points in each 10 per cent of the total. For example, the 20 readings of sheet steel thickness given in Table 13-2, when grouped in pairs of consecutive values, give Table 13-3.

Table 13-3　Readings of Sheet-steel Thickness

No. of group	Average reading	No. of group	Average reading
1 (lowest 10 per cent)	24.25	6	25.25
2 (next lowest)	24.45	7	25.45
3 (etc.)	24.60	8	25.60
4	24.75	9 (next to highest)	25.75
5	24.95	10 (highest 10 per cent)	25.95

In this way, a large number of observations may be combined into a small number of well-defined points that can be conveniently compared with other data. Plotting the readings vertically against the number of the group horizontally provides a graphical picture of the whole that enables any irregularity to be located. If the plot is made on ordinary graph paper with a linear scale, and if the data follow the normal distribution law, the middle group points will be closely spaced and the extreme points will be widely separated, since most of the readings should be concentrated about the mid-point.

The important thing to find out from such a graph is how nearly the data fit the normal law. To make it easy to do this, a special form of graph paper, called *probability paper*, has been prepared which has the horizontal coordinates expanded on both sides of the center in such a way that points following the normal error function (P_1 curve, Appendix G) will lie along a straight line. For example, the data of Table 13-3 have been plotted on probability paper in Fig. 13-3. The first point, representing the lowest 10 per cent of the readings, has the value 24.25 and thus is plotted vertically at the mid-point of its group, or 5 on the per cent scale. The second point, 24.45, is plotted above its mid-point, or 15 per cent, etc. The resulting curve has a point of inflection at the center and is not at all a straight line. Thus, the data are shown not to obey the normal law, confirming the conclusion reached by the calculations made in Sec. 13-6.

On the other hand, when the ten measurements of an angle given in Table 13-1 are plotted in the same way, as also shown in Fig. 13-3, the points fall almost exactly on a straight line, showing that these data do follow the normal law. The point at which the line crosses the 50 per cent line gives the mean value of all the readings. Also, the vertical distance between the points at which the line crosses the 15.8 and 50 per cent lines gives the standard deviation of the measurements. Thus, the use of probability paper reduces the labor of calculation, as well as aiding the analysis.

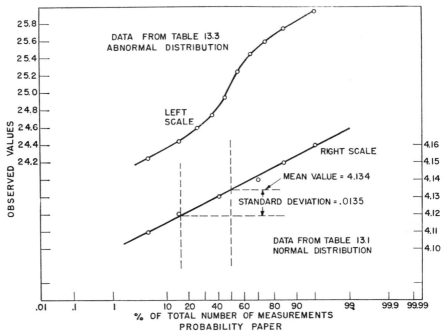

Fig. 13-3   Percentage of total number of measurements, probability paper.

13-9   Adjustment of Observations.   Frequently a quantity may be determined by two or more independent methods, as when measurements are made with different instruments or by different observers. To find the most probable value, considering all the data, the different results must be combined, with due regard to their different degrees of precision.

Evidently, if m measurements give M as the average of the readings and n additional measurements of equal precision give an average of N, the most probable true value is the same as found by considering the $m + n$ measurements as a single set of data. Thus the most probable value is

$$M_0 = \frac{mM + nN}{m + n} \tag{13-23}$$

In combining the results of different numbers of measurements of the same precision, therefore, each should be given a weight proportional to the number of measurements it represents (Eq. 1-31).

If the standard deviation is s_1 for each of the m measurements and s_2 for each of the n measurements, the standard deviation of M will be $s_1/\sqrt{m}$ and of N will be $s_2/\sqrt{n}$. Therefore, in combining the two means, a weight m/s_1^2 should be applied to M, and a weight n/s_2^2 to N, giving for the most probable true value

$$M = \frac{mMs_2^2 + nNs_1^2}{ms_2^2 + ns_1^2} \tag{13-24}$$

If $s_2 = s_1$, this reduces to Eq. 13-23.

This illustrates the importance of knowing the precision of each quantity employed in engineering calculations. For each 10 per cent increase in the standard deviation of a measurement, 20 per cent more measurements will be required for the same over-all accuracy.

It often occurs that we know the form of equations connecting two or more variables but do not know the coefficients of the several terms in the equations. For example, we may believe that the stray losses of an induction motor are made up of three distinct elements, each related in a definite way to the motor dimensions, speed, current, etc.; and we then wish to determine the proper coefficients to apply to these separate elements in order to arrive at the best possible equation for the loss that will apply to other machines. We have

$$W = aA + bB + cC + \cdots \tag{13-25}$$

where A, B, C, . . . are known quantities calculated from the motor dimensions, current, etc., a, b, c, . . . are unknown coefficients to be determined, and aA, bB, cC, . . . are the separate elements (of watts loss) whose sum equals the total (watts stray loss) that we wish to calculate.

Since formulas of this kind generally leave out of consideration a large number of minor factors and since the values of A, B, C, etc., are approximations at best, the final values of a, b, c, etc., will be inexact. To find the most probable values of a, b, c, . . . , the procedure is to obtain actual test results (values of W) on as many machines as practicable, say n in all, and arrange the data in the form of n simultaneous equations:

$$\begin{aligned}
W_1 &= aA_1 + bB_1 + cC_1 + \cdots \\
W_2 &= aA_2 + bB_2 + cC_2 + \cdots \\
W_n &= aA_n + bB_n + cC_n + \cdots
\end{aligned} \tag{13-26}$$

Since the values of W, A, B, C, etc., are all known, this gives n equations in the small number of unknowns, a, b, c, ... The problem then is to find the values of a, b, c that will give the best fit with the n equations, that is, the values that will make the sum of the squares of the differences between the actual and the calculated values of W_1, W_2, etc., a minimum.

The most probable value of a will be that which makes the sum of the squares of the difference in W due to a small change in a a minimum. The differences between the calculated and the actual values of W are

$$x_1 = aA_1 + bB_1 + cC_1 + \cdots - W_1$$
$$x_2 = aA_2 + bB_2 + cC_2 + \cdots - W_2 \qquad (13\text{-}27)$$
$$\cdots\cdots\cdots\cdots\cdots\cdots\cdots$$

To make the sum of the squares of x_1, x_2, x_3, . . . a minimum, each of the derivatives with respect to a, b, c, . . . of $x_1{}^2 + x_2{}^2 + x_3{}^2 + \ldots$ must be zero. That is,

$$\frac{d}{da}[(aA_1 + bB_1 + \cdots - W_1)^2$$
$$+ (aA_2 + bB_2 + \cdots - W_2)^2 + \cdots] = 0$$

$$\frac{d}{db}[(aA_1 + bB_1 + \cdots - W_1)^2$$
$$+ (aA_2 + bB_2 + \cdots - W_2)^2 + \cdots] = 0 \quad (13\text{-}28)$$

$$\frac{d}{dc}[(aA_1 + bB_1 + \cdots - W_1)^2$$
$$+ (aA_2 + bB_2 + \cdots - W_2)^2 + \cdots] = 0$$

Differentiating with respect to a gives

$$2A_1(aA_1 + bB_1 + \cdots - W_1)$$
$$+ 2A_2(aA_2 + bB_2 + \cdots - W_2) + \cdots = 0 \quad (13\text{-}29)$$

or, dropping the factor 2 and rearranging, we have

$$a(A_1{}^2 + A_2{}^2 + \cdots) + b(A_1B_1 + A_2B_2 + \cdots)$$
$$+ c(A_1C_1 + A_2C_2 + \cdots) + \cdots = (A_1W_1 + A_2W_2 + \cdots)$$

$$a(A_1B_1 + A_2B_2 + \cdots) + b(B_1{}^2 + B_2{}^2 + \cdots)$$
$$+ c(B_1C_1 + B_2C_2 + \cdots) + \cdots = (B_1W_1 + B_2W_2 + \cdots)$$

$$a(A_1C_1 + A_2C_2 + \cdots) + b(B_1C_1 + B_2C_2 + \cdots)$$
$$+ c(C_1{}^2 + C_2{}^2 + \cdots) + \cdots = (C_1W_1 + C_2W_2 + \cdots)$$
$$(13\text{-}30)$$

As all the numerical values of A_n, B_n, C_n, . . . , W_n are known, it is just a matter of arithmetic to compute the coefficients of a, b, c, . . . in these equations, giving finally just as many equations as there are unknowns:

$$a\Sigma A^2 + b\Sigma AB + c\Sigma AC + \cdots = \Sigma AW$$
$$a\Sigma AB + b\Sigma B^2 + c\Sigma BC + \cdots = \Sigma BW \qquad (13\text{-}31)$$
$$a\Sigma AC + b\Sigma BC + c\Sigma C^2 + \cdots = \Sigma CW$$
$$. \quad . \quad . \quad . \quad . \quad . \quad . \quad . \quad . \quad . \quad . \quad . \quad .$$

which can be solved simultaneously to find the desired values of a, b, c, etc. (Σ indicates the sum of all like terms from 1 to n.)

These should be substituted in Eq. 13-27 to find the actual values of the differences, x_1, x_2, x_3, . . . , x_n; and then the a.d. and s values should be calculated. If the ratio a.d./s is nearly 0.80 and if there are no values of x greater than about $2s$, so that the distribution is normal, the problem can be considered solved. If, however, a.d./s differs considerably from 0.80, or if there are values of x greater than $2s$, or at any rate $3s$, it follows that some of the tests do not fit the normal pattern. By reexamination of the data for the cases that do not conform, it is usually possible to detect some error, or an omitted factor, and to adjust the results accordingly, leading to revised values of a, b, c, etc., or the inclusion of additional terms in the equation until finally the desired accuracy of fit is secured.

An example of this method is given in Sec. 7-3, where the data in Table 7-1 have been used to determine the coefficients of an empirical power series that will best fit the tests.

13-10 The Binomial Law—Permutations and Combinations. We have seen in Sec. 13-4 that, in tossing a coin, the chance of a head coming up on a single trial is 0.5. More generally, if the chance of an event happening on a particular trial is p, so that the chance of its not happening on any trial is $1 - p$, then the chance that it will happen every time in n independent trials is

$$P_n(0) = p^n \qquad (13\text{-}32)$$

and the chance of its not happening at all in n trials is

$$P_0(n) = (1 - p)^n \qquad (13\text{-}33)$$

For example, if, on the average, one out of ten telephones is busy at any moment, the chance of getting four different calls through without delay is

$$P_4(0) = (0.9)^4 = 0.6561$$

and the chance of getting a busy signal every time is

$$P_0(4) = (0.1)^4 = 0.0001$$

What is the chance of getting just one busy signal in the four trials? The chance of getting a busy signal the first time, and then three clear signals, is $(0.1)(0.9)^3$. There are three other possible sequences: a busy signal on the second, third, or fourth trial, and all the rest clear signals. The sum of all these chances is

$$P_3(1) = (0.1)(0.9)^3 + (0.9)(0.1)(0.9)^2 + (0.9)^2(0.1)(0.9)$$
$$+ (0.9)^3(0.1) = 4(0.1)(0.9)^3 = 0.2916$$

Similarly, the chance of getting just two busy signals in the four trials is

$$P_2(2) = (0.1)[0.1(0.9)^2 + 0.9(0.1)(0.9) + (0.9)^2(0.1)]$$
$$+ 0.9(0.1)[(0.1)(0.9) + (0.9)(0.1)] + (0.9)^2(0.1)^2$$
$$= 6(0.1)^2(0.9)^2 = 0.0486$$

and the chance of getting three busy signals in the four trials is

$$P_1(3) = (0.1)^3(0.9) + (0.1)^2(0.9)(0.1) + (0.1)(0.9)(0.1)^2$$
$$+ (0.9)(0.1)^3$$
$$= 4(0.1)^3(0.9) = 0.0036$$

The sum of all these five chances is unity, as it should be:

$$0.6561 + 0.2916 + 0.0486 + 0.0036 + 0.0001 = 1$$

This method of analysis, carried further, leads to the general rule that the chance of just m successes in n independent trials, when the chance of success on each trial is p, will be

$$P_m(n - m) = \frac{n(n - 1)(n - 2) \cdots (n - m + 1)}{m!} (p)^m(1 - p)^{n-m}$$

$$(13\text{-}34)$$

As a check, in the cases considered above, with $n = 4$, $p = 0.9$, the chances of making $m = 4$, 3, 2, 1, or 0 successful calls are, by Eq. 13-34,

$$P_4(0) = (1)(0.9)^4(0.1)^0 = 0.6561$$
$$P_3(1) = (4)(0.9)^3(0.1) = 0.2916$$
$$P_2(2) = (6)(0.9)^2(0.1)^2 = 0.0486$$
$$P_1(3) = (4)(0.9)(0.1)^3 = 0.0036$$
$$P_0(4) = (1)(0.9)^0(0.1)^4 = 0.0001$$

which agree with the values already found.

We recognize the numerical coefficient of Eq. 13-34 as an old friend, the coefficient of the *m*th term in the binomial series expression (Eq. 5-22). For convenience, this binomial coefficient is often represented by the shorthand expression $C(n,m)$:

$$C(n,m) = \frac{n(n-1)(n-2) \cdots (n-m+1)}{m!} = \frac{n!}{m!(n-m)!}$$

(13-35)

Suppose we have *n* different objects, *a*, *b*, *c*, . . . , *n*, and we take out *m* of them at random. How many different combinations is it possible to have? If $m = 1, 2, 3$, etc., we find the possibilities given in Table 13-4.

Table 13-4   Total Number of Possible Combinations for *m* Number of Objects

m, No. of objects in group	Possible combinations	Total number of possibilities
1	*a*, *b*, *c*, . . . , *n*	*n*
2	*ab*, *ac*, . . . , *an*; *bc*, *bd*, . . . , *bn*; . . .	$\dfrac{n(n-1)}{2}$
3	*abc*, *abd*, . . . , *abn*; *acd*, *ace*, . . . , *acn*; . . . *bcd*, *bce*, . . . , *bcn*; *bde*, *bdf*, . . . , *bdn*; . . .	$\dfrac{n(n-1)(n-2)}{6}$

The total is again equal to the binomial coefficient.

Thus, we find that $C(n,m)$ (Eq. 13-35) is also equal to the total possible number of different combinations of *n* things taken *m* at a time.

We can see that *m* different things can be arranged in *m*! different sequences or permutations, for

If $m = 1$, we can have only *a*   total = 1
If $m = 2$, we can have *ab* or *ba*   total = 2
If $m = 3$, we can have *abc*, *acb*, *bac*, *bca*, *cab*, or *cba*   total = 6

. . . .

Thus the total number of different arrangements, or permutations, of *n* different things, taken *m* at a time, is

$$m!C(n,m) = \frac{n!}{(n-m)!}$$

(13-36)

If $m = 1$, this is *n*!

These relations are useful in determining how many different happenings can occur under different circumstances, and hence what the probability is that a desired event or series of events actually will occur. Knowing this probability, the engineer can provide an alternate procedure, or adequate reserve capacity, or check tests, or protective devices, to ensure that the risk of damage or extra cost or delay is held within tolerable limits.

13-11   Correlation Coefficients.   Suppose that it is desired to improve the quality and uniformity of an alloy steel whose properties have been found to vary considerably. The first step is to obtain test data, giving numerical values of such properties as ultimate strength at various temperatures, creep, hardness, ductility, etc., for a large number of samples of different kinds. If feasible, special compositions or treatments may be procured, chosen in such a way as to cover the range of practicable variations. Or, available samples, from different suppliers, or made at different times, etc., may be utilized. Data on the composition, processing, heat treatment, etc., of each sample are also collected. Then the different samples are listed in parallel columns, first in the order of excellence in one quality, such as ductility, and then, successively, in the order of magnitude of each of the factors suspected as causes of variation.

For example, suppose eight samples of steel have been prepared with varying contents of three different alloying elements, X, Y, and Z, and their properties have been carefully measured. Then, the samples are numbered consecutively in the order of their quality with respect to ductility, say, and they are also ranked in the order of their alloy contents, as shown in Table 13-5.

Table 13-5   Different Order Rankings for Eight Samples of Steel

(1) Ductility	(2) Alloy X content	(3) Alloy Y content	(4) Alloy Z content
1	7	3	4
2	3	1	2
3	6	2	5
4	1	4	8
5	5	6	1
6	8	5	6
7	4	8	7
8	2	7	3

The table shows that the sample 1 is best in the selected quality of ductility, that it has the fourth greatest content of alloy X, the second greatest of Y, and the fifth greatest of Z. If the rank of all the samples was just the same for alloy X, say, as for ductility, it would be highly probable that the X content and ductility had a close cause-and-effect relation. On this basis, experiments could be undertaken to increase further, and control, the X content, in the confident expectation that a more ductile steel would result. Actually, the rankings are not consistent, and it seems to be anybody's guess whether X, Y, or Z has an important effect or not.

The method of deciding the question is to compute the rank correlation coefficient t between each two columns that are to be compared, by the following process:

1. The n samples are ranked in order of merit with respect to a selected quality in column 1.

2. With the same numbers assigned, the samples are arranged in column 2 in the order of another quality (as their alloy content).

3. For each sample in column 2, the other samples that have higher assigned numbers, but are ranked lower in the column, are counted.

4. The sum of all the numbers obtained by step 3, called Z, is multiplied by $4/n(n-1)$ and unity is subtracted from the result.

The result is the rank correlation coefficient

$$t = \frac{4Z}{n(n-1)} - 1 \tag{13-37}$$

If the orders of rank in the two columns are the same, Z will be equal to $n(n-1)/2$ and t will be 1. If the orders of rank are exactly inverse, Z will be 0 and t will be -1. If all possible ways of ranking the second column are tried, it will be found that the most frequent value of t will be 0. The probability of a particular value of t, therefore, follows a curve quite similar to the normal probability law (Fig. 13-1). The similarity is greater the greater the value of n.

From Eq. 13-36, the total number of possible rankings (permutations) of n samples taken one at a time is $n!$ Only one of these rankings will be the same as the ranking of the samples with respect to another quality. Hence, the probability that the rankings of n samples with respect to two unrelated qualities will be identical, giving $t = 1$, is only $1/n!$

Applying these rules to compare column 1 with columns 2, 3, and 4 of Table 13-5, we find the results of Table 13-6.

We find that t is -0.21 for column 2, showing that the X alloy has a slight, but hardly significant, tendency to decrease the ductility.

For column 3, t is 0.71, showing that alloy Y has a strong and highly significant tendency to increase the ductility. For column 4, t is 0 showing that alloy Z has no noticeable effect.

Table 13-6 Correlation of Samples

	(2)			(3)		(4)	
Sample	Higher numbered samples below it	Sum	Sample	Sum	Sample	Sum
7	8	1	3	5	4	4
3	4, 5, 6, 8	4	1	6	2	5
6	8	1	2	5	5	1
1	2, 4, 5, 8	4	4	4	8	0
5	8	1	6	2	1	3
8	. . . .	0	5	2	6	1
4	. . . .	0	8	0	7	0
2	. . . .	0	7	0	3	0
Total Z:		11		24		14
$t = \dfrac{Z - 14}{14}$		-0.21		0.71		0.00

In this way, by computing correlation coefficients between parallel columns of factual data, or merely of opinions, we may obtain definite conclusions as to the probability of various alternatives, or the credibility of different witnesses, etc.

13-12   Sampling.   If a small sample from a large production lot is examined, the number of defectives found is likely to indicate a better quality than the true average. This curious conclusion is proved by the binomial law. Eq. 13-34 shows that if the average number of defectives is 10 per cent and if successive lots of 10 are tested, 35 per cent of them will have no defects, 39 per cent will have one defect, and 26 per cent will have more than one defect. That is, 39 per cent will show the true average quality, while 35 per cent will be better, and only 26 per cent will be worse than average quality. Hence, some knowledge of probability theory is required to decide how many items should be inspected and to draw correct conclusions from the test results.

When large numbers of similar items are to be produced, the number that needs to be inspected can be reduced whenever the production process has been stabilized, so that the variations are small and follow the normal law. The usual (single sampling) inspection process requires that n items be selected at random for inspection from each lot of N and that if c or less defectives are found, the entire lot of N items shall be accepted without further inspection. If more than c defectives are found in the sample of n, the entire lot of N must be inspected, and all defectives corrected or replaced. Thus, so long as the quality is high, only n/N of the items need to be inspected, but when the quality falls, more and more items must be tested. Such an increase in inspection time and cost calls attention to the trouble and provides an incentive for correcting it.

H. F. Dodge and H. G. Romig have published extensive charts and tables that give values of n and c, determined by the binomial theorem, that will give the lowest inspection cost, while insuring that the desired maximum permissible value of per cent defectives, called the lot tolerance percent defective, or LTPD, shall not be exceeded for any chosen value of the consumer's risk. The consumer's risk is defined as the chance that any given lot that is passed by the inspection system will have a quality lower than the LTPD. The values of n and c can be smaller if the production process gives a small per cent defective, so this value should be known before the n and c values are selected.

For example, Table 13-7[1] gives the n and c values for any production lot size N up to $N = 5000$, and for values of the process average defectives between 0.06 and 2.00 per cent, all on the basis of a consumer's risk of 10 per cent. The table shows, for example, that if a lot of $N = 900$ items is to be produced by a process that has been found to give a process average of between 0.51 and 1.00 per cent defectives and if the consumer is to have a 90 per cent certainty that no lot will pass inspection that has more than 5.0 per cent defectives, then the producer should inspect 105 of the 900 items, selected at random, and he should pass all 900 if the number of defectives found is two or less. The table shows also that if no more than two defectives are allowed in each 105 items tested, the average outgoing quality level, or AOQL, should have less than 1.2 per cent defective. This is lower than indicated by the c/n ratio, because some of the N lots will be fully inspected (when more than two defectives are found in a sample of 105), and these will have zero defectives, assuming the inspectors throw out or replace all the defective items, as they are supposed to do.

13-13 Randomization—Latin Squares. When a new device, or drug, or seed, or treatment is to be evaluated, it is essential to distinguish the numerous variations due to extraneous causes from those due to the treatment itself. It is not practical to keep all the test con-

[1] Dodge and Romig, "Sampling Inspection Tables," John Wiley & Sons, Inc., 2d ed., New York, 1959.

Table 13-7 Single Sampling Table for Consumer's Risk of 10%
and for LTPD = 5.0%

Lot size	Process average 0.06 to 0.50%			Process average 0.51 to 100%			Process average 1.01 to 1.50%			Process average 1.51 to 2.00%		
N	n	c	AOQL %	n	c	AOQL %	n	c	AOQL %	n	c	AOQL %
1–30	All	0	0	All	0	0	All	0	0	All	0	0
31–50	30	0	0.49	30	0	0.49	30	0	0.49	30	0	0.49
51–100	37	0	0.63	37	0	0.63	37	0	0.63	37	0	0.63
101–200	40	0	0.74	40	0	0.74	40	0	0.74	40	0	0.74
201–300	43	0	0.74	70	1	0.92	70	1	0.92	95	2	0.99
301–400	44	0	0.74	70	1	0.99	100	2	1.0	120	3	1.1
401–500	75	1	0.95	100	2	1.1	100	2	1.1	125	3	1.2
501–600	75	1	0.98	100	2	1.1	125	3	1.2	150	4	1.3
601–800	75	1	1.0	100	2	1.2	130	3	1.2	175	5	1.4
801–1000	75	1	1.0	105	2	1.2	155	4	1.4	180	5	1.4
1001–2000	75	1	1.0	130	3	1.4	180	5	1.6	230	7	1.7
2001–3000	105	2	1.3	135	3	1.4	210	6	1.7	280	9	1.9
3001–4000	105	2	1.3	160	4	1.5	210	6	1.7	305	10	2.0
4001–5000	105	2	1.3	160	4	1.5	235	7	1.8	330	11	2.0

n = Sample size.
c = Acceptance number.
AOQL = Average outgoing quality limit.

ditions the same, except for the treatment, and at any rate, it is useful to find out what happens when the conditions change.

To do this, a large number of tests should be made with all the conditions that may affect the results varied systematically, so that each condition can be averaged out in the analysis. For this purpose, Latin squares may be used, as shown in Fig. 13-4. For example, suppose it is desired to measure the relative growth rates of plants when treated in four different ways A, B, C, and D. The land in which they are to be grown may then be divided into sixteen similar plots, designated by the four rows and four columns of the 4×4 Latin square in Fig. 13-4. The four treatments will be applied to the plants in a random manner, but so that each treatment will be applied to one plot in each row and one in each column, as indicated.

When the measurements of growth are obtained, the four results for each treatment will come one from each row and from each column, so the averages will cancel out any variations due to the soil. And the averages of each column and of each row will show whether there actually was any difference in the fertility of the 16 plots. The mean

3 × 3	A B C
	B C A
	C A B

4 × 4	A B C D
	B D A C
	C A D B
	D C B A

5 × 5	A B C D E
	B A E C D
	C D A E B
	D E B A C
	E C D B A

6 × 6	A B C D E F
	B F D C A E
	C D E F B A
	D A F E C B
	E C A B F D
	F E B A D C

Fig. 13-4 Latin Squares.

3 × 3	$A\alpha$ $B\beta$ $C\gamma$
	$B\gamma$ $C\alpha$ $A\beta$
	$C\beta$ $A\gamma$ $B\alpha$

4 × 4	$A1\alpha$ $B2\beta$ $C3\gamma$ $D4\delta$
	$B4\gamma$ $A3\delta$ $D2\alpha$ $C1\beta$
	$C2\delta$ $D1\gamma$ $A4\beta$ $B3\alpha$
	$D3\beta$ $C4\alpha$ $B1\delta$ $A2\gamma$

5 × 5	$A0\alpha5$ $B1\beta6$ $C2\gamma7$ $D3\delta8$ $E4x9$
	$B2\delta9$ $C3\epsilon5$ $D4\alpha6$ $E0\beta7$ $A1\gamma8$
	$C4\beta8$ $D0\gamma9$ $E1\delta5$ $A2\epsilon6$ $B3\alpha7$
	$D1\epsilon7$ $E2\alpha8$ $A3\beta9$ $B4\gamma5$ $C0\delta6$
	$E3\gamma6$ $A4\delta7$ $B0\epsilon8$ $C1\alpha9$ $D2\beta5$

Fig. 13-5 Graeco-Latin Squares.

deviation of the measurements from each average will show the accuracy of the results and will disclose whether there was any irregularity requiring further study. By repeating the program, with a different allocation of the treatments to the plots, or with additional plots, the project may be carried on until the desired accuracy has been obtained.

When it is desired to learn the effects of additional variables, a Graeco-Latin square may be used, as shown in Fig. 13-5. Here, there are four extra conditions α, β, γ, and δ in addition to the four treatments A, B, C, and D. Each combination of a Greek and a Latin letter occurs once, and each letter occurs once in each row and each column. Of course, any two or more of the letters may be used for the same treatment or condition, if it is desired to obtain more data on one rather than exploring additional treatments. By averaging results for each Greek and each Latin letter separately, the values of each can be determined, and their effects on each other can be determined by averaging other selected test results.

The art of designing experiments to allow for large numbers of variables and of analyzing the results, called the *analysis of variance*, has been developed at great length, as explained in books such as those listed in the bibliography of this chapter. Tables of Latin and Graeco-Latin squares,[1] and of random numbers for randomizing test conditions, are available also.

[1] R. A. Fisher, *Contributions to Mathematical Statistics*, John Wiley & Sons, Inc., New York, 1950.

13.14   Magic Squares.   The design of Latin squares is closely allied to that of magic squares. The simplest type of magic square is an array of n^2 numbers arranged in a square with n numbers in each row and column in such a way that the sum of the numbers in each row, column, and diagonal is the same, equal to $n(n^2 + 1)/2$ (see Eq. 5-14). There is no simple rule for forming magic squares with an even value of n, but squares with n an odd value can be formed very simply by placing 1 in the center of the bottom line and putting the succeeding

4	9	2
3	5	7
8	1	6

n = 3   each sum = 15

11	18	25	2	9
10	12	19	21	3
4	6	13	20	22
23	5	7	14	16
17	24	1	8	15

n = 5   each sum = 65

22	31	40	49	2	11	20
21	23	32	41	43	3	12
13	15	24	33	42	44	4
5	14	16	25	34	36	45
46	6	8	17	26	35	37
38	47	7	9	18	27	29
30	39	48	1	10	19	28

n = 7   each sum = 175

Fig. 13-6   Magic squares with an odd number on a side.

numbers, 2, 3, 4, etc., in a diagonal line down to the right. When the side of the square is reached, the next number goes in the box corresponding to the next position in an adjoining square. When the next box is already filled, the next number goes in the box immediately above. Squares with 3, 5, and 7 numbers on a side are shown in Fig. 13-6.

There are a great many different squares that can be formed when n is large. A thorough discussion of the subject can be found in the Encyclopaedia Britannica.

PROBLEMS

1. In 1,000 observations of the same quantity how many may be expected to differ from the mean value by less than the probable error, by less than the mean absolute error, and by less than the root-mean-square error, respectively?

2. Ten measurements of the density of a body made with equal precision give the following results:

$$
\begin{array}{ccccc}
9.662 & 9.664 & 9.677 & 9.663 & 9.645 \\
9.673 & 9.659 & 9.662 & 9.680 & 9.654
\end{array}
$$

What is the probable value of the density of the body and the probable error of that value?

3. It is required to determine an angle with a probable error less than 0.25″. The mean of twenty measurements gives a probable error of 0.38″. How many additional measurements are necessary?

4. A micrometer was used to measure the distance between the threads of a screw. Forty measurements were taken to determine the error in the machining of the screw, and to estimate the apparent distance in mils: ₑ

600.0	606.1	602.4	603.4	602.7	602.7	600.7
599.7	604.8	600.7	601.4	602.0	602.6	600.0
599.5	604.7	601.6	603.1	603.7	600.9	601.4
604.6	602.1	601.7	601.8	602.1	601.4	602.9
603.9	602.2	601.4	600.6	602.3	600.8	602.9
602.4	602.4	602.1	603.6	603.6		

Find the probable distance between the threads and its probable error.

5. Regarding the alphabet as consisting of 21 consonants and 5 vowels, how many distinct five-letter words are possible, each having three consonants and two vowels alternated?

6. A firm has four positions available, and a list of eleven applicants. How many possible ways are there of filling them?

7. Show that the probability of throwing a seven on the first throw of a pair of dice is greater than for any other number that may be thrown.

8. A horseshoe contains eight nails. In how many different orders may they be driven? What is the probability that the four shoes on a certain horse will be driven in the same order?

9. How many straight lines can be drawn through five points in such a way that each line contains two points?

10. How many distinct hands of bridge (13 cards) can be dealt from a full pack without a joker (52 cards)?

11. Show that for $m = 2, 3, 5$, the following form of the binomial theorem is valid:

$$(x + y)^m = \sum_{n=0}^{m} C_n{}^m x^{m-n} y_n$$

where
$$C_n{}^m = \frac{m!}{n!\,(m - n)!}$$

and may be defined as the number of combinations of m things taken n at a time.

12. How many different connections must a telephone exchange be capable of setting up, if it accommodates 10,000 subscribers?

13. The letters of the word *tooth* are written on cards, which are then thoroughly shuffled. If two are drawn in order, what is the chance that they yield the word *to?*

Bibliography

1. Adams, J. K.: "Basic Statistical Concepts," McGraw-Hill Book Company, New York, 1955.
2. American Society for Testing Materials: "ASTM Manual on the Presentation of Data," New York.
3. Cochran, W. C., and G. M. Cox: "Experimental Designs," John Wiley & Sons, Inc., New York, 1952.
4. Deming, W. E.: "Statistical Adjustment of Data," John Wiley & Sons, Inc., New York, 1943.
5. Dodge, H. F., and H. G. Romig: "Sampling Inspection Tables," 2d ed., John Wiley & Sons, Inc., New York, 1959.
6. Feller, W.: "An Introduction to Probability Theory and Its Applications," John Wiley & Sons, Inc., New York, 1950.
7. Fisher, R. A.: "The Design of Experiments," Oliver & Boyd, Ltd., Edinburgh, 1949.
8. Fisher, R. A., and F. Yates: "Statistical Tables," Hafner Publishing Company, Inc., New York, 1949.
9. Fry, T. C.: "Probability and Its Engineering Uses," D. Van Nostrand Company, Inc., Princeton, N.J., 1928.
10. Hald, A.: "Statistical Theory with Engineering Applications," John Wiley & Sons, Inc., New York, 1952.
11. Kempthorne, O.: "The Design and Analysis of Experiments," John Wiley & Sons, Inc., New York, 1952.
12. Kendall, M.: "Rank Correlation Methods," Charles Griffin & Company, Ltd., London, 1948.
13. Newman, J. R.: "The World of Mathematics," parts VII and VIII, Simon and Schuster, Inc., New York, 1956.
14. Simon, L. E.: "An Engineers' Manual of Statistical Methods," John Wiley & Sons, Inc., New York, 1941.
15. Whittaker, E. T., and G. Robinson: "The Calculus of Observations," D. Van Nostrand Company, Inc., Princeton, N.J., 1924.
16. Wilks, S.: "Mathematical Statistics," Princeton University Press, Princeton, N.J., 1943.
17. Wilks, S.: "Elementary Statistical Analysis," Princeton University Press, Princeton, N. J., 1948.
18. Williams, J. D.: "The Compleat Strategyst—A Primer on the Theory of Games of Strategy," McGraw-Hill Book Company, New York, 1954.

Chapter 14 MATHEMATICAL MODELS, ELECTRIC CIRCUITS, AND COMPUTERS

14-1 The Duality of Nature and of Mathematics. There are two ways of explaining many natural phenomena, in terms of corpuscles or waves; of point charges or fields; or, generally, in terms of lumped or distributed effects.

Many of the properties of light, such as shadows, can be explained by the once accepted theory that light rays consist of corpuscles moving in straight lines. Other properties, such as polarization and interference patterns, are explained by the now accepted theory that light rays consist of waves, whose frequencies determine whether they are heat, light, or radio waves or are X rays.

The old Newtonian mechanics assumed that matter and energy could be subdivided without limit, while the new quantum mechanics and modern physics state that all matter is made up of discrete particles, and that energy, too, is made up of indivisible units. Each theory is useful within its limits, and each has advantages for particular purposes.

There are two corresponding methods of mathematical treatment of physical problems; one dealing with continuous variables, called *point-set topology*, the other dealing with discrete quantities, called *combinatorial*, or *algebraic*, *topology*. Point-set topology underlies calculus, function theory, differential equations, and other methods of dealing with the properties of points infinitesimally distant from one another along curves or surfaces. Under algebraic topology are included the theory of groups and of networks, and other methods of dealing with distinct entities. The former is especially adapted to deal with problems in the small, the latter to deal with problems in the large. However, there is no sharp line separating the two methods, since each overlaps the other, and the elementary mathematics covered in this book is common to both.

[325]

Likewise there are two forms of computers, or "mechanical brains," that have been developed to perform mathematical operations. The analog computer is adapted to receive its data and to give out its answers in the form of plotted curves that represent continuous variables. The digital computer receives its instructions and gives out its results in the form of tables of numbers representing discrete entities. Both forms of computer are being used more and more by engineers.

14-2   Models for Aid in Analysis.   From the earliest times, engineers have used models as aids to understanding and for checking their results. The Greeks, having no adequate numeration system, founded their mathematical reasoning on geometry and used drawings or geometrical shapes to demonstrate their conclusions. When numerical computations became important, the abacus (Sec. 1-7) was developed to provide a physical model, in which beads strung on wires represent the objects to be counted.

The early engineers used ropes, pulleys, springs, and other devices to form many sorts of mechanical models that were used to explain and verify their ideas. As physics and electricity grew in importance, vector diagrams and geometrical models in great variety have been used, many of which are basic factors in engineering education today (see Fig. 11-5). With the growing complexity of the problems to be solved, however, and the increased number of variables to be considered, the older forms of model are less and less adequate. The concepts of quantum mechanics, atomic physics, and of economic systems cannot be explained in terms of two-dimensional drawings or three-dimensional structures.

One line of progress in devising better models has been the development by mathematicians of many new forms of geometry that deal with the properties of curves and surfaces in space of more than three dimensions. Problems that involve n variables are considered as problems in the behavior of curves in n-dimensional space or as the behavior of groups of two- or three-dimensional structures immersed in a space of n dimensions. Since we cannot construct physical models with more than the three dimensions of length, width, and height, such models as are used to illustrate these more complex mathematical concepts enable only a part of the variables to be visualized.

A second line of progress has been to accept the mathematical equations themselves as sufficient, without using any physical models. Physicists and mathematicians say that, after all, any physical model has a particular color and size and many other properties that are not pertinent to the problem, so that the model may restrict full understanding. Witness the case of the student who wanted to know the color of a ball before he calculated how high it would bounce!

Nevertheless, the need for models persists. Engineers, especially, need models to assure the safety and proper functioning of related parts. They have made progress by using dimensional analysis (Sec. 3-9) to design small-scale replicas of large structures, with their parts so proportioned that measurements made on the small model can be used to predict the performance of the full-scale design. For example, if a model of a structure is made with all its dimensions exactly one-nth as large as those of the full-scale design, and of the same materials, it is known that the resonant frequencies of vibration measured on the model will be just n times as great as those of the n times larger structure.

Models used without regard to mathematical analysis can be very misleading, for the strength of a given cross section of muscle, or of steel, is proportional to its area, or the square of its mean diameter. And the deflection of a beam of a given area under a given force goes up as the cube of its length, while its own weight increases as the product of the area by its length. Therefore, although a flea can jump two feet, or hundreds of times its own height, an elephant can hardly jump at all. Therefore, also, the legs of a daddy longlegs can be extremely long and thin, while those of a rhinoceros must be very short and thick. All the properties of a physical structure change radically in different ways when its dimensions are changed by a factor of 10 or more, so that the proportions of large and small structures must be radically different if they are to be equally successful. Similarly, it appears that the best forms of government, and of all social institutions, are different for large and small organizations.

Of course, whenever time and expense permit, engineers build one full-scale model and put it through type tests, before building a large number of duplicate designs; and they learn all they can by field tests and service experience on machines that are in use. The best model of all is a machine that has performed well through years of service under severe conditions.

14-3 Electrical Network Models. Electrical engineers have built great electric power systems and an immense variety of equipment for using and controlling electric power and for communication. All of these systems employ electrical networks, whereby various windings, devices, and controls are connected together by conductors that carry electric currents, thereby transmitting power and information in any desired manner. These networks are made up of a series of meshes, or closed loops in which different currents flow, and of junction-pairs, or points of interconnection of the meshes (Fig. 14-1). The behavior of such a network is similar whether the currents are measured in microamperes, in amperes, or in thousands of amperes. Hence an electrical network constructed on a miniature scale provides a highly satisfactory model of an indefinitely large electric power system. As a result, electrical engineers have developed a great familiarity with, and ingenuity in, the use of electrical networks. The network analyzer is an example of an electric circuit model that is widely used by electrical engineers as an analog computer to study and forecast the behavior of power systems.

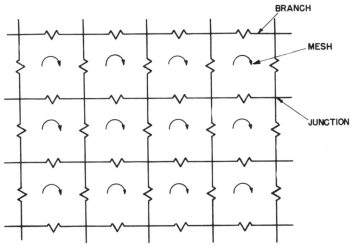

Fig. 14-1 Part of a stationary electrical network representing a complex physical system. Each branch of the network represents one degree of freedom of motion of the system. The sum of the voltages around each mesh is zero. Each connection point, or junction, represents a constraint on the motion of the system. The sum of the currents entering each junction is zero. Each conductor, or branch, has an impedance, which represents the combination of a mass, a spring, and friction. The voltage across each branch, divided by the current in the branch, is equal to the impedance of the branch.

Ohm's law, $E = IR$, is the basic law of electric circuits. It states that, in a circuit containing only resistance, R ohms, the voltage, E volts, is equal to the product of R by the current, I amperes. The law is generalized to state that $E = IZ$, where Z is the impedance of the circuit (Eq. 3-19). Kirchhoff, in 1847, was the first to state the two laws governing the flow of currents in electrical networks: that the sum of all the voltages around a closed loop, or mesh, is zero; and that the sum of all the currents entering any junction point is also zero.

In the hundred years since then, mathematicians have built up an extensive theory on the foundation Kirchhoff laid. They consider each junction point to be a space of zero dimensions, and each connecting branch a one-dimensional space. The network concept has been extended in this way to form a complex of one-, two-, and more dimensional spaces interconnected in any manner, all immersed in an *n*-dimensional enveloping space. Such a collection of spaces is called *topological structure*. These concepts form a part of modern combinatorial topology. In their development by mathematicians, however, nearly all traces of their electrical origin have been lost.

Superimposed on the topological structure of a network, there is an algebraic structure formed by the live relations among the electric currents and voltages in the various branches and meshes of the dead underlying structure. Also associated with the network are the electrostatic fields that represent the energy stored in the capacitance, *C*, of each branch and the electromagnetic fields that similarly represent the energy stored in the inductance, *L*. Thus, an electrical network, as a whole, embodies many concepts of both forms of topology. Since an electrical network can be extended without limit, by adding more branches and interconnecting them in an infinite variety of ways, it forms a realizable model of a collection of one-, two-, three-, and *n*-dimensional structures that goes far beyond the possibilities of any mechanical or three-dimensional geometric model.

As pointed out in Sec. 12-1, the same, typical, linear second-order differential equation that represents the motion of a spring-supported weight, with friction, represents also the behavior of an electric circuit with inductance, resistance, and capacitance. Furthermore, it is easy to make precise measurements of voltage, current, and power in an electric circuit, whereas it is not at all easy to make similar measurements on mechanical, thermal, and other systems. Hence a physical model formed of an electrical network provides a convenient and adequate representation of a great many physical systems whose behaviors are defined by linear differential equations.

In constructing an actual circuit, however, the resistance, inductance, and capacitance must all be positive quantities. There is no such thing in Nature as a true negative resistance. Yet the differential equations that represent some physical systems, such as occur in heat flow, may include negative terms that correspond to positive terms in the analogous electric-circuit equations. Therefore, it is not feasible to construct actual electric-circuit models of some physical systems, even though the corresponding sets of equations differ only in the signs of some of the terms.

This obstacle is readily overcome by employing equivalent electric circuits, or circuits written down on paper, instead of using actual electric circuits. *R*, *L*, and *C* can be made either + or − on paper as desired, and the mathematical solutions of the equations can be found equally well for either choice. Thus, the equivalent electric circuit, or paper model, has an even wider usefulness than a model constructed of an actual electric circuit. Experience gained with measurements on actual circuits can be used to check the mathematical results on the corresponding equivalent circuits and thereby to check indirectly the similar mathematical results for equivalent circuits that are not physically realizable in electrical terms.

If R, L, and C are considered to be distributed along each branch of a network, the current and voltage will vary from point to point, and their steady-state values will be defined by differential equations. If R, L, and C are considered to be lumped at particular places in the network, their steady-state values will be defined by algebraic equations relating the separate quantities. Whether the distributed or lumped circuit theory is preferable, or a combination of them, will depend on the particular problem to be solved.

14-4   Equations versus Equivalent Electric Circuits.   When we represent a complex physical system by a set of equations, we ignore a great many of the properties of the system itself, which may or may not be important in a particular problem. A moment's consideration shows that we cannot reconstruct an actual physical structure, using solely the information contained in the equations; or, rather, we find that infinitely many different systems are equally well represented by the same equations. This is natural because the essence of mathematics is to condense the pertinent factors into the fewest possible symbols, so that the equations developed will have great generality and will apply to as many different cases as possible.

On the other hand, when we represent a physical system by an electric circuit model, we are able to retain in the network a great many additional properties that are left out of the equations. The circuit expresses both the mesh and the junction point equations, and it embodies the physical laws of energy conservation and flow. Each separate branch of the circuit represents a distinct degree of freedom of motion of the physical system. By opening the connections between the different circuit elements, the properties of the primitive network can be studied, and the effects of different methods of connection can be analyzed, without loss of contact with physical reality.

The equations of the actual system define the relationships existing with a particular arrangement, as expressed by a particular set of circuit connections. To tear apart the equations and attempt to form from them the independent equations for all the degrees of freedom of the actual system is something like trying to separate scrambled eggs into the original yolks and whites. As Gabriel Kron has shown, by his method of "diakoptics," an electrical network, including hundreds, or thousands, of branches, can be torn apart, analyzed and solved in small pieces, and the results put together again, in a manner quite impractical when dealing with equations alone.

Kron has also remarked that the information embodied in the equivalent electric circuit of a physical system embodies precisely and completely the instructions needed by a digital computer to calculate the system performance, whereas the equations alone are insufficient. And, the electric-circuit diagram provides a mathematical shorthand whereby the needed information can be presented more compactly as well as more completely than in the form of equations.

Without elaborating further, it is clear that equivalent electric circuits provide paper models of all sorts of physical systems that are of great value to engineers in the mathematical analysis of system performance. There is no doubt that their importance will grow and will be increasingly recognized in the years ahead.

14-5 Basic Laws of Electric Circuits—Steady State. Every engineer should be familiar with the laws of simple electric circuits and their equivalent linear second-order differential equations. By simple circuits are meant circuits that include only stationary electrical devices (no rotating machines) and only circuit elements whose impedances are constant, independent of changes in current, voltage, or other factors.

The current i in a circuit branch is measured in amperes and is proportional to the rate of flow of electrons (negative electric charge) past a given point. The voltage e impressed across the branch is measured in volts and is proportional to the rate of change of the magnetic flux linkages in the power supply generator, less the voltage drop in the circuit external to the considered branch. The power W, or rate of energy flow into the branch at any instant, is measured in watts and is equal to the product ei.

The net voltage around any closed circuit is zero. That is, when a voltage is impressed on a circuit, a current will flow and will increase until the sum of the voltage drops across the various elements (impedances) of the circuit builds up to a value equal and opposite to the voltage impressed. This is entirely analogous to what happens when a mechanical force is impressed on a mass (Eq. 12-1).

There are three basic elements that make up the impedance of a circuit branch, an inductance L, a resistance R, and a capacitance C, as indicated in Fig. 14-2.

A current i flowing through an inductance, L henries, creates a magnetic field in the surrounding space, which stores an amount of energy equal to $Li^2/2$ watts. The voltage drop across the inductance at any instant is $L\,di/dt$, and the product of this by the current, or $Li\,di/dt$, is the energy flowing into the magnetic field at any instant. Thus, the inductance in an electrical system corresponds to a mass in a mechanical system, and the magnetic energy corresponds to kinetic energy.

A current i, flowing through a resistance R ohms, creates an energy loss, which appears as heat in the conductor at this point. The rate of energy loss occurring at any instant is i^2R watts. The voltage drop across the resistance is iR volts (Eq. 3-15). Thus, the resistance loss in an electrical system corresponds to the friction loss, or damping, in a mechanical system.

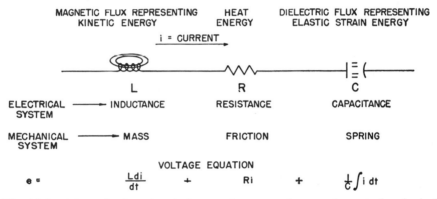

Fig. 14-2   A branch of an electrical network representing one element of a physical system.

When a current i flows into a capacitance, C farads, electrons (negative electric charge) are stored in the dielectric field, the total amount of stored charge at any instant being equal to $q = \int i\,dt$. The corresponding voltage across the capacitor is $e = \int i\,dt/C$, and the total dielectric field energy is $Ce^2/2$. Thus, a capacitance in an electrical system corresponds to a spring in a mechanical system, and the dielectric field energy corresponds to elastic strain energy.

The voltage equation of the branch, therefore, is

$$\frac{L\,di}{dt} + Ri + \frac{1}{C}\int i\,dt = e \qquad \text{volts} \qquad (14\text{-}1)$$

Substituting $q = \int i\,dt$, $\dfrac{dq}{dt} = i$, $\dfrac{d^2q}{dt^2} = \dfrac{di}{dt}$, we have

$$\frac{L\,d^2q}{dt^2} + \frac{R\,dq}{dt} + \frac{q}{C} = e \text{ volts} \qquad (14.2)$$

or
$$\left(Lp^2 + Rp + \frac{1}{C}\right)q = e = f(t) \text{ volts} \qquad (14.3)$$

which is the same linear second-order differential equation (12-2) that we found for a mechanical system.

If the applied voltage e is sinusoidal (Eq. 3-16), so that

$$e = \sqrt{2}\, E \sin (\omega t - \phi) \qquad \text{volts} \qquad (14\text{-}4)$$

then

$$f(t) = pe = \sqrt{2}\, \omega E \cos (\omega t - \phi) = j\omega e \qquad \text{volts per second} \quad (14\text{-}5)$$

where ω is the frequency in radians per second (Sec. 12-4).

Since R, L, and C are assumed to be constant, the steady-state current i in Eq. 14-3 must also be sinusoidal, so that $pi = j\omega i$ and $p^2 i = -\omega^2 i$. Hence, the particular, or steady-state, solution of Eq. 14-3 is

$$
\begin{aligned}
i &= \frac{j\omega e}{(-\omega^2 L + j\omega R + 1/C)} = \frac{e}{R + j(\omega L - 1/\omega C)} \\
&= \frac{\sqrt{2}\, E}{Z} \sin (\omega t - \phi - \theta) = \sqrt{2}\, I \sin (\omega t - \phi - \theta) \qquad \text{amperes}
\end{aligned}
$$

$$(14\text{-}6)$$

where

$$Z = \sqrt{R^2 + \left(\omega L - \frac{1}{\omega C}\right)^2} = \sqrt{R^2 + X^2} \qquad \text{ohms} \quad (14\text{-}7)$$

is the impedance of the branch and

$$\theta = \cos^{-1} \frac{R}{Z} \qquad (14\text{-}8)$$

θ is called the *power factor angle*, and $\cos \theta = R/Z$ is called the *power factor* (see Sec. 3-13).

The instantaneous power flow is ei watts. From Eqs. 14-4 and 14-6

$$
\begin{aligned}
ei &= \frac{2E^2}{Z} \sin (\omega t - \phi) \sin (\omega t - \phi - \theta) \\
&= \frac{E^2}{Z} [\cos \theta - \cos (2\omega t - 2\phi - \theta)] \qquad (14\text{-}9)
\end{aligned}
$$

As shown in Fig. 14-3, the first term of Eq. 14-9 represents the continuous power flow, equal to $I^2 R$, called the *active power*. The second term represents an alternating power flow, called the *reactive power*, equal to $I^2 X$, where

$$X = \omega L - \frac{1}{\omega C} \qquad \text{ohms} \qquad (14\text{-}10)$$

is the net reactance of the branch.

As discussed in Sec. 3-13, it is customary to use the root-mean-square values of current and voltage, I and E, in alternating-current circuit calculations. When these are represented by phasors, we have (Eq. 3-20)

$$E \backslash \phi = E (\cos \phi - j \sin \phi) \tag{14-11}$$

and
$$\overline{I \backslash \phi + \theta} = \frac{E}{Z} = I [\cos (\phi + \theta) - j \sin (\phi + \theta)] \tag{14-12}$$

The reactive power has a frequency twice that of the current and voltage, as shown by Eq. 14-9. Hence the apparent power obtained by

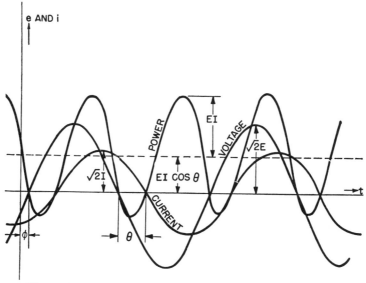

Fig. 14-3   Current, voltage, and power in a single-phase circuit.

multiplying E and I directly, when represented as a phasor (see Sec. 3-4), rotates twice as fast as E and I and the phase angle of this product with reference to the current or voltage has no useful meaning.

To obtain the power referred to the voltage as a base, it is necessary to subtract the phase angle of I from that of E, instead of adding as in ordinary multiplication of phasors. Therefore, we should multiply E by the conjugate of I, which is a phasor equal to I but with the j term reversed in sign, as indicated by an asterisk:

$$I^* = I \underline{/\phi + \theta} = I[\cos (\phi + \theta) + j \sin (\phi + \theta)] \tag{14-13}$$

The product EI^* gives for the power, from Eqs. 14-11 and 14-13,

$$W = EI^* = EI[\cos \phi \cos (\phi + \theta) + \sin \phi \sin (\phi + \theta)]$$
$$+ j[\cos \phi \sin (\phi + \theta) - \sin \phi \cos (\phi + \theta)]$$
$$= EI(\cos \theta + j \sin \theta) = \text{active power} + j(\text{reactive power})$$
$$\tag{14-14}$$

The reversal of the j term of the current, rather than of the voltage, is chosen to agree with the convention that reactive power delivered to an inductive load is positive. If the C term in Eq. 14-10 predominated, X would become negative and the reactive power delivered would also be negative.

From the foregoing, it is seen that the general rule (Sec. 12-4) for solving the differential equations of electric circuits with sinusoidal impressed voltages is to substitute $j\omega$ for p (and $-\omega^2$ for p^2) and to solve the resulting equations by ordinary complex algebra, as in Sec. 3-13, except that in multiplying voltage by current to obtain power, the conjugate of the current phasor should be used.

14-6   Basic Laws of Electric Circuits—Transient State.   To find the complete solution of the electric-circuit equation, when a sinusoidal voltage is suddenly applied

$$\frac{L\,di}{dt} + Ri + \frac{1}{C}\int i\,dt = HE \sin{(\omega t - \phi)} \tag{14-15}$$

we substitute q for $\int i\,dt$, to eliminate the integral sign, replace d/dt by p, and apply the methods of Sec. 12-8 or Sec. 12-9. This gives

$$\left(Lp^2 + Rp + \frac{1}{C}\right)q = HE \sin{(\omega t - \phi)} \tag{14-16}$$

Since Eq. 14-16 is like Eq. 12-70, which we solved previously, the desired solution will be obtained if we substitute $y = q$, $a = R/2L$, $b = 1/LC$, and $F = E/L$ in Eq. 12-77. The result is

$$Hq = -\frac{HE}{\omega Z} \sin{(\omega t - \phi + \alpha)} - \frac{HE}{\omega Z} e^{-Rt/2L} \sin{(\phi - \alpha)} \cos{mt}$$
$$+ \frac{HEe^{-Rt/2L}\sqrt{R^2 + 4\omega^2 L^2}\cos{(\phi - \beta)}\sin{mt}}{2\omega mLZ} \tag{14-17}$$

where $m = \sqrt{1/LC - R^2/4L^2}$
$\tan \alpha = R/X$
$\tan \beta = R(2\omega L - X)/(R^2 + 2\omega LX)$
The reactance is $X = \omega L - 1/\omega C$, and the impedance is

$$Z = \sqrt{R^2 + X^2}$$

The frequency of the applied voltage is $\omega/2\pi$ cycles per second if t is measured in seconds. The resonant frequency of the circuit in cycles per second is $m/2\pi$.

To find the current i, we differentiate Eq. 14-17:

$$Hi = H\frac{dq}{dt} = -\frac{HE}{Z}\cos(\omega t - \phi + \alpha)$$

$$+ \frac{HEe^{-Rt/2L}}{2\omega LZ}\left\{\left[2mL\sin(\phi - \alpha)\right.\right.$$

$$-\frac{R\sqrt{R^2 + 4\omega^2 L^2}}{2mL}\cos(\phi - \beta)\right]\sin mt$$

$$+ [R\sin(\phi - \alpha) + \sqrt{R^2 + 4\omega^2 L^2}\cos(\phi - \beta)]\cos mt\bigg\} \quad (14\text{-}18)$$

or

$$Hi = \frac{HE}{Z}\sin(\omega t - \phi - \theta) - \frac{HEe^{-Rt/2L}}{\omega Z\sqrt{LC}}\left[\cos(\phi + \theta)\sin(mt + \gamma)\right.$$

$$-\frac{\sqrt{R^2 + 4\omega^2 L^2}\cos(\phi - \beta)\cos(mt + \gamma)}{2mL}\right] \quad (14\text{-}19)$$

where $\theta = 90° - \alpha = \tan^{-1}(X/R)$ = power factor angle
    $\gamma = \tan^{-1}(R/2mL)$
    The first term of Eq. 14-19 is the steady-state current, when a voltage $e = E\sin(\omega t - \phi)$ is suddenly applied to the branch circuit of Fig. 14-2, with q and dq/dt both equal to zero initially. This agrees with Eq. 14-6 found previously as the particular solution of the circuit, except that in Eq. 14-19 we have used E to represent the peak voltage, whereas in Eq. 14-6 the peak voltage was taken to be $\sqrt{2}\,E$.
    If the resistance is zero. the current will be given by placing $R = 0$ in Eq. 14-19, or

$$Hi = \frac{HE}{X}\sin(\omega t - \phi - 90°)$$

$$+ \frac{HE}{X}\left(\frac{1}{\omega\sqrt{LC}}\sin\phi\sin mt + \cos\phi\cos mt\right) \quad (R = 0) \quad (14\text{-}20)$$

If the circuit is tuned, so that $\omega L = 1/\omega C$, and, therefore, $X = 0$, we have $\theta = 0$, $m = \sqrt{\omega^2 - R^2/4L^2}$, $Z = R$, $\tan\beta = 2\omega L/R$, and $\tan\gamma = R/2mL$, so that Eq. 14-19 becomes

$$Hi = \frac{HE}{R}\sin(\omega t - \phi) - \frac{HEe^{-Rt/2L}}{2mRL}[(2\omega L\cos\phi + R\sin\phi)\sin mt$$

$$- 2mL\sin\phi\cos mt] \quad (\omega L = 1/\omega C) \quad (14\text{-}21)$$

If the circuit is critically damped, so that $R^2 = 4L/C$, we have $m = 0$. Equation 12-80, instead of Eq. 12-77, provides the basis for the solution in this case, since making $m = 0$ in Eq. 12-77 gives an indeterminate result. Substituting in Eq. 12-80, we find for q

$$Hq = \frac{-HE \cos (\omega t - \phi - \theta)}{\omega Z} + \frac{HEe^{-Rt/2L}}{\omega Z} \cos (\phi + \theta)$$

$$+ \frac{HEte^{-Rt/2L} \cos (\phi - \beta)}{\sqrt{\omega LZ}} \quad (14\text{-}22)$$

where $\tan \theta = X/R$

$\tan \beta = R/2\omega L$, and $Z = \omega L + R^2/4\omega L$

($\theta = 90° - \alpha$ is used in place of α that was used in Eq. 12-80.)

Differentiating, the current is found to be

$$Hi = \frac{HE}{Z} \sin (\omega t - \phi - \theta) - \frac{HREe^{-Rt/2L}}{2\omega LZ} \cos (\phi + \theta)$$

$$+ \frac{HEe^{-Rt/2L}}{\sqrt{\omega LZ}} \left(1 - \frac{Rt}{2L}\right) \cos (\phi - \beta) \quad \left(R^2 = \frac{4L}{C}\right) \quad (14\text{-}23)$$

If the circuit is overdamped, so that $R^2 > 4L/C$, m becomes a quadrature number and the circuit is no longer oscillatory. For this case, let:

$$m = jn = j\sqrt{\frac{R^2}{4L^2} - \frac{1}{LC}}$$

and, from Eqs. 9-32 and 9-33, Eq. 14-19 becomes

$$Hi = \frac{HE}{Z} \sin (\omega t - \phi - \theta) + \frac{HEe^{-Rt/2L}}{2\omega LZ} \left\{ \left[2nL \sin (\phi - \alpha) \right. \right.$$

$$\left. - \frac{R\sqrt{R^2 + 4\omega^2 L^2}}{2nL} \cos (\phi - \beta) \right] \sinh nt + [R \sin (\phi - \alpha)$$

$$+ \sqrt{R^2 + 4\omega^2 L^2} \cos (\phi - \beta)] \cosh nt \right\} \quad \left(R^2 > \frac{4L}{C}\right) \quad (14\text{-}24)$$

Finally, if the circuit has resistance R and inductance L only, so that $1/C = 0$, the solution is found from Eq. 12-81, by substituting $R/2L$ for a, E/L for F, and q for y:

$$Hq = \frac{HE}{R\omega} [\cos \phi - \cos (\omega t - \phi)]$$

$$- \frac{HEL}{RZ} [\sin (\omega t - \phi - \theta) + e^{-Rt/L} \sin (\phi + \theta)] \quad (14\text{-}25)$$

where $Z = \sqrt{R^2 + \omega^2 L^2}$
$x = \omega L$

$$\theta = \tan^{-1} \frac{X}{R}$$

The current i is found by differentiating the charge q:

$$Hi = \frac{Hdq}{dt} = \frac{HE}{RZ} [Z \sin (\omega t - \phi) - X \cos (\omega t - \phi - \theta)]$$

$$+ \frac{HE}{Z} e^{-Rt/L} \sin (\phi + \theta) \qquad \left(\frac{1}{C} = 0 \right)$$

$$= \frac{HE}{Z} \sin (\omega t - \phi - \theta) + \frac{HE}{Z} e^{-Rt/L} \sin (\phi + \theta) \qquad (14\text{-}26)$$

The steady-state current is the same as before, Eq. 14-19, but the transient current now decays smoothly instead of oscillating.

These equations enable the current, power, etc., to be calculated when a sinusoidal voltage is impressed on any electric circuit with fixed values of R, L, and C. If the applied voltage is an arbitrary function of time instead of being sinusoidal, the voltage-time curve can be resolved into a series of harmonics by the methods of Chap. 10, and the complete solution then will be given by the sum of the solutions for the separate harmonics.

14-7. Boolean Algebra. Engineers often want to design electric circuits for control or communication purposes in which the exact value of the current is of no importance, the question being merely whether a current does or does not flow.

In such cases, when we have to deal with questions of truth and falsity, which can be answered by yes or no, and we are not concerned with numerical magnitudes, we can employ Boolean algebra with advantage. This method of logical reasoning was originated by George Boole* in 1847. In brief, it is the algebra which results when there are only two numbers, 1 and 0. Shannon and other writers have recently applied the method to the design of electric control circuits, with the special object of performing complex switching operations with the fewest possible number of switches, or "contacts."

In Fig. 14-4(1), there is shown an electrical switch X_1, which we shall simply designate by the term *gate*, that can be used to open or close an electric circuit between a and b. The *hindrance* h of the circuit is defined as a quantity which is 0 if the gate is closed and is 1 if the gate is open:

---

* "Pure mathematics was discovered by Boole in a work which he called the *Laws of Thought* (1854)."—Bertrand Russell.

$h = 0$ means Yes, a current can flow; and $h = 1$ means No, a current cannot flow. The hindrances of a number of independently operated gates may be designated by X_1, X_2, X_3, etc. If two or more gates are operated by the same relay, so that they open and close together, they all have the same value of hindrance. When one gate opens at the

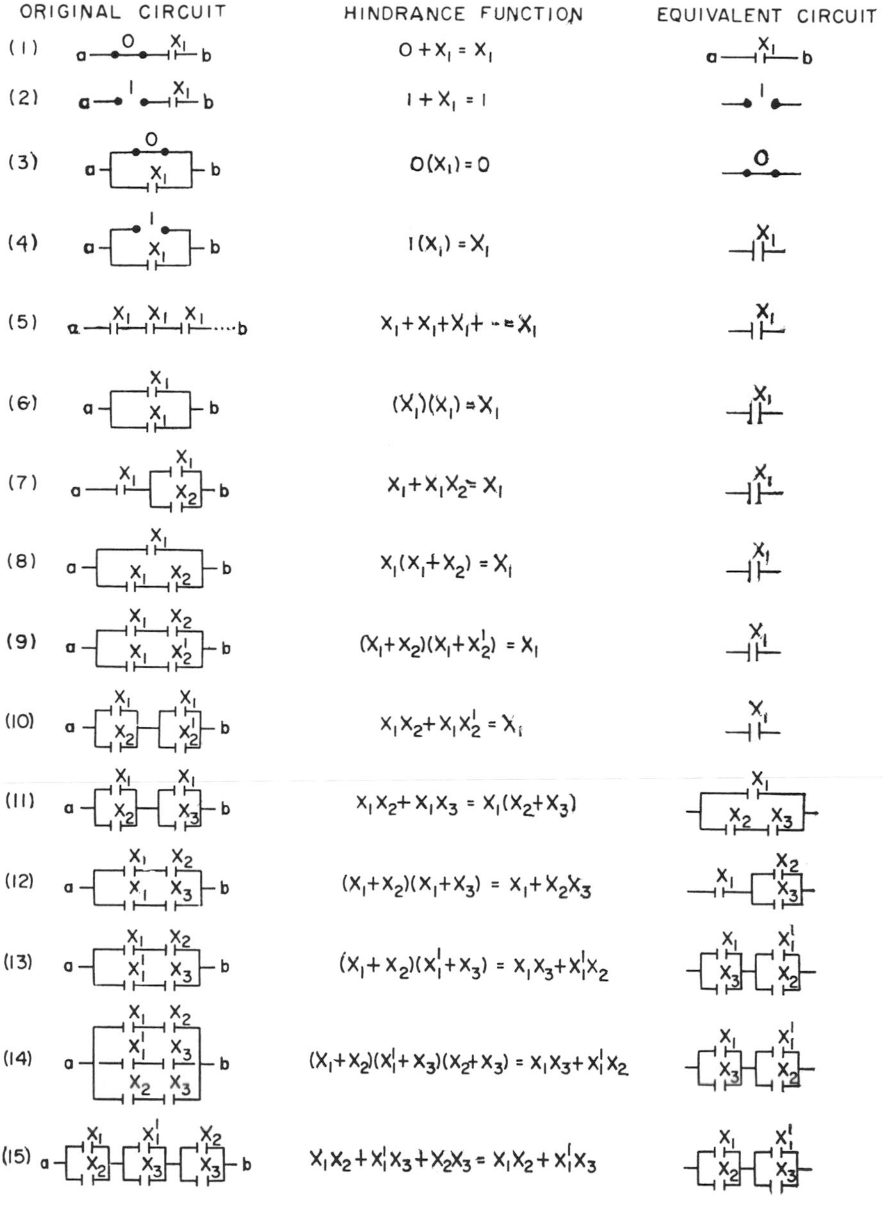

ORIGINAL CIRCUIT	HINDRANCE FUNCTION	EQUIVALENT CIRCUIT
(1)	$0 + X_1 = X_1$	
(2)	$1 + X_1 = 1$	
(3)	$0(X_1) = 0$	
(4)	$1(X_1) = X_1$	
(5)	$X_1 + X_1 + X_1 + \cdots = X_1$	
(6)	$(X_1)(X_1) = X_1$	
(7)	$X_1 + X_1 X_2 = X_1$	
(8)	$X_1(X_1 + X_2) = X_1$	
(9)	$(X_1 + X_2)(X_1 + X_2') = X_1$	
(10)	$X_1 X_2 + X_1 X_2' = X_1$	
(11)	$X_1 X_2 + X_1 X_3 = X_1(X_2 + X_3)$	
(12)	$(X_1 + X_2)(X_1 + X_3) = X_1 + X_2 X_3$	
(13)	$(X_1 + X_2)(X_1' + X_3) = X_1 X_3 + X_1' X_2$	
(14)	$(X_1 + X_2)(X_1' + X_3)(X_2 + X_3) = X_1 X_3 + X_1' X_2$	
(15)	$X_1 X_2 + X_1' X_3 + X_2 X_3 = X_1 X_2 + X_1' X_3$	

Fig. 14-4 Simple electric switching circuits.

same time that another one closes, their hindrances are designated by X and X'. That is, $X' = 1$ when $X = 0$, and $X' = 0$ when $X=1$.

If there are several gates, X_1, X_2, X_3, . . . , in series (circuit 5, Fig. 14-4), opening any one gate will prevent current flow, and opening or closing the other gates will then have no effect.

The hindrance of the circuit is the sum of all the hindrance values of all the series-connected gates:

$$h = X_1 + X_2 + X_3 + \cdots \qquad (14\text{-}27)$$

and, if any one of the gates is open, say, $X_1 = 1$, no current can flow, so that h will be 1 also. If all the gates are open, h still is equal to 1. This leads to the first rule of Boolean algebra, that no matter how many like quantities are added together, their sum is equal to only one of them:

$$X + X + X + \cdots = X \qquad (14\text{-}28)$$

Likewise, if a number of gates are connected in parallel (Fig. 14-4), and if any one of the gates is closed, say, $X_1 = 0$, a current can flow from a to b, so that $h = 0$. No matter whether the other parallel-connected gates are open or closed, h will still be 0. Therefore, the hindrance of parallel-connected gates is

$$h = X_1 X_2 X_3 \cdots \qquad (14\text{-}29)$$

and making $X_1 = X_2 = X_3 = X$ gives the second rule of Boolean algebra, that no matter how many like quantities are multiplied together, the product is equal to only one of them:

$$h = (X)\,(X)\,(X) \cdots = X \qquad (14\text{-}30)$$

Equation (14-30) is true for the numbers 0 and 1 and is not true for any other numbers. In Boolean algebra, there is no need for exponents, since $X^n = X$, and no need for numeral coefficients, since $nX = X$. Thus, the expressions are much easier to work with than those in ordinary algebra.

Proceeding in this way, it is a simple matter to build up the table of circuit relations shown in Fig. 14-4. The hindrance function of each left-hand circuit is given in the center column. In the right-hand column, equivalent but simpler circuits are given which represent the hindrance functions of the center column after reduction to their simplest forms. Considering circuit (9), for example, if $X_1 = 1$, no current can flow in either branch of the circuit, so the hindrance is $X_1 = 1$. If $X_1 = 0$, the current can flow through either X_2 or X_2'. If $X_2 = 0$, $X_2' = 1$; if $X_2 = 1$, $X_2' = 0$. In either case, a current can flow from a to b, so that the hindrance is 0, or is again equal to X_1.

Hence, the four gates of circuit (9) can be replaced by the single gate X_1, in so far as the current path from a to b is concerned.

In a circuit which consists of a gate X_1 in series with a group of other circuits among which duplicate gates X_1 also occur, the hindrance function can be simplified by the principle that

$$h = X_1 + f(X_1, X_2, X_3, \ldots) = X_1 + f(0, X_2, X_3, \ldots) \quad (14\text{-}31)$$

For, if $X_1 = 1$, no current can flow, regardless of the other circuit conditions. And if $X_1 = 0$, the hindrance will be that obtained by substituting $X_1 - 0$ throughout.

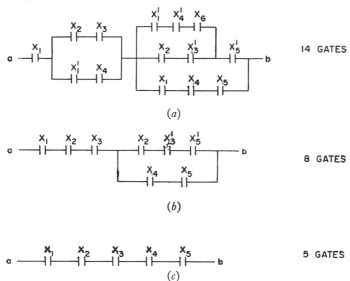

14 GATES

(a)

8 GATES

(b)

5 GATES

(c)

Fig. 14-5   Simplification of complex switching circuit.

Similarly, if the circuit consists of X_1 in series with a group of other circuits in which oppositely operated gates X_1' occur, the hindrance function can be simplified by the principle that

$$h = X_1 + f(X_1', X_2, X_3, \ldots) = X_1 + f(1, X_2, X_3, \ldots) \quad (14\text{-}32)$$

As an example of the use of these rules to simplify a circuit, we may consider the circuit having 14 gates, shown in Fig. 14-5a. Since X_1 is in series with the entire circuit, we can replace X_1 by 0 and X_1' by 1 wherever they occur in the remainder of the circuit. This reduces the circuit to (b) with eight gates. Since X_3 is now in series with the entire circuit, we may replace X_3' by 1. This simplifies the circuit to (c) with only five gates.

Instead of employing the hindrance function h, which is 0 when a gate is closed and 1 when it is open, we can equally well use the trans mission function *t*, which is 0 when a gate is open and 1 when it is closed. The equations for the parallel and series connections are then interchanged, giving a dual relationship between the hindrance and the transmission formulas.

14-8 Computers.   Over the years, as needs have grown for more and more complex calculations, men have invented machines to do the work. The Roman numerals were not adapted to extensive calculations because a new symbol was required for each larger unit—*V* for 5, *X* for 10, *L* for 50, *C* for 100, *D* for 500, and *M* for 1,000. With this system the order of the numerals made no difference, 155 could just as well be *LCV* or *VCL* as the normal *CLV*. This made adding simple, as whenever 5 *I*'s accumulated they were replaced by a *V*, two *L*'s became a *C*, etc. There was no carrying over to the next decimal place, and there were no fractions, but multiplication was not easy.

The Hindu invention of the symbol *0*, leading to the decimal system, enabled 10 symbols to represent any number, however large or small, and the wide use of the abacus (Sec. 1-7) paved the way for the first mechanical calculators. These used the angular position of a toothed wheel to represent the numerals from 0 to 9, with an extra wheel for each multiple of 10, as proposed by Pascal in 1642 and improved on by Leibnitz, Thomas, Odhner, and many others. About 1833 Charles Babbage proposed his "Analytical Engine" for performing arithmetic calculations whose operations were controlled by Jacquard cards, as used to control the cloth patterns in weaving. The first really practical adding and listing machines were made by Felt and Burroughs about 1890. Since then more than a hundred different models of the Burroughs machine have been made, and many millions of these and other desk calculators, cash registers, and tabulating machines have been produced. Further steps toward the modern computer were marked by the player piano, controlled by punched paper tapes, and the Hollerith cards for sorting and tabulating. These had punched holes through which connections were made to electric circuits by metal brushes sliding over them. The development of relays for actuating switches in extensive telephone networks led in 1938 to the Stibitz relay computer that adds, subtracts, multiplies, and divides with remote control.

From these various sources, automatic digital computers began to appear in the 1940s, and since then they have come forward very rapidly, so that now they are indispensable in many business operations, process controls, and research and engineering activities. The versatility and fantastic speeds of the modern electronic digital computers are chiefly due to the use of electronic "gates" and "storage elements." A gate is a semiconductor (diode or transistor) that will or will not allow a current to pass through, depending on the presence or absence of a voltage impulse, or signal, supplied to it. Thus, an electric circuit can be opened or closed in less than 10^{-8} second by supplying a voltage pulse to its gate.

A storage element may consist of an area on a magnetic tape or a ferrite core which can be magnetized by applying a pulsed magnetic field and which will retain this magnetism until it is changed by another pulse. A typical "memory unit" may consist of a space 3 by 5 by 5 inches that holds 150,000 tiny ferrite cores. Fifteen or more such units may be used, giving the computer the ability to store more than two million bits of information. Or, a storage element may be a bit of ceramic insulation or a capacitor that can be given an electric charge by a voltage impulse and that will retain this charge until it is changed by another signal. As there are only two conditions for a gate—open or closed (empty or filled)—it is desirable to use Boolean algebra (Sec. 14-7) for all equations and to make all calculations in the binary system (Sec. 1-7), since these employ only two numbers, 0 and 1.

The early calculating machines, using toothed wheels, required about one second for each operation, as it takes that time to accelerate, rotate, and stop a wheel. The relays that came in 30 years ago operated a thousand times faster, since a spring-loaded contact can be opened or closed in about 1 millisecond. The vacuum tubes used in the first digital computers were still a thousand times faster, as they had no moving parts. But the semiconductors used in present-day computers can change their state in a billionth of a second, 10^9 times as fast as the cogwheel adding machines. To use this fantastic speed of operation, it has been necessary to speed up the ways for putting information into the computer and for taking it out. For example, the so-called peripherals of a computer include a card reader that reads standard 80-column cards column by column. As it reads, the information is automatically translated into the binary language of the computer. There is also a card punch that can punch 80-column cards at 100 cards a minute—it prints an entire 136-character line at once, instead of only one character at a time.

A most important step in this speeding up has been the development of many "computer languages" that give the computer precise instructions in very few "words," which the computer translates into an extended series of commands to perform the required operations. And, "subroutines" have been developed, such as that for finding the square root of a number. By storing in the computer's memory the complete procedure for any such operation, it will only be necessary to feed in a few letters, SQRT, and the number, when the computer will immediately give out the answer. For each kind of calculation an appropriate language is used—Fortran, Algol, Basic, or Mad for numerical calculations; Cobal for business purposes; Lisp for list processing; and many others.

The basic features of a digital computer are its control, logic (arithmetic), memory, and input/output units. Each location in the memory unit has its own "address" or distinct number so that when the control unit calls for a needed item, the gate to that address is opened, and its data are transferred to the arithmetic unit or elsewhere by an appropriate series of voltage pulses. The control unit may include a clock or motor-driven drum with a magnetic trace that provides a timed series of voltage pulses which may be directed to any desired address. The memory unit is stored with instructions for solving the problem and with the needed data for a particular case. The arithmetic unit adds, subtracts, or multiplies the given numbers as directed by the control unit. The control unit may compare the answer received from the arithmetic unit with a desired result and if it is not satisfactory may ask the arithmetic unit to repeat the process or iterate until the answer is satisfactory. This is especially necessary when approximation methods or infinite series are used, since the desired accuracy may require only one, two, or three terms of the series and since many problems with nonlinear equations require that the parameters be changed to match the valued found by calculation, as when magnetic saturation changes the reactance of a circuit.

Despite all that has been done to speed up the input and ouput procedures, the electronic circuit speeds are so great that the computer cannot be fully occupied if it waits for instructions from a single user. There has grown up, therefore, the concept of "shared-time" computers. This means that there may be a large number of input consoles, located in many and distant places, all having free access to the computer. Then, the successive problems may be stacked up in a waiting line and fed in turn into the computer. Most users want to get one answer, consider it, and then return to the computer for another answer. In this case, the computer sets aside in its memory the procedure for each problem as soon as an answer has been given out, takes up the next problem, and returns to the former whenever it is called for. In this way, even the highest-speed computers with the largest memories can be kept fully occupied if there are a sufficient number of users. It seems likely that this way of solving problems will prove to be so versatile, speedy, and economical that nearly every business group will subscribe to shared-time computer service.

14-9   Solving a Problem on the Computer.   Instructions to the computer are typed out on a keyboard that has only capital letters and symbols. In the Fortran language, generally used for numerical calculations, some of the principal words and symbols used are:

HELLO   This tells the computer to be ready to start a new program.

INPUT   This tells the computer to store in its memory the immediately following symbols or data.

READ   This tells the computer to take the immediately following numbers from its memory for use in the next computation.

RUN   This tells the computer to go ahead with the calculations.

PRINT   This tells the computer to print out the numbers corresponding to the immediately following symbols or addresses.

GØTØ   This tells the computer to go to the address indicated by the immediately following number. (Ø is used in place of O to avoid confusion with the number 0.)

STOP   This tells the computer to stop until it has new instructions.

END   This tells the computer that the program is finished.

A + B tells the computer to add B to A.

A − B tells the computer to subtract B from A.

A/B tells the computer to divide A by B.

A*B tells the computer to multiply B by A.

A**B tells the computer to raise A to the power B.

SQRT A tells the computer to find the square root of A

The trigonometric sine and cosine are indicated by SIN and CØS, and the natural logarithm by LØG.

Each operation by the computer must be spelled out in a separate line, preceded by a number that gives the sequence of steps. For example, to solve two simultaneous equations

$$AX + BY = E \quad \text{and} \quad CX + DY = F$$

the solution is found by these equations:

$$X = (DE - BF)/G \quad \text{and} \quad Y = (AF - CE)/G$$

where $G = (DA - BC)$

The computer instructions or program will then be

0010	INPUT, A, B, C, D, E, F
10	G = D*A − B*C
20	X = (D*E − B*F)/G
30	Y = (A*F − C*E)/G
40	PRINT X,Y,G
50	GØTØ
60	END

The number 10 before INPUT is an address that is quite distinct from the numbers at the start of each line, which merely indicate the sequence.

To use the program, the actual numbers are given to the computer; each value is given in the place of its letter symbol. Suppose that $A = 1$, $B = 2$, $C = 3$, $D = 4$, $E = 17$, $F = 39$. Then, when the computer instructions call for them, the user types in the numbers 1, 2, 3, 4, 17, 39, which are the values of A, B, C, D, E, and F for the particular problem. The computer will immediately perform the calculations and will print out the answers $X = 5$, $Y = 6$, $G = -2$.

As another example, suppose we wish to find the impedance equivalent to two other impedances connected in parallel. We work out the needed equations:

$$Z1 = A + jB \qquad Z2 = 3 + jD$$
$$Y1 = 1/Z1 = (A - jB)/(A^2 + B^2)$$
$$= E - jF$$
$$Y2 = 1/Z2 = (C - jD)/(C^2 + D^2)$$
$$= G - jH$$
$$Y = Y1 + Y2 = (E + G) - j(F + H) = M - jN$$
$$Z = 1/Y = (M + jN)/(M^2 + N^2) = R + jX$$

The computer instructions would then be

0010	INPUT A, B, C, D
10	$E = A/(A**2 + B**2)$
20	$F = B/(A**2 + B**2)$
30	$G = C/(C**2 + D**2)$
40	$H = D/(C**2 + D**2)$
50	$M = E + G$
60	$N = F + H$
70	$R = M/(M**2 + N**2)$
80	$X = N/(M**2 + N**2)$
90	PRINT R, X
95	GØTØ 10
100	END

If we also desired to find the numerical value of the impedance, we would put in one more line and change line 90 to

85	$Z = SQRT (R**2 + X**2)$
90	PRINT R, X, Z

The line 95, telling the computer to return to the starting point, is put in because in general the computations are to be repeated with a different set of numbers.

Bibliography

1. Berkeley, E. C.: "Giant Brains: or Machines That Think," John Wiley & Sons, Inc., New York, 1949.
2. Bewley, L. V.: "Tensor Analysis of Electric Circuits and Machines," Ronald Press Company, New York, 1961.
3. Birkhoff, G., and S. MacLane: "A Survey of Modern Algebra," The Macmillan Company, New York, 1953.
4. Cundy, H. M., and A. P. Rollett: "Mathematical Models," Oxford University Press, New York, 1952.
5. Clarke, Edith: "Circuit Analysis of A-C Power Systems," vols. I and II, John Wiley & Sons, Inc., New York, 1950.
6. Davis, Gordon B.: "An Introduction to Electronic Computers," McGraw-Hill Book Company, New York, 1966.
7. Flores, Ivan: "Computer Logic," Prentice-Hall, Inc., Englewood Cliffs, N.J., 1960.
8. Guillemin, E. A.: "Introductory Circuit Theory," John Wiley & Sons, Inc., New York, 1953.
9. Guillemin, E. A.: "The Mathematics of Circuit Analysis," John Wiley & Sons, Inc., New York, 1949.
10. Hildebrand, F. B.: "Introduction to Numerical Analysis," McGraw-Hill Book Company, New York, 1956.
11. Kármán, T. V., and M. A. Biot: "Mathematical Methods in Engineering," McGraw-Hill Book Company, New York, 1940.
12. Kron, Gabriel: "Equivalent Circuits of Electric Machinery," John Wiley & Sons, New York, 1951.
13. Langhaar, H. L.: "Dimensional Analysis and Theory of Models," John Wiley & Sons, Inc., New York, 1951.
14. Lawden, D. F.: "Mathematics of Engineering Systems (Linear and Non-Linear)," John Wiley & Sons, Inc., New York, 1955.
15. Stigant, Austen: "Determinants, Matrices, and Tensors," MacDonald and Co., London, 1959.
16. Swann, W. F. G.: *Nature and the Mind of Man, J. of the Franklin Inst.*, vol. 261, no. 6, pp. 591–613, 1956.
17. Ver Planck, D. W., and B. R. Teare, Jr.: "Engineering Analysis," John Wiley & Sons, Inc., New York, 1954.
18. Shannon, E. S.: A Symbolic Analysis of Relay and Switching Circuits, *Trans. AIEE*, vol. 57, p. 713, 1938.
19. Weber, Ernst: "Linear Transient Analysis," John Wiley & Sons, Inc., New York, 1954.

Appendix

	0	1	2	3	4	5	6	7	8	9
10	00000	00432	00860	01284	01703	02119	02531	02938	03342	03743
11	04139	04532	04922	05308	05690	06070	06446	06819	07188	07555
12	07918	08279	08636	08991	09342	09691	10037	10380	10721	11059
13	11394	11727	12057	12385	12710	13033	13354	13672	13988	14301
14	14613	14922	15229	15534	15836	16137	16435	16732	17026	17319
15	17609	17898	18184	18469	18752	19033	19312	19590	19866	20140
16	20412	20683	20952	21219	21484	21748	22011	22272	22531	22789
17	23045	23300	23553	23805	24055	24304	24551	24797	25042	25285
18	25527	25768	26007	26245	26482	26717	26951	27184	27416	27646
19	27875	28103	28330	28556	28780	29003	29226	29447	29667	29885
20	30103	30320	30535	30750	30963	31175	31387	31597	31806	32015
21	32222	32428	32634	32838	33041	33244	33445	33646	33846	34044
22	34242	34439	34635	34830	35025	35218	35411	35603	35793	35984
23	36173	36361	36549	36736	36922	37107	37291	37475	37658	37840
24	38021	38202	38382	38561	38739	38917	39094	39270	39445	39620
25	39794	39967	40140	40312	40483	40654	40824	40993	41162	41330
26	41497	41664	41830	41996	42160	42325	42488	42651	42813	42975
27	43136	43297	43457	43616	43775	43993	44091	44248	44404	44560
28	44716	44871	45025	45179	45332	45484	45637	45788	45939	46090
29	46240	46389	46538	46687	46835	46982	47129	47276	47422	47567
30	47712	47857	48001	48144	48287	48430	48572	48714	48855	48996
31	49136	49276	49415	49554	49693	49831	49969	50106	50243	50379
32	50515	50651	50786	50920	51055	51188	51322	51455	51587	51720
33	51851	51983	52114	52244	52375	52504	52634	52763	52892	53020
34	53148	53275	53403	53529	53656	53782	53908	54033	54158	54283
35	54407	54531	54654	54777	54900	55023	55145	55267	55388	55509
36	55630	55751	55871	55991	56110	56229	56348	56467	56585	56703
37	56820	56937	57054	57171	57287	57403	57519	57634	57749	57864
38	57978	58092	58206	58320	58433	58546	58659	58771	58883	58995
39	59106	59218	59329	59439	59550	59660	59770	59879	59988	60097
40	60206	60314	60423	60531	60638	60746	60853	60959	61066	61172
41	61278	61384	61490	61595	61700	61805	61909	62014	62118	62221
42	62325	62428	62531	62634	62737	62839	62941	63043	63144	63246
43	63347	63448	63548	63649	63749	63849	63949	64048	64147	64246
44	64345	64444	64542	64640	64738	64836	64933	65031	65128	65225
45	65321	65418	65514	65610	65706	65801	65896	65992	66087	66181
46	66276	66370	66464	66558	66652	66745	66839	66932	67025	67117
47	67210	67302	67394	67486	67578	67669	67761	67852	67943	68034
48	68124	68215	68305	68395	68485	68574	68664	68753	68842	68931
49	69020	69108	60197	69285	69373	69461	69548	69636	69723	69810
50	69897	69984	70070	70157	70243	70329	70415	70501	70586	70672
51	70757	70842	70927	71012	71096	71181	71265	71349	71433	71517
52	71600	71684	71767	71850	71933	72016	72099	72181	72263	72346
53	72428	72509	72591	72673	72754	72835	72916	72997	73078	73159
54	73239	73320	73400	73480	73560	73640	73719	73799	73878	73957
55	74036	74115	74194	74273	74351	74429	74507	74586	74663	74741
56	74819	74896	74975	75061	75128	75205	75282	75358	75435	75511
57	75587	75664	75740	75815	75891	75967	76042	76118	76193	76268
58	76343	76418	76492	76567	76641	76716	76790	76864	76938	77012
59	77085	77159	77232	77305	77379	77452	77525	77597	77670	77743

Appendix A LOGARITHMS OF NUMBERS (*Continued*)

	0	1	2	3	4	5	6	7	8	9
60	77815	77887	77960	78032	78104	78176	78247	78319	78390	78462
61	78533	78604	78675	78746	78817	78888	78958	79029	79099	79169
62	79239	79309	79379	79449	79518	79588	79657	79727	79796	79865
63	79934	80003	80072	80140	80209	80277	80346	80414	80482	80550
64	80618	80686	80754	80821	80889	80956	81023	81090	81158	81224
65	81291	81358	81425	81491	81558	81624	81690	81757	81823	81889
66	81954	82020	82086	82151	82217	82282	82347	82413	82478	82543
67	82607	82672	82737	82802	82866	82930	82995	83059	83123	83187
68	83251	83315	83378	83442	83506	83569	83632	83696	83759	83822
69	83885	83948	84011	84073	84136	84198	84261	84323	84386	84448
70	84510	84572	84634	84696	84757	84819	84880	84942	85003	85065
71	85126	85187	85248	85309	85370	85431	85491	85552	85612	85673
72	85733	85794	85854	85914	85974	86034	86094	86153	86213	86273
73	86332	86392	86451	86510	86570	86629	86688	86747	86806	86864
74	86923	86982	87040	87099	87157	87216	87274	87332	87390	87448
75	87506	87564	87622	87679	87737	87795	87852	87910	87967	88024
76	88081	88138	88195	88252	88309	88366	88423	88480	88536	88593
77	88649	88705	88762	88818	88874	88930	88986	89042	89098	89154
78	89209	89265	89321	89376	89432	89487	89542	89597	89653	89708
79	89763	89818	89873	89927	89982	90037	90091	90146	90200	90255
80	90309	90363	90417	90472	90526	90580	90634	90687	90741	90795
81	90849	90902	90956	91009	91062	91116	91169	91222	91275	91328
82	91381	91434	91487	91540	91593	91645	91698	91751	91803	91855
83	91908	91960	92012	92065	92117	92169	92221	92273	92324	92376
84	92428	92480	92531	92583	92634	92686	92737	92788	92840	92891
85	92942	92993	93044	93095	93146	93197	93247	93298	93349	93399
86	93450	93500	93551	93601	93651	93702	93752	93802	93852	93902
87	93952	94002	94052	94101	94151	94201	94250	94300	94349	94399
88	94448	94498	94547	94596	94645	94694	94743	94792	94841	94890
89	94939	94988	95036	95085	95134	95182	95231	95279	95328	95376
90	95424	95472	95521	95569	95617	95665	95713	95761	95809	95856
91	95904	95952	95999	96047	96095	96142	96190	96237	96284	96332
92	96379	96426	96473	96529	96567	96614	96661	96708	96755	96802
93	96848	96895	96942	96988	97035	97081	97128	97174	97220	97267
94	97313	97359	97405	97451	97497	97543	97589	97635	97681	97727
95	97772	97818	97864	97909	97955	98000	98046	98091	98137	98182
96	98227	98272	98318	98363	98408	98453	98498	98543	98588	98632
97	98677	98722	98767	98811	98856	98900	98945	98989	99034	99078
98	99123	99167	99211	99255	99300	99344	99388	99432	99476	99520
99	99564	99607	99651	99695	99739	99782	99826	99870	99913	99957
100	00000	00043	00087	00130	00173	00217	00260	00303	00346	00389
101	00432	00475	00518	00561	00604	00647	00689	00732	00775	00817
102	00860	00903	00945	00988	01030	01072	01115	01157	01199	01242
103	01284	01326	01368	01410	01452	01494	01536	01578	01620	01662
104	01703	01745	01787	01828	01870	01912	01953	01995	02036	02078
105	02119	02160	02202	02243	02284	02325	02366	02407	02449	02490
106	02531	02572	02612	02643	02694	02735	02776	02816	02857	02898
107	02938	02979	03019	03060	03100	03141	03181	03222	03262	03302
108	03342	03383	03423	03463	03503	03543	03583	03623	03663	03703
109	03743	03782	03822	03862	03902	03941	03981	04021	04060	04100

Appendix B NATURAL TRIGONOMETRIC FUNCTIONS

Angle	sin	tan	cot	cos	Angle	Angle	sin	tan	cot	cos	Angle
0° 0′	0.0000	0.0000	—	1.0000	90° 0′	7° 30′	0.1305	0.1317	7.5958	0.9914	82° 30′
10	0.0029	0.0029	343.77	1.0000	50	40	0.1334	0.1346	7.4287	0.9911	20
20	0.0058	0.0058	171.89	1.0000	40	50	0.1363	0.1376	7.2687	0.9907	10
30	0.0087	0.0087	114.59	1.0000	30	8° 0′	0.1392	0.1405	7.1154	0.9903	82° 0′
40	0.0116	0.0116	85.940	0.9999	20	10	0.1421	0.1435	6.9682	0.9899	50
50	0.0145	0.0145	68.750	0.9999	10	20	0.1449	0.1465	6.8269	0.9894	40
1° 0′	0.0175	0.0175	57.290	0.9998	89° 0′	30	0.1478	0.1495	6.6912	0.9890	30
10	0.0204	0.0204	49.104	0.9998	50	40	0.1507	0.1524	6.5606	0.9886	20
20	0.0233	0.0233	42.964	0.9997	40	50	0.1536	0.1554	6.4348	0.9881	10
30	0.0262	0.0262	38.188	0.9997	30	9° 0′	0.1564	0.1584	6.3138	0.9877	81° 0′
40	0.0291	0.0291	34.368	0.9996	20	10	0.1593	0.1614	6.1970	0.9872	50
50	0.0320	0.0320	31.242	0.9995	10	20	0.1622	0.1644	6.0844	0.9868	40
2° 0′	0.0349	0.0349	28.636	0.9994	88° 0′	30	0.1650	0.1673	5.9758	0.9863	30
10	0.0378	0.0378	26.432	0.9993	50	40	0.1679	0.1703	5.8708	0.9858	20
20	0.0407	0.0407	24.542	0.9992	40	50	0.1708	0.1733	5.7694	0.9853	10
30	0.0436	0.0437	22.904	0.9990	30	10° 0′	0.1736	0.1763	5.6713	0.9848	80° 0′
40	0.0465	0.0466	21.470	0.9989	20	10	0.1765	0.1793	5.5764	0.9843	50
50	0.0494	0.0495	20.206	0.9988	10	20	0.1794	0.1823	5.4845	0.9838	40
3° 0′	0.0523	0.0524	19.081	0.9986	87° 0′	30	0.1822	0.1853	5.3955	0.9833	30
10	0.0552	0.0553	18.075	0.9985	50	40	0.1851	0.1883	5.3093	0.9827	20
20	0.0581	0.0582	17.169	0.9983	40	50	0.1880	0.1914	5.2257	0.9822	10
30	0.0610	0.0612	16.350	0.9981	30	11° 0′	0.1908	0.1944	5.1446	0.9816	79° 0′
40	0.0640	0.0641	15.605	0.9980	20	10	0.1937	0.1974	5.0658	0.9811	50
50	0.0669	0.0670	14.924	0.9978	10	20	0.1965	0.2004	4.9894	0.9805	40
4° 0′	0.0698	0.0699	14.301	0.9976	86° 0′	30	0.1994	0.2035	4.9152	0.9799	30
10	0.0727	0.0729	13.727	0.9974	50	40	0.2022	0.2065	4.8430	0.9793	20
20	0.0756	0.0758	13.197	0.9971	40	50	0.2051	0.2095	4.7729	0.9787	10
30	0.0785	0.0787	12.706	0.9969	30	12° 0′	0.2079	0.2126	4.7046	0.9781	78° 0′
40	0.0814	0.0816	12.251	0.9967	20	10	0.2108	0.2156	4.6382	0.9775	50
50	0.0843	0.0846	11.826	0.9964	10	20	0.2136	0.2186	4.5736	0.9769	40
5° 0′	0.0872	0.0875	11.430	0.9962	85° 0′	30	0.2164	0.2217	4.5107	0.9763	30
10	0.0901	0.0904	11.059	0.9959	50	40	0.2193	0.2247	4.4494	0.9757	20
20	0.0929	0.0934	10.712	0.9957	40	50	0.2221	0.2278	4.3897	0.9750	10
30	0.0958	0.0963	10.385	0.9954	30	13° 0′	0.2250	0.2309	4.3315	0.9744	77° 0′
40	0.0987	0.0992	10.078	0.9951	20	10	0.2278	0.2339	4.2747	0.9737	50
50	0.1016	0.1022	9.7882	0.9948	10	20	0.2306	0.2370	4.2193	0.9730	40
6° 0′	0.1045	0.1051	9.5144	0.9945	84° 0′	30	0.2334	0.2401	4.1653	0.9724	30
10	0.1074	0.1080	9.2553	0.9942	50	40	0.2363	0.2432	4.1126	0.9717	20
20	0.1103	0.1110	9.0098	0.9939	40	50	0.2391	0.2462	4.0611	0.9710	10
30	0.1132	0.1139	8.7769	0.9936	30	14° 0′	0.2419	0.2493	4.0108	0.9703	76° 0′
40	0.1161	0.1169	8.5555	0.9932	20	10	0.2447	0.2524	3.9617	0.9696	50
50	0.1190	0.1198	8.3450	0.9929	10	20	0.2476	0.2555	3.9136	0.9689	40
7° 0′	0.1219	0.1228	8.1443	0.9925	83° 0′	30	0.2504	0.2586	3.8667	0.9681	30
10	0.1248	0.1257	7.9530	0.9922	50	40	0.2532	0.2617	3.8208	0.9674	20
20	0.1276	0.1287	7.7704	0.9918	40	50	0.2560	0.2648	3.7760	0.9667	10
30	0.1305	0.1317	7.5958	0.9914	30	15° 0′	0.2588	0.2679	3.7321	0.9659	75° 0′
Angle	cos	cot	tan	sin	Angle	Angle	cos	cot	tan	sin	Angle

Appendix B NATURAL TRIGONOMETRIC FUNCTIONS (*Continued*)

Angle	sin	tan	cot	cos	Angle	Angle	sin	tan	cot	cos	Angle
15° 0'	0.2588	0.2679	3.7321	0.9659	75° 0'	22° 30'	0.3827	0.4142	2.4142	0.9239	67° 30'
10	0.2616	0.2711	3.6891	0.9652	50	40	0.3854	0.4176	2.3945	0.9228	20
20	0.2644	0.2742	3.6470	0.9644	40	50	0.3881	0.4210	2.3750	0.9216	10
30	0.2672	0.2773	3.6059	0.9636	30	23° 0'	0.3907	0.4245	2.3559	0.9205	67° 0'
40	0.2700	0.2805	3.5656	0.9628	20	10	0.3934	0.4279	2.3369	0.9194	50
50	0.2728	0.2836	3.5261	0.9621	10	20	0.3961	0.4314	2.3183	0.9182	40
16° 0'	0.2756	0.2867	3.4874	0.9613	74° 0'	30	0.3987	0.4348	2.2998	0.9171	30
10	0.2784	0.2899	3.4495	0.9605	50	40	0.4014	0.4383	2.2817	0.9159	20
20	0.2812	0.2931	3.4124	0.9596	40	50	0.4041	0.4417	2.2637	0.9147	10
30	0.2840	0.2962	3.3759	0.9588	30	24° 0'	0.4067	0.4452	2.2460	0.9135	66° 0'
40	0.2868	0.2994	3.3402	0.9580	20	10	0.4094	0.4487	2.2286	0.9124	50
50	0.2896	0.3026	3.3052	0.9572	10	20	0.4120	0.4522	2.2113	0.9112	40
17° 0'	0.2924	0.3057	3.2709	0.9563	73° 0'	30	0.4147	0.4557	2.1943	0.9100	30
10	0.2952	0.3089	3.2371	0.9555	50	40	0.4173	0.4592	2.1775	0.9088	20
20	0.2979	0.3121	3.2041	0.9546	40	50	0.4200	0.4628	2.1609	0.9075	10
30	0.3007	0.3153	3.1716	0.9537	30	25° 0'	0.4226	0.4663	2.1445	0.9063	65° 0'
40	0.3035	0.3185	3.1397	0.9528	20	10	0.4253	0.4699	2.1283	0.9051	50
50	0.3062	0.3217	3.1084	0.9520	10	20	0.4279	0.4734	2.1123	0.9038	40
18° 0'	0.3090	0.3249	3.0777	0.9511	72° 0'	30	0.4305	0.4770	2.0965	0.9026	30
10	0.3118	0.3281	3.0475	0.9502	50	40	0.4331	0.4806	2.0809	0.9013	20
20	0.3145	0.3314	3.0178	0.9492	40	50	0.4358	0.4841	2.0655	0.9001	10
30	0.3173	0.3346	2.9887	0.9483	30	26° 0'	0.4384	0.4877	2.0503	0.8988	64° 0'
40	0.3201	0.3378	2.9600	0.9474	20	10	0.4410	0.4913	2.0353	0.8975	50
50	0.3228	0.3411	2.9319	0.9465	10	20	0.4436	0.4950	2.0204	0.8962	40
19° 0'	0.3256	0.3443	2.9042	0.9455	71° 0'	30	0.4462	0.4986	2.0057	0.8949	30
10	0.3283	0.3476	2.8770	0.9446	50	40	0.4488	0.5022	1.9912	0.8936	20
20	0.3311	0.3508	2.8502	0.9436	40	50	0.4514	0.5059	1.9768	0.8923	10
30	0.3338	0.3541	2.8239	0.9426	30	27° 0'	0.4540	0.5095	1.9626	0.8910	63° 0'
40	0.3365	0.3574	2.7980	0.9417	20	10	0.4566	0.5132	1.9486	0.8897	50
50	0.3393	0.3607	2.7725	0.9407	10	20	0.4592	0.5169	1.9347	0.8884	40
20° 0'	0.3420	0.3640	2.7475	0.9397	70° 0'	30	0.4617	0.5206	1.9210	0.8870	30
10	0.3448	0.3673	2.7228	0.9387	50	40	0.4643	0.5243	1.9074	0.8857	20
20	0.3475	0.3706	2.6985	0.9377	40	50	0.4669	0.5280	1.8940	0.8843	10
30	0.3502	0.3739	2.6746	0.9367	30	28° 0'	0.4695	0.5317	1.8807	0.8829	62° 0'
40	0.3529	0.3772	2.6511	0.9356	20	10	0.4720	0.5354	1.8676	0.8816	50
50	0.3557	0.3805	2.6279	0.9346	10	20	0.4746	0.5392	1.8546	0.8802	40
21° 0'	0.3584	0.3839	2.6051	0.9336	69° 0'	30	0.4772	0.5430	1.8418	0.8788	30
10	0.3611	0.3872	2.5826	0.9325	50	40	0.4797	0.5467	1.8291	0.8774	20
20	0.3638	0.3906	2.5605	0.9315	40	50	0.4823	0.5505	1.8165	0.8760	10
30	0.3665	0.3939	2.5386	0.9304	30	29° 0'	0.4848	0.5543	1.8040	0.8746	61° 0'
40	0.3692	0.3973	2.5172	0.9293	20	10	0.4874	0.5581	1.7917	0.8732	50
50	0.3719	0.4006	2.4960	0.9283	10	20	0.4899	0.5619	1.7796	0.8718	40
22° 0'	0.3746	0.4040	2.4751	0.9272	68° 0'	30	0.4924	0.5658	1.7675	0.8704	30
10	0.3773	0.4074	2.4545	0.9261	50	40	0.4950	0.5696	1.7556	0.8689	20
20	0.3800	0.4108	2.4342	0.9250	40	50	0.4975	0.5735	1.7437	0.8675	10
30	0.3827	0.4142	2.4142	0.9239	30	30° 0'	0.5000	0.5774	1.7321	0.8660	60° 0'
Angle	cos	cot	tan	sin	Angle	Angle	cos	cot	tan	sin	Angle

Appendix B NATURAL TRIGONOMETRIC FUNCTIONS (*Continued*)

Angle	sin	tan	cot	cos	Angle	Angle	sin	tan	cot	cos	Angle
30° 0'	0.5000	0.5774	1.7321	0.8660	60° 0'	37° 30'	0.6088	0.7673	1.3032	0.7934	52° 30'
10	0.5025	0.5812	1.7205	0.8646	50	40	0.6111	0.7720	1.2954	0.7916	20
20	0.5050	0.5851	1.7090	0.8631	40	50	0.6134	0.7766	1.2876	0.7898	10
30	0.5075	0.5890	1.6977	0.8616	30	38° 0'	0.6157	0.7813	1.2799	0.7880	52° 0'
40	0.5100	0.5930	1.6864	0.8601	20	10	0.6180	0.7860	1.2723	0.7862	50
50	0.5125	0.5969	1.6753	0.8587	10	20	0.6202	0.7907	1.2647	0.7844	40
31° 0'	0.5150	0.6009	1.6643	0.8572	59° 0'	30	0.6225	0.7954	1.2572	0.7826	30
10	0.5175	0.6048	1.6534	0.8557	50	40	0.6248	0.8002	1.2497	0.7808	20
20	0.5200	0.6088	1.6426	0.8542	40	50	0.6271	0.8050	1.2423	0.7790	10
30	0.5225	0.6128	1.6319	0.8526	30	39° 0'	0.6293	0.8098	1.2349	0.7771	51° 0'
40	0.5250	0.6168	1.6212	0.8511	20	10	0.6316	0.8146	1.2276	0.7753	50
50	0.5275	0.6208	1.6107	0.8496	10	20	0.6338	0.8195	1.2203	0.7735	40
32° 0'	0.5299	0.6249	1.6003	0.8480	58° 0'	30	0.6361	0.8243	1.2131	0.7716	30
10	0.5324	0.6289	1.5900	0.8465	50	40	0.6383	0.8292	1.2059	0.7698	20
20	0.5348	0.6330	1.5798	0.8450	40	50	0.6406	0.8342	1.1988	0.7679	10
30	0.5373	0.6371	1.5697	0.8434	30	40° 0'	0.6428	0.8391	1.1918	0.7660	50° 0'
40	0.5398	0.6412	1.5597	0.8418	20	10	0.6450	0.8441	1.1847	0.7642	50
50	0.5422	0.6453	1.5497	0.8403	10	20	0.6472	0.8491	1.1778	0.7623	40
33° 0'	0.5446	0.6494	1.5399	0.8387	57° 0'	30	0.6494	0.8541	1.1708	0.7604	30
10	0.5471	0.6536	1.5301	0.8371	50	40	0.6517	0.8591	1.1640	0.7585	20
20	0.5495	0.6577	1.5204	0.8355	40	50	0.6539	0.8642	1.1571	0.7566	10
30	0.5519	0.6619	1.5108	0.8339	30	41° 0'	0.6561	0.8693	1.1504	0.7547	49° 0'
40	0.5544	0.6661	1.5013	0.8323	20	10	0.6583	0.8744	1.1436	0.7528	50
50	0.5568	0.6703	1.4919	0.8307	10	20	0.6604	0.8796	1.1369	0.7509	40
34° 0'	0.5592	0.6745	1.4826	0.8290	56° 0'	30	0.6626	0.8847	1.1303	0.7490	30
10	0.5616	0.6787	1.4733	0.8274	50	40	0.6648	0.8899	1.1237	0.7470	20
20	0.5640	0.6830	1.4641	0.8258	40	50	0.6670	0.8952	1.1171	0.7451	10
30	0.5664	0.6873	1.4550	0.8241	30	42° 0'	0.6691	0.9004	1.1106	0.7431	48° 0'
40	0.5688	0.6916	1.4460	0.8225	20	10	0.6713	0.9057	1.1041	0.7412	50
50	0.5712	0.6959	1.4370	0.8208	10	20	0.6734	0.9110	1.0977	0.7392	40
35° 0'	0.5736	0.7002	1.4281	0.8192	55° 0'	30	0.6756	0.9163	1.0913	0.7373	30
10	0.5760	0.7046	1.4193	0.8175	50	40	0.6777	0.9217	1.0850	0.7353	20
20	0.5783	0.7089	1.4106	0.8158	40	50	0.6799	0.9271	1.0786	0.7333	10
30	0.5807	0.7133	1.4019	0.8141	30	43° 0'	0.6820	0.9325	1.0724	0.7314	47° 0'
40	0.5831	0.7177	1.3934	0.8124	20	10	0.6841	0.9380	1.0661	0.7294	50
50	0.5854	0.7221	1.3848	0.8107	10	20	0.6862	0.9435	1.0599	0.7274	40
36° 0'	0.5878	0.7265	1.3764	0.8090	54° 0'	30	0.6884	0.9490	1.0538	0.7254	30
10	0.5901	0.7310	1.3680	0.8073	50	40	0.6905	0.9545	1.0477	0.7234	20
20	0.5925	0.7355	1.3597	0.8056	40	50	0.6926	0.9601	1.0146	0.7214	10
30	0.5948	0.7400	1.3514	0.8039	30	44° 0'	0.6947	0.9657	1.0355	0.7193	46° 0'
40	0.5972	0.7445	1.3432	0.8021	20	10	0.6967	0.9713	1.0295	0.7173	50
50	0.5995	0.7490	1.3351	0.8004	10	20	0.6988	0.9770	1.0235	0.7153	40
37° 0'	0.6018	0.7536	1.3270	0.7986	53° 0'	30	0.7009	0.9827	1.0176	0.7133	30
10	0.6041	0.7581	1.3190	0.7969	50	40	0.7030	0.9884	1.0117	0.7112	20
20	0.6065	0.7627	1.3111	0.7951	40	50	0.7050	0.9942	1.0058	0.7092	10
30	0.6088	0.7673	1.3032	0.7934	30	45° 0'	0.7071	1.0000	1.0000	0.7071	45° 0'
Angle	cos	cot	tan	sin	Angle	Angle	cos	cot	tan	sin	Angle

Appendix C NUMERICAL SERIES

$$1 - \frac{1}{3} + \frac{1}{5} - \frac{1}{7} + \cdots = \frac{\pi}{4}$$

$$1 - \frac{1}{3^2} + \frac{1}{5^2} - \frac{1}{7^2} + \cdots = 0.9159656 \cdots$$

$$1 - \frac{1}{3^3} + \frac{1}{5^3} - \frac{1}{7^3} + \cdots = \frac{\pi^3}{32}$$

$$1 - \frac{1}{3^5} + \frac{1}{5^5} - \frac{1}{7^5} + \cdots = \frac{5\pi^5}{1,536}$$

$$1 - \frac{1}{3^7} + \frac{1}{5^7} - \frac{1}{7^7} + \cdots = \frac{61\pi^7}{64(2,880)}$$

$$1 + \frac{1}{3^2} + \frac{1}{5^2} + \frac{1}{7^2} + \cdots = \frac{\pi^2}{8}$$

$$1 + \frac{1}{3^4} + \frac{1}{5^4} + \frac{1}{7^4} + \cdots = \frac{\pi^4}{96}$$

$$1 + \frac{1}{3^6} + \frac{1}{5^6} + \frac{1}{7^6} + \cdots = \frac{\pi^6}{960}$$

$$1 + \frac{1}{3^8} + \frac{1}{5^8} + \frac{1}{7^8} + \cdots = \frac{17\pi^8}{161,280}$$

$$1 + \frac{1}{2^2} + \frac{1}{3^2} + \frac{1}{4^2} + \cdots = \frac{\pi^2}{6}$$

$$1 + \frac{1}{2^4} + \frac{1}{3^4} + \frac{1}{4^4} + \cdots = \frac{\pi^4}{90}$$

$$1 + \frac{1}{2^6} + \frac{1}{3^6} + \frac{1}{4^6} + \cdots = \frac{\pi^6}{945}$$

$$1 + 2 + 3 + 4 + \cdots + n = \frac{n(n + 1)}{2}$$

$$1 + 2^2 + 3^2 + 4^2 + \cdots + n^2 = \frac{n(n + 1)(2n + 1)}{6}$$

$$1 + 2^3 + 3^3 + 4^3 + \cdots + n^3 = \frac{n^2(n + 1)^2}{4}$$

$$1 + 2^4 + 3^4 + 4^4 + \cdots + n^4 = \frac{n(n + 1)(2n + 1)(3n^2 + 3n - 1)}{30}$$

Appendix D INTEGRALS

The constant of integration has been omitted in each case.

CERTAIN ELEMENTARY FORMS

(1) $\displaystyle\int k\,dx = k\int dx$

(2) $\displaystyle\int (du + dv + \cdots + dw) = \int du + \int dv + \cdots + \int dw$

(3) $\displaystyle\int u\,dv = uv - \int v\,du$

(4) $\displaystyle\int u^n\,du = \frac{u^{n+1}}{n+1} \qquad n \neq -1$

(5) $\displaystyle\int \frac{du}{u} = \ln|u|$

FORMS CONTAINING $(a + bx)$

(6) $\displaystyle\int \frac{x\,dx}{a+bx} = \frac{x}{b} - \frac{a}{b^2}\ln|a+bx|$

(7) $\displaystyle\int \frac{x\,dx}{(a+bx)^2} = \frac{a}{b^2(a+bx)} + \frac{1}{b^2}\ln|a+bx|$

(8) $\displaystyle\int x(a+bx)^n\,dx = \frac{x(a+bx)^{n+1}}{b(n+1)} - \frac{(a+bx)^{n+2}}{b^2(n+1)(n+2)} \qquad n \neq -1, -2$

(9) $\displaystyle\int \frac{dx}{x(a+bx)} = \frac{1}{a}\ln\left|\frac{x}{a+bx}\right|$

(10) $\displaystyle\int \frac{dx}{x(a+bx)^2} = \frac{1}{a(a+bx)} + \frac{1}{a^2}\ln\left|\frac{x}{a+bx}\right|$

(11) $\displaystyle\int x\sqrt{a+bx}\,dx = \frac{2}{15b^2}(3bx - 2a)(a+bx)^{3/2}$

(12) $\displaystyle\int x^n\sqrt{a+bx}\,dx = \frac{2x^n(a+bx)^{3/2}}{(2n+3)b} - \frac{2an}{(2n+3)b}\int x^{n-1}\sqrt{a+bx}\,dx$

$$2n + 3 \neq 0$$

(13) $\displaystyle\int \frac{x\,dx}{\sqrt{a+bx}} = \frac{2}{3b^2}(bx - 2a)\sqrt{a+bx}$

[356]

Appendix D   INTEGRALS (*Continued*)

(14) $\displaystyle\int \frac{x^n\,dx}{\sqrt{a+bx}} = \frac{2x^n\sqrt{a+bx}}{(2n+1)b} - \frac{2an}{(2n+1)b}\int \frac{x^{n-1}\,dx}{\sqrt{a+bx}}$ $2n+1 \neq 0$

(15) $\displaystyle\int \frac{dx}{x\sqrt{a+bx}} = \begin{cases} \dfrac{1}{\sqrt{a}} \ln \left| \dfrac{\sqrt{a+bx}-\sqrt{a}}{\sqrt{a+bx}+\sqrt{a}} \right| & a>0 \\[4pt] \qquad\qquad \text{or} \\[4pt] \dfrac{2}{\sqrt{-a}} \arctan \sqrt{\dfrac{a+bx}{-a}} & a<0 \end{cases}$

(16) $\displaystyle\int \frac{dx}{x^n\sqrt{a+bx}} = -\frac{\sqrt{a+bx}}{(n-1)ax^{n-1}} - \frac{(2n-3)b}{2(n-1)a}\int \frac{dx}{x^{n-1}\sqrt{a+bx}}$ $n \neq 1$

FORMS CONTAINING $(a^2 - x^2)$

(17) $\displaystyle\int \frac{dx}{a^2-x^2} = \begin{cases} \dfrac{1}{2a} \ln \dfrac{a+x}{a-x} = \dfrac{1}{a} \operatorname{argtanh} \dfrac{x}{a} & x^2 < a^2 \\[4pt] \qquad\qquad \text{or} \\[4pt] \dfrac{1}{2a} \ln \dfrac{x+a}{x-a} = \dfrac{1}{a} \operatorname{argcoth} \dfrac{x}{a} & x^2 > a^2 \end{cases}$

(18) $\displaystyle\int \sqrt{a^2-x^2}\,dx = \frac{x}{2}\sqrt{a^2-x^2} + \frac{a^2}{2}\arcsin \frac{x}{a}$

(19) $\displaystyle\int (a^2-x^2)^{3/2}\,dx = \frac{x}{4}(a^2-x^2)^{3/2} + \frac{3}{8}a^2 x\sqrt{a^2-x^2} + \frac{3}{8}a^4 \arcsin \frac{x}{a}$

(20) $\displaystyle\int x^2\sqrt{a^2-x^2}\,dx = -\frac{x}{4}(a^2-x^2)^{3/2} + \frac{a^2}{8}x\sqrt{a^2-x^2} + \frac{a^4}{8}\arcsin \frac{x}{a}$

(21) $\displaystyle\int x^n\sqrt{a^2-x^2}\,dx = -\frac{x^{n-1}(a^2-x^2)^{3/2}}{n+2} + \frac{(n-1)a^2}{n+2}\int x^{n-2}\sqrt{a^2-x^2}\,dx$
$$n \neq -2$$

(22) $\displaystyle\int \frac{dx}{\sqrt{a^2-x^2}} = \arcsin \frac{x}{a}$

(23) $\displaystyle\int \frac{dx}{(a^2-x^2)^{3/2}} = \frac{x}{a^2\sqrt{a^2-x^2}}$

(24) $\displaystyle\int \frac{x^2\,dx}{\sqrt{a^2-x^2}} = -\frac{x}{2}\sqrt{a^2-x^2} + \frac{a^2}{2}\arcsin \frac{x}{a}$

(25) $\displaystyle\int \frac{x^n\,dx}{\sqrt{a^2-x^2}} = -\frac{x^{n-1}\sqrt{a^2-x^2}}{n} + \frac{(n-1)a^2}{n}\int \frac{x^{n-2}\,dx}{\sqrt{a^2-x^2}}$ $n \neq 0$

(26) $\displaystyle\int \frac{dx}{x\sqrt{a^2-x^2}} = -\frac{1}{a}\ln \left| \frac{a+\sqrt{a^2-x^2}}{x} \right|$

(27) $\displaystyle\int \frac{dx}{x^2\sqrt{a^2-x^2}} = -\frac{\sqrt{a^2-x^2}}{a^2 x}$

(28) $\displaystyle\int \frac{dx}{x^n\sqrt{a^2-x^2}} = -\frac{\sqrt{a^2-x^2}}{(n-1)a^2 x^{n-1}} + \frac{n-2}{(n-1)a^2}\int \frac{dx}{x^{n-2}\sqrt{a^2-x^2}}$ $n \neq 1$

Appendix D INTEGRALS (*Continued*)

FORMS CONTAINING $(x^2 \pm a^2)$

(29) $\displaystyle\int \frac{dx}{x^2 + a^2} = \frac{1}{a} \arctan \frac{x}{a}$

(30) $\displaystyle\int \sqrt{x^2 \pm a^2}\, dx = \frac{x}{2} \sqrt{x^2 \pm a^2} \pm \frac{a^2}{2} \ln |x + \sqrt{x^2 \pm a^2}|$

(31) $\displaystyle\int (x^2 \pm a^2)^{3/2}\, dx = \frac{x}{4} (x^2 \pm a^2)^{3/2} \pm \frac{3}{8} a^2 x \sqrt{x^2 \pm a^2}$

$$+ \frac{3}{8} a^4 \ln |x + \sqrt{x^2 \pm a^2}|$$

(32) $\displaystyle\int x^2 \sqrt{x^2 \pm a^2}\, dx = \frac{x}{4} (x^2 \pm a^2)^{3/2} \mp \frac{a^2}{8} x \sqrt{x^2 \pm a^2} - \frac{a^4}{8} \ln |x + \sqrt{x^2 \pm a^2}|$

(33) $\displaystyle\int x^n \sqrt{x^2 \pm a^2}\, dx = \frac{x^{n-1}(x^2 \pm a^2)^{3/2}}{n + 2} \mp \frac{(n - 1)a^2}{n + 2} \int x^{n-2} \sqrt{x^2 \pm a^2}\, dx$

$$n \neq -2$$

(34) $\displaystyle\int \frac{dx}{\sqrt{x^2 + a^2}} = \ln (x + \sqrt{x^2 + a^2}) = \operatorname{argsinh} \frac{x}{a}$

(35) $\displaystyle\int \frac{dx}{\sqrt{x^2 - a^2}} = \ln |x + \sqrt{x^2 - a^2}| = \operatorname{argcosh} \frac{x}{a}$

(36) $\displaystyle\int \frac{dx}{(x^2 \pm a^2)^{3/2}} = \frac{\pm x}{a^2 \sqrt{x^2 \pm a^2}}$

(37) $\displaystyle\int \frac{x^2\, dx}{\sqrt{x^2 \pm a^2}} = \frac{x}{2} \sqrt{x^2 \pm a^2} \mp \frac{a^2}{2} \ln |x + \sqrt{x^2 \pm a^2}|$

(38) $\displaystyle\int \frac{x^n\, dx}{\sqrt{x^2 \pm a^2}} = \frac{x^{n-1} \sqrt{x^2 \pm a^2}}{n} \mp \frac{(n - 1)a^2}{n} \int \frac{x^{n-2}\, dx}{\sqrt{x^2 \pm a^2}} \qquad n \neq 0$

(39) $\displaystyle\int \frac{dx}{x \sqrt{x^2 + a^2}} = -\frac{1}{a} \ln \frac{a + \sqrt{x^2 + a^2}}{|x|} = -\frac{1}{a} \operatorname{argcsch} \frac{x}{a}$

(40) $\displaystyle\int \frac{dx}{x \sqrt{x^2 - a^2}} = \frac{1}{a} \operatorname{arcsec} \frac{x}{a}$

(41) $\displaystyle\int \frac{dx}{x^2 \sqrt{x^2 \pm a^2}} = \mp \frac{\sqrt{x^2 \pm a^2}}{a^2 x}$

(42) $\displaystyle\int \frac{dx}{x^n \sqrt{x^2 \pm a^2}} = \mp \frac{\sqrt{x^2 \pm a^2}}{(n - 1)a^2 x^{n-1}} \mp \frac{(n - 2)}{(n - 1)a^2} \int \frac{dx}{x^{n-2} \sqrt{x^2 \pm a^2}}$

$$n \neq 1$$

BINOMIAL DIFFERENTIALS

(43) $\displaystyle\int \frac{dx}{(a + bx^2)^2} = \frac{x}{2a(a + bx^2)} + \frac{1}{2a \sqrt{ab}} \arctan \sqrt{\frac{b}{a}}\, x$

(44) $\displaystyle\int \frac{dx}{x(a + bx^2)} = \frac{1}{2a} \ln \frac{x^2}{|a + bx^2|}$

Appendix D   INTEGRALS (*Continued*)

(45) $\displaystyle \int x^m(a + bx^n)^r \, dx = \frac{x^{m-n+1}(a + bx^n)^{r+1}}{(nr + m + 1)b}$

$$- \frac{(m - n + 1)a}{(nr + m + 1)b} \int x^{m-n}(a + bx^n)^r \, dx \qquad nr + m + 1 \neq 0$$

(46) $\displaystyle \int x^m(a + bx^n)^r \, dx = \frac{x^{m+1}(a + bx^n)^r}{nr + m + 1} + \frac{anr}{nr + m + 1} \int x^m(a + bx^n)^{r-1} \, dx$

$$nr + m + 1 \neq 0$$

(47) $\displaystyle \int x^m(a + bx^n)^r \, dx = \frac{x^{m+1}(a + bx^n)^{r+1}}{a(m + 1)}$

$$- \frac{b(nr + n + m + 1)}{a(m + 1)} \int x^{m+n}(a + bx^n)^r \, dx \qquad m \neq -1$$

(48) $\displaystyle \int x^m(a + bx^n)^r \, dx = -\frac{x^{m+1}(a + bx^n)^{r+1}}{n(r + 1)a}$

$$+ \frac{nr + n + m + 1}{n(r + 1)a} \int x^m(a + bx^n)^{r+1} \, dx \qquad r \neq -1$$

EXPONENTIAL AND LOGARITHMIC FORMS

(49) $\displaystyle \int e^x \, dx = e^x$

(50) $\displaystyle \int a^x \, dx = \frac{a^x}{\ln a} = a^x \log_a e \qquad a > 0, a \neq 1$

(51) $\displaystyle \int x e^{ax} \, dx = \frac{e^{ax}}{a^2} (ax - 1)$

(52) $\displaystyle \int x^n e^{ax} \, dx = \frac{x^n e^{ax}}{a} - \frac{n}{a} \int x^{n-1} e^{ax} \, dx$

(53) $\displaystyle \int \ln x \, dx = x \ln x - x$

(54) $\displaystyle \int x \ln x \, dx = \frac{x^2}{4} (2 \ln x - 1)$

(55) $\displaystyle \int x^n \ln x \, dx = \frac{x^{n+1}}{n + 1} \ln x - \frac{x^{n+1}}{(n + 1)^2} \qquad n \neq -1$

(56) $\displaystyle \int (\ln x)^n \, dx = x(\ln x)^n - n \int (\ln x)^{n-1} \, dx \qquad n > 0$

FORMS CONTAINING TRIGONOMETRIC FUNCTIONS

(57) $\displaystyle \int \sin x \, dx = -\cos x$

(58) $\displaystyle \int \cos x \, dx = \sin x$

(59) $\displaystyle \int \tan x \, dx = \ln |\sec x|$

Appendix D INTEGRALS (*Continued*)

$$(60) \quad \int \cot x \, dx = \ln |\sin x|$$

$$(61) \quad \int \sec x \, dx = \ln |\sec x + \tan x|$$

$$(62) \quad \int \csc x \, dx = \ln |\csc x - \cot x| = -\ln |\csc x + \cot x|$$

$$(63) \quad \int \sec^2 x \, dx = \tan x$$

$$(64) \quad \int \csc^2 x \, dx = -\cot x$$

$$(65) \quad \int \sec x \tan x \, dx = \sec x$$

$$(66) \quad \int \csc x \cot x \, dx = -\csc x$$

$$(67) \quad \int \sin^2 x \, dx = \tfrac{1}{2}x - \tfrac{1}{4}\sin 2x$$

$$(68) \quad \int \sin^3 x \, dx = -\cos x + \tfrac{1}{3}\cos^3 x$$

$$(69) \quad \int \sin^4 x \, dx = \tfrac{3}{8}x - \tfrac{1}{4}\sin 2x + \tfrac{1}{32}\sin 4x$$

$$(70) \quad \int \sin^n x \, dx = -\frac{1}{n}\sin^{n-1} x \cos x + \frac{n-1}{n}\int \sin^{n-2} x \, dx \qquad n \text{ integer} > 0$$

$$(71) \quad \int \cos^2 x \, dx = \tfrac{1}{2}x + \tfrac{1}{4}\sin 2$$

$$(72) \quad \int \cos^3 x \, dx = \sin x - \tfrac{1}{3}\sin^3 x$$

$$(73) \quad \int \cos^4 x \, dx = \tfrac{3}{8}x + \tfrac{1}{4}\sin 2x + \tfrac{1}{32}\sin 4x$$

$$(74) \quad \int \cos^n x \, dx = \frac{1}{n}\cos^{n-1} x \sin x + \frac{n-1}{n}\int \cos^{n-2} x \, dx \qquad n \text{ integer} > 0$$

$$(75) \quad \int \sin^m x \cos^n x \, dx = \frac{\sin^{m+1} x \cos^{\,n-1} x}{m+n} + \frac{n-1}{m+n}\int \sin^m x \cos^{n-2} x \, dx$$
$$m+n \neq 0$$

$$(76) \quad \int \sin^m x \cos^n x \, dx = -\frac{\sin^{m-1} x \cos^{n+1} x}{m+n} + \frac{m-1}{m+n}\int \sin^{m-2} x \cos^n x \, dx$$
$$m+n \neq 0$$

$$(77) \quad \int \sin^m x \cos^n x \, dx = -\frac{\sin^{m+1} x \cos^{n+1} x}{n+1} + \frac{m+n+2}{n+1}\int \sin^m x \cos^{n+2} x \, dx$$
$$n \neq -1$$

$$(78) \quad \int \sin^m x \cos^n x \, dx = \frac{\sin^{m+1} x \cos^{n+1} x}{m+1} + \frac{m+n+2}{m+1}\int \sin^{m+2} x \cos^n x \, dx$$
$$m \neq -1$$

Appendix D INTEGRALS (*Continued*)

(79) $\displaystyle\int \sin mx \sin nx \, dx = \frac{\sin (m-n)x}{2(m-n)} - \frac{\sin (m+n)x}{2(m+n)} \qquad m^2 \neq n^2$

(80) $\displaystyle\int \sin mx \cos nx \, dx = -\frac{\cos (m-n)x}{2(m-n)} - \frac{\cos (m+n)x}{2(m+n)} \qquad m^2 \neq n^2$

(81) $\displaystyle\int \cos mx \cos nx \, dx = \frac{\sin (m-n)x}{2(m-n)} + \frac{\sin (m+n)x}{2(m+n)} \qquad m^2 \neq n^2$

(82) $\displaystyle\int x \sin x \, dx = \sin x - x \cos x$

(83) $\displaystyle\int x^n \sin x \, dx = -x^n \cos x + n \int x^{n-1} \cos x \, dx$

(84) $\displaystyle\int x \sin^n x \, dx = \frac{\sin^{n-1} x(\sin x - nx \cos x)}{n^2} + \frac{n-1}{n} \int x \sin^{n-2} x \, dx$

$$n \neq 0$$

(85) $\displaystyle\int x \cos x \, dx = \cos x + x \sin x$

(86) $\displaystyle\int x^n \cos x \, dx = x^n \sin x - n \int x^{n-1} \sin x \, dx$

(87) $\displaystyle\int x \cos^n x \, dx = \frac{\cos^{n-1} x(\cos x + nx \sin x)}{n^2} + \frac{n-1}{n} \int x \cos^{n-2} x \, dx$

$$n \neq 0$$

(88) $\displaystyle\int e^{ax} \sin bx \, dx = \frac{e^{ax}}{a^2 + b^2} (a \sin bx - b \cos bx)$

(89) $\displaystyle\int e^{ax} \cos bx \, dx = \frac{e^{ax}}{a^2 + b^2} (a \cos bx + b \sin bx)$

(90) $\displaystyle\int \tan^2 x \, dx = \tan x - x$

(91) $\displaystyle\int \tan^n x \, dx = \frac{\tan^{n-1} x}{n-1} - \int \tan^{n-2} x \, dx \qquad n \neq 1$

(92) $\displaystyle\int \cot^2 x \, dx = -\cot x - x$

(93) $\displaystyle\int \cot^n x \, dx = -\frac{\cot^{n-1} x}{n-1} - \int \cot^{n-2} x \, dx \qquad n \neq 1$

(94) $\displaystyle\int \sec^n x \, dx = \frac{\tan x \sec^{n-2} x}{n-1} + \frac{n-2}{n-1} \int \sec^{n-2} x \, dx \qquad n \neq 1$

(95) $\displaystyle\int \csc^n x \, dx = -\frac{\cot x \csc^{n-2} x}{n-1} + \frac{n-2}{n-1} \int \csc^{n-2} x \, dx \qquad n \neq 1$

(96) $\displaystyle\int \frac{dx}{1 + \sin x} = \tan\left(\frac{1}{2}x - \frac{\pi}{4}\right)$

(97) $\displaystyle\int \frac{dx}{1 - \sin x} = \tan\left(\frac{1}{2}x + \frac{\pi}{4}\right)$

Appendix D   INTEGRALS (*Continued*)

(98) $\displaystyle\int \frac{dx}{a + b\sin x} = \begin{cases} \dfrac{2}{\sqrt{a^2 - b^2}}\arctan\left(\dfrac{a\tan\frac{1}{2}x + b}{\sqrt{a^2 - b^2}}\right) & a^2 > b^2 \\[2ex] \dfrac{1}{\sqrt{b^2 - a^2}}\ln\left|\dfrac{a\tan\frac{1}{2}x + b - \sqrt{b^2 - a^2}}{a\tan\frac{1}{2}x + b + \sqrt{b^2 - a^2}}\right| & a^2 < b^2 \end{cases}$

(99) $\displaystyle\int \frac{dx}{1 + \cos x} = \tan\tfrac{1}{2}x$

(100) $\displaystyle\int \frac{dx}{1 - \cos x} = -\cot\tfrac{1}{2}x$

(101) $\displaystyle\int \frac{dx}{a + b\cos x} = \begin{cases} \dfrac{2}{\sqrt{a^2 - b^2}}\arctan\left(\dfrac{\sqrt{a^2 - b^2}\tan\frac{1}{2}x}{a + b}\right) & a^2 > b^2 \\[2ex] \dfrac{1}{\sqrt{b^2 - a^2}}\ln\left|\dfrac{\sqrt{b^2 - a^2}\tan\frac{1}{2}x + a + b}{\sqrt{b^2 - a^2}\tan\frac{1}{2}x - a - b}\right| & a^2 < b^2 \end{cases}$

(102) $\displaystyle\int \frac{dx}{\sin x + \cos x} = \frac{1}{\sqrt{2}}\ln\left|\tan\left(\frac{1}{2}x + \frac{\pi}{8}\right)\right|$

FORMS CONTAINING INVERSE TRIGONOMETRIC FUNCTIONS

(103) $\displaystyle\int \arcsin x\, dx = x\arcsin x + \sqrt{1 - x^2}$

(104) $\displaystyle\int x^n \arcsin x\, dx = \frac{x^{n+1}}{n + 1}\arcsin x - \frac{1}{n + 1}\int \frac{x^{n+1}\, dx}{\sqrt{1 - x^2}} \qquad n \neq -1$

(105) $\displaystyle\int \arctan x\, dx = x\arctan x - \ln\sqrt{1 + x^2}$

(106) $\displaystyle\int \operatorname{arcsec} x\, dx = x\operatorname{arcsec} x - \ln|x + \sqrt{x^2 - 1}|$

FORMS CONTAINING HYPERBOLIC FUNCTIONS

(107) $\displaystyle\int \sinh x\, dx = \cosh x$

(108) $\displaystyle\int \cosh x\, dx = \sinh x$

(109) $\displaystyle\int \tanh x\, dx = \ln\cosh x$

(110) $\displaystyle\int \coth x\, dx = \ln|\sinh x|$

(111) $\displaystyle\int \operatorname{sech} x\, dx = 2\arctan e^x$

(112) $\displaystyle\int \operatorname{csch} x\, dx = \ln\left|\tanh\frac{x}{2}\right|$

(113) $\displaystyle\int \operatorname{sech}^2 x\, dx = \tanh x$

Appendix D INTEGRALS (*Continued*)

(114) $\displaystyle\int \operatorname{csch}^2 x\, dx = -\coth x$

(115) $\displaystyle\int \operatorname{sech} x \tanh x\, dx = -\operatorname{sech} x$

(116) $\displaystyle\int \operatorname{csch} x \coth x\, dx = -\operatorname{csch} x$

(117) $\displaystyle\int \sinh^2 x\, dx = \tfrac{1}{2}\sinh x \cosh x - \tfrac{1}{2}x$

(118) $\displaystyle\int \cosh^2 x\, dx = \tfrac{1}{2}\sinh x \cosh x + \tfrac{1}{2}x$

(119) $\displaystyle\int x \sinh x\, dx = x \cosh x - \sinh x$

(120) $\displaystyle\int x^2 \sinh x\, dx = (x^2 + 2)\cosh x - 2x \sinh x$

(121) $\displaystyle\int x \cosh x\, dx = x \sinh x - \cosh x$

(122) $\displaystyle\int \tanh^2 x\, dx = x - \tanh x$

(123) $\displaystyle\int \coth^2 x\, dx = x - \coth x$

(124) $\displaystyle\int \operatorname{argsinh} x\, dx = x \operatorname{argsinh} x - \sqrt{1 + x^2}$

(125) $\displaystyle\int \operatorname{argcosh} x\, dx = x \operatorname{argcosh} x - \sqrt{x^2 - 1} \qquad x^2 > 1$

(126) $\displaystyle\int \operatorname{argtanh} x\, dx = x \operatorname{argtanh} x + \tfrac{1}{2}\ln(1 - x^2) \qquad x^2 < 1$

Appendix E   INFINITE SERIES

1. $(1 + x)^m = 1 + mx + \dfrac{m(m - 1)x^2}{2} + \cdots$

$\qquad\qquad\qquad + \dfrac{m(m - 1) \cdots (m - n + 2)x^{n-1}}{(n - 1)!} + \cdots \qquad x^2 < 1$

2. $(a + b)^n = a^n + na^{n-1}b + \dfrac{n(n - 1)a^{n-2}b^2}{2!} + \dfrac{n(n - 1)(n - 2)a^{n-3}b^3}{3!}$

$\qquad\qquad\qquad\qquad\qquad\qquad\qquad + \cdots \qquad b^2 < a^2$

3. $\dfrac{1}{1 + x} = 1 - x + x^2 - x^3 + \cdots + (-1)^{n+1}x^{n-1} + \cdots$

4. $\dfrac{1}{1 - x} = 1 + x + x^2 + \cdots + x^{n-1} + \cdots$

5. $\sin x = x - \dfrac{x^3}{6} + \dfrac{x^5}{120} - \cdots + \dfrac{(-1)^{n+1}x^{2n-1}}{(2n - 1)!} + \cdots$

6. $\cos x = 1 - \dfrac{x^2}{2} + \dfrac{x^4}{24} - \dfrac{x^6}{720} + \cdots + \dfrac{(-1)^{n+1}x^{2n-2}}{(2n - 2)!} + \cdots$

7. $\tan x = x + \dfrac{x^3}{3} + \dfrac{2x^5}{15} + \dfrac{17x^7}{315} + \cdots$

8. $\sin^{-1} x = x + \dfrac{x^3}{6} + \dfrac{3x^5}{40} + \dfrac{5x^7}{112} + \cdots + \dfrac{[1 \cdot 3 \cdots (2n - 3)]x^{2n-1}}{[2 \cdot 4 \cdots (2n - 2)](2n - 1)}$

9. $\tan^{-1} x = x - \dfrac{x^3}{3} + \dfrac{x^5}{5} - \dfrac{x^7}{7} + \cdots + \dfrac{(-1)^{n+1}x^{2n-1}}{2n - 1} + \cdots$

10. $\cos^2 x = 1 - x^2 + \dfrac{x^4}{3} - \dfrac{2x^6}{45} + \cdots + \dfrac{(-1)^{n-1}(2)^{2n-3}x^{2n-2}}{(2n - 2)!} + \cdots$

11. $\sin^2 x = x^2 - \dfrac{x^4}{3} + \dfrac{2x^6}{45} - \cdots + \dfrac{(-1)^{n+1}(2)^{2n-1}x^{2n}}{(2n)!} + \cdots$

12. $\sinh x = x + \dfrac{x^3}{6} + \dfrac{x^5}{120} + \cdots + \dfrac{x^{2n-1}}{(2n - 1)!} + \cdots$

13. $\cosh x = 1 + \dfrac{x^2}{2} + \dfrac{x^4}{24} + \cdots + \dfrac{x^{2n-2}}{(2n - 2)!} + \cdots$

14. $\tanh x = x - \dfrac{x^3}{3} + \dfrac{2x^5}{15} - \dfrac{17x^7}{315} + \cdots$

15. $e^x = 1 + x + \dfrac{x^2}{2} + \dfrac{x^3}{6} + \cdots + \dfrac{x^{n-1}}{(n - 1)!} + \cdots$

16. $e^{\sin x} = 1 + x + \dfrac{x^2}{2} - \dfrac{x^4}{4} - \dfrac{x^5}{15} + \dfrac{x^6}{240} + \cdots$

17. $e^{\tan x} = 1 + x + \dfrac{x^2}{2} + \dfrac{x^3}{2} + \dfrac{3x^4}{8} + \dfrac{37x^5}{120} + \cdots \qquad x^2 < \dfrac{\pi^2}{4}$

18. $\ln (1 + x) = x - \dfrac{x^2}{2} + \dfrac{x^3}{3} - \dfrac{x^4}{4} + \cdots + \dfrac{(-1)^{n+1}x^n}{n} + \cdots$

19. $\ln (\sin x) = \ln x - \dfrac{x^2}{6} - \dfrac{x^4}{180} - \dfrac{x^6}{2,835} - \cdots \qquad x^2 < \pi^2$

20. $\ln (\cos x) = -\dfrac{x^2}{2} - \dfrac{x^4}{12} - \dfrac{x^6}{45} - \dfrac{17x^8}{2,520} - \cdots \qquad x^2 < \dfrac{\pi^2}{4}$

21. $\ln (\tan x) = \ln x + \dfrac{x^2}{3} + \dfrac{7x^4}{90} + \dfrac{62x^6}{2,835} + \cdots \qquad x^2 < \dfrac{\pi^2}{4}$

[364]

x	eˣ	e⁻ˣ	sinh x	cosh x	tanh x
.00	1.000	1.000	.000	1.000	.000
.01	1.010	.990	.010	1.000	.010
.02	1.020	.980	.020	1.000	.020
.03	1.030	.970	.030	1.000	.030
.04	1.041	.961	.040	1.001	.040
.05	1.051	.951	.050	1.001	.050
.06	1.062	.942	.060	1.002	.060
.07	1.073	.932	.070	1.002	.070
.08	1.083	.923	.080	1.003	.080
.09	1.094	.914	.090	1.004	.090
.1	1.105	.905	.100	1.005	.100
.2	1.221	.819	.201	1.020	.197
.3	1.350	.741	.305	1.045	.291
.4	1.492	.670	.411	1.081	.380
.5	1.649	.607	.521	1.128	.462
.6	1.822	.549	.637	1.185	.537
.7	2.014	.497	.759	1.255	.604
.8	2.226	.449	.888	1.337	.664
.9	2.460	.407	1.027	1.433	.716
1.0	2.718	.368	1.175	1.543	.762
1.1	3.004	.333	1.336	1.669	.800
1.2	3.320	.301	1.509	1.811	.834
1.3	3.669	.273	1.698	1.971	.862
1.4	4.055	.247	1.904	2.151	.885
1.5	4.482	.223	2.129	2.352	.905
1.6	4.953	.202	2.376	2.577	.922
1.7	5.474	.183	2.646	2.828	.935
1.8	6.050	.165	2.942	3.107	.947
1.9	6.686	.150	3.268	3.418	.956
2.0	7.389	.135	3.627	3.762	.964
2.1	8.166	.122	4.022	4.144	.970
2.2	9.025	.111	4.457	4.568	.976
2.3	9.974	.100	4.937	5.037	.980
2.4	11.023	.091	5.466	5.557	.984
2.5	12.182	.082	6.050	6.132	.987
2.6	13.464	.074	6.695	6.769	.989
2.7	14.880	.067	7.406	7.473	.991
2.8	16.445	.061	8.192	8.253	.993
2.9	18.174	.055	9.060	9.115	.994
3.0	20.086	.050	10.018	10.068	.995
3.1	22.20	.045	11.08	11.12	.996
3.2	24.53	.041	12.25	12.29	.997
3.3	27.11	.037	13.54	13.57	.997
3.4	29.96	.033	14.97	15.00	.998
3.5	33.12	.030	16.54	16.57	.998
3.6	36.60	.027	18.29	18.31	.999
3.7	40.45	.025	20.21	20.24	.999
3.8	44.70	.022	22.34	22.36	.999
3.9	49.40	.020	24.69	24.71	.999
4.0	54.60	.018	27.29	27.31	.999
4.1	60.34	.017	30.16	30.18	.999
4.2	66.69	.015	33.34	33.35	1.000
4.3	73.70	.014	36.84	36.86	1.000
4.4	81.45	.012	40.72	40.73	1.000
4.5	90.02	.011	45.00	45.01	1.000
4.6	99.48	.010	49.74	49.75	1.000
4.7	109.95	.0090	54.97	54.98	1.000
4.8	121.51	.0082	60.75	60.76	1.000
4.9	134.29	.0074	67.14	67.15	1.000
5.0	148.41	.0067	74.20	74.21	1.000
6.0	403.4	.0025	201.7		1.000
7.0	1096.6	.00091	548.3		1.000
8.0	2981.0	.00034	1490.5		1.000
9.0	8103.1	.00012	4051.5		1.000
10.0	22026.5	.000045	11013.2		1.000

$+x/s$	Y	P_1	x/s	Y	P_1
0.00	0.399	1.000	1.00	0.242	0.317
0.05	0.398	0.960	1.10	0.218	0.271
0.10	0.397	0.920	1.20	0.194	0.230
0.15	0.394	0.881	1.30	0.171	0.194
0.20	0.391	0.842	1.40	0.150	0.162
0.25	0.386	0.803	1.50	0.130	0.134
0.30	0.381	0.764	1.60	0.111	0.110
0.35	0.375	0.726	1.70	0.094	0.089
0.40	0.368	0.689	1.80	0.079	0.072
0.45	0.360	0.653	1.90	0.066	0.057
0.50	0.352	0.617	2.00	0.054	0.046
0.55	0.343	0.582	2.10	0.044	0.036
0.60	0.333	0.549	2.20	0.035	0.028
0.65	0.323	0.516	2.30	0.028	0.021
0.70	0.312	0.484	2.40	0.022	0.016
0.75	0.301	0.453	2.50	0.018	0.012
0.80	0.290	0.424	3.00	0.0044	0.0027
0.85	0.278	0.395	3.50	0.0009	0.0005
0.90	0.266	0.368	4.00	0.0001	0.0001
0.95	0.254	0.342			

$$Y = \frac{1}{\sqrt{2\pi}} \exp\left(-\frac{x^2}{2s^2}\right) \tag{13-11}$$

$$P_1 = \sqrt{\frac{2}{\pi}} \int_x^\infty \exp\left(-\frac{x^2}{2s^2}\right) \frac{dx}{s} \tag{13-18}$$

The fraction x/s is the ratio of a particular error, x, to the standard deviation, s (Eq. 13-9). $Y\, dx/s$ is the fraction of all the errors that will normally occur with values between $x - dx/2$ and $x + dx/2$. P_1 is the fraction of all the errors that (normally) will have numerical values greater than x

Appendix H   OPERATIONAL FORMULAS

1. $\dfrac{H}{p^m} = \dfrac{Ht^m}{m!}$

2. $\dfrac{H}{p+a} = \dfrac{H}{a}\left(1 - e^{-at}\right)$

3. $\dfrac{pH}{p+a} = He^{-at}$

4. $\dfrac{apH}{p^2 + a^2} = H \sin at$

5. $\dfrac{H}{p(p+a)} = \dfrac{H}{a^2}\left(at - 1 + e^{-at}\right)$

6. $\dfrac{apH}{p^2 - a^2} = H \sinh at$

7. $\dfrac{p^2 H}{p^2 + a^2} = H \cos at$

8. $\dfrac{a^2 H}{p^2 + a^2} = H(1 - \cos at)$

9. $\dfrac{p^2 H}{p^2 - a^2} = H \cosh at$

10. $\dfrac{pH}{(p+a)^2} = Hte^{-at}$

11. $\dfrac{H}{(p+a)^2} = \dfrac{H}{a^2}[1 - e^{-at}(1 + at)]$

12. $\dfrac{pH}{(p+a)^n} = \dfrac{Ht^{n-1}e^{-at}}{(n-1)!}$

13. $\dfrac{p^2 H}{(p^2 + a^2)^2} = \dfrac{Ht \sin at}{2a}$

14. $\dfrac{p^2 H}{(p+a)^2} = H(1 - at)e^{-at}$

15. $\dfrac{apH}{(p+b)^2 + a^2} - He^{-bt} \sin at$

16. $\dfrac{apH}{(p+b)^2 - a^2} = He^{-bt} \sinh at$

17. $\dfrac{(p^2 + bp)H}{(p+b)^2 + a^2} = He^{-bt} \cos at$

18. $\dfrac{(p^2 + bp)H}{(p+b)^2 - a^2} = He^{-bt} \cosh at$

19. $\dfrac{pH}{(p+a)(p+b)} = \dfrac{H}{a-b}\left(e^{-bt} - e^{-at}\right)$

20. $\dfrac{p^2 H}{(p+a)(p+b)} = \dfrac{H}{b-a}\left(be^{-bt} - ae^{-at}\right)$

21. $\dfrac{(p^2 + 2a^2)H}{p^2 + 4a^2} = H \cos^2 at$

22. $\dfrac{pH}{p^2 + 2ap + b} = \dfrac{He^{-at} \sin t \sqrt{b - a^2}}{\sqrt{b - a^2}}$

23. $\dfrac{H}{(p+a)(p+b)} = \dfrac{H}{ab} + \dfrac{H}{b-a}\left(\dfrac{e^{-bt}}{b} - \dfrac{e^{-at}}{a}\right)$

24. $\dfrac{H}{p^2 + 2ap + b} = H\left\{\dfrac{1}{b} - \dfrac{e^{-at} \sin\left[t \sqrt{b - a^2} + \cos^{-1}\left(a/\sqrt{b}\right)\right]}{\sqrt{b} \sqrt{b - a^2}}\right\}$

$$F(s) = \mathcal{L}[f(t)] = \int_0^\infty f(t)e^{-st}\,dt \qquad f(t) = \mathcal{L}^{-1}[F(s)] \begin{array}{l} = 0 \text{ for } t < 0 \\ = f(t) \text{ for } t > 0 \end{array}$$

1. $\dfrac{a}{s}$

1. a

2. $\dfrac{1}{s+a}$

2. ϵ^{-at}

3. $\dfrac{\omega}{s^2+\omega^2}$

3. $\sin \omega t$

4. $\dfrac{s}{s^2+\omega^2}$

4. $\cos \omega t$

5. $\dfrac{As+B}{s^2+\omega^2}$

5. $C \cos (\omega t + \phi)$
   where $C = \sqrt{A^2 + (B/\omega)^2}$
   $\phi = \tan^{-1}(-B/A)$

6. $\dfrac{\omega}{(s+a)^2+\omega^2}$

6. $\epsilon^{-at}\sin \omega t$

7. $\dfrac{s+a}{(s+a)^2+\omega^2}$

7. $\epsilon^{-at}\cos \omega t$

8. $\dfrac{n!}{s^{n+1}}$

8. t^n

8a. $\dfrac{1}{s^2}$

8a. t

9. $\dfrac{1}{(s+a)^n}$

9. $\dfrac{1}{(n-1)!}t^{n-1}\epsilon^{-at}$

9a. $\dfrac{1}{(s+a)^2}$

9a. $t\epsilon^{-at}$

10. $sF(s) - f(0+)$

10. $f'(t)$

11. $s^2F(s) - sf(0+) - f'(0+)$

11. $f''(t)$

12. $\dfrac{F(s)}{s} + \dfrac{F^{-1}(0+)}{s}$

12. $f^{-1}(t)$ or $\int f(t)\,dt$

where $F^{-1}(0+) = \displaystyle\int_{-\infty}^{0+} f(t)\,dt.$

13. $\epsilon^{-as}F(s)$

13. $f(t-a)H(t-a)$

14. Sum of transforms of individual terms

14. Sum of terms

15. $\dfrac{s \sin \theta + \omega \cos \theta}{s^2+\omega^2}$

15. $\sin(\omega t + \theta)$

16. $\dfrac{\omega}{s^2-\omega^2}$

16. $\sinh \omega t$

   or $\dfrac{\epsilon^{\omega t} - \epsilon^{-\omega t}}{2}$

17. $\dfrac{s}{s^2-\omega^2}$

17. $\cosh \omega t$

   or $\dfrac{\epsilon^{\omega t} + \epsilon^{-\omega t}}{2}$

18. $\dfrac{\epsilon^{-s}}{s}$

18. $f(t) = 0,\ t < 1$
    $= 1,\ t > 1$

[368]

Appendix I   ELEMENTARY LAPLACE TRANSFORM PAIRS (*Continued*)

19. $\dfrac{1 - \epsilon^{-s}}{s}$

19. $f(t) = 1,\ t < 1$
    $ = 0,\ t > 1$

20. $\dfrac{1 - (1 + s)\epsilon^{-s}}{s^2}$

20. $f(t) = t,\ t < 1$
    $ = 0,\ t > 1$

21. $\dfrac{\epsilon^{-s}}{s} + \dfrac{\epsilon^{-s}}{s^2}$

21. $f(t) = 0,\ t < 1$
    $ = t,\ t > 1$

22. $\dfrac{1 - \epsilon^{-s}}{s^2}$

22. $f(t) = t,\ t < 1$
    $ = 1,\ t > 1$

23. $\dfrac{(1 - \epsilon^{-s})^2}{s^2}$

23. $f(t) = t,\ t < 1$
    $ = 2 - t,\ 1 < t < 2$
    $ = 0,\ t > 2$

24. $\dfrac{1}{s} - \dfrac{(1 - \epsilon^{-s})}{s^2}$

24. $f(t) = 1 - t,\ t < 1$
    $ = 0,\ t > 1$

25. $\dfrac{s}{(s + a)^2}$

25. $(1 - at)\epsilon^{-at}$

26. $\dfrac{s}{(s + a)^3}$

26. $t\left(1 - \dfrac{at}{2}\right)\epsilon^{-at}$

27. $\dfrac{1}{(s + a)(s + b)}$

27. $\dfrac{\epsilon^{-bt} - \epsilon^{-at}}{a - b}$

28. $\dfrac{s}{(s + a)(s + b)}$

28. $\dfrac{a\epsilon^{-at} - b\epsilon^{-bt}}{a - b}$

29. $\dfrac{1}{(s + a)(s + b)^2}$

29. $\dfrac{\epsilon^{-at} - \epsilon^{-bt}[1 - (a - b)t]}{(a - b)^2}$

30. $\dfrac{s}{(s + a)(s + b)^2}$

30. $\dfrac{a - b(a - b)t\epsilon^{-bt} - a\epsilon^{-at}}{(a - b)^2}$

31. $\dfrac{s}{(s + a)^2 + b^2}$

31. $\epsilon^{-at}\left(\cos bt - \dfrac{a}{b}\sin bt\right)$

32. $\dfrac{1}{(s + a)(s + b)(s + c)}$

32. $\dfrac{(c - b)\epsilon^{-at} + (a - c)\epsilon^{-bt} + (b - a)\epsilon^{-ct}}{(a - b)(b - c)(c - a)}$

33. $\dfrac{s}{(s + a)(s + b)(s + c)}$

33. $\dfrac{a(b - c)\epsilon^{-at} + b(c - a)\epsilon^{-bt} + c(a - b)\epsilon^{-ct}}{(a - b)(b - c)(c - a)}$

34. $\dfrac{1}{s(s + a)}$

34. $\dfrac{1}{a}\left(1 - \epsilon^{-at}\right)$

35. $\dfrac{1}{(s + a)(s^2 + \omega^2)}$

35. $\dfrac{1}{a^2 + \omega^2}\left(\epsilon^{-at} + \dfrac{a}{\omega}\sin \omega t - \cos \omega t\right)$

36. $\dfrac{1}{(s^2 + \omega^2)^2}$

36. $\dfrac{1}{2\omega^3}(\sin \omega t - \omega t \cos \omega t)$

37. $\dfrac{s}{(s^2 + \omega^2)^2}$

37. $\dfrac{t}{2\omega}\sin \omega t$

Index

[371]